Stevan
whithead

THE TREASURE HUNTERS

THE TREASURE HUNTERS

by

Enid Blyton

Illustrated by BARBARA FREEMAN

COLLINS
LONDON AND GLASGOW

This Impression 1962

PRINTED AND MADE IN GREAT BRITAIN BY
WM. COLLINS SONS AND CO. LTD.
LONDON AND GLASGOW

CONTENTS

CHAPTER ONE

GRANNY'S OLD HOUSE

JEFFERY was sticking some stamps into his album when Susan and John came tearing into the playroom.

"Jeffery! What do you think! We're going to stay with Granny and Granpa in their old, old house!" cried Susan.

"Really?" said Jeffery, surprised and pleased. "How do you know?"

"Because Daddy said so," said Susan, dancing round the room. "Isn't it lovely! John has never been to Granny's, and I hardly remember the house —but you've told us so much about it, Jeffery, that I feel as if I know it inside and out!"

Mother came into the room, and smiled at the three excited faces.

"Yes," she said, "it *is* fun for you, isn't it? Daddy's father and mother are such dear old people, and you will be very happy with them for a few weeks. Daddy is taking me away for a while, because the doctor says I need strong sea-air—and Granny and Granpa have offered to have you till we come back."

"Let me see their letter, Mother!" begged Jeffery. He took it and read it.

"We shall so love to have our grandchildren," he read. "Especially as this may be the last year we shall be able to live here. It will almost break our hearts to leave this old house, which has been in our family for three hundred years."

"Oh, Mother!" said Jeffery, looking up in dismay. "Are they really leaving their old home? I thought Daddy said it would be his and ours some day."

"Yes, we thought so too," said Mother. "But you see, since the War, things have been very difficult, and Granny and Granpa have very little money.

They will have to sell the old place, and live in a smaller house."

"Well, it's a good thing we're going to stay with them whilst they've still got the old house," said Jeffery. "I remember it quite well, Mother—it's simply lovely!"

"I've never been there," said John, who was the youngest. "Last time you and Susan went I had chicken pox."

"I don't remember it *very* well," said Susan, "but Jeffery has told us all about it heaps of times. I'm longing to go!"

"Well, you haven't long to wait!" said Mother. "You are going to-morrow! So I am going to be very, very busy to-day, packing for you all!"

"To-morrow!" cried Susan, jumping for joy. "Oh, how lovely! I must go and pack for my dolls."

To-morrow came very quickly indeed. In no time at all the three children were packed into Daddy's car, with the luggage behind, and off they went! Mother sat in front with Daddy, and the three children were behind.

"You'll love Granny's old house," said Jeffery, as they sped along. "It's the sort of place where all kinds of things have happened, you know—and where you feel anything might still happen."

"Oh, I *do* love places like that," said Susan, happily. "Are there good walks round, Jeffery?"

"Most exciting ones," said Jeffery. "There is a deep, dark wood nearby, where we can go exploring. And there is a river that flows through the wood and makes part of it very marshy. And there is a lovely farm, where Farmer Timbles lives, and his wife—she's fat and kind, and she makes the most lovely cakes."

"We'll go there to tea then!" said Susan, jumping up and down on the seat. "This will be a lovely holiday."

"I hope you will remember to be quiet in the house, and to be kind and obedient to your grandparents," said Daddy. "They have had a lot of trouble lately, and it is kind of them to have you."

"We really will do our best," promised John. "Jeffery, was there a dog at Granny's? Or a cat?"

"There was a dog called Rags," said Jeffery, who never forgot anything. "He was a darling, but he may not be there now."

"You'll soon see!" said Mother. "We are nearly there!"

"Look! That's the wood I was telling you about," said Jeffery. The children pressed their noses against the car window and peered out. They saw a thick, dark wood with one or two narrow paths running into it. It looked very exciting.

The car turned into a drive between two big gate-posts. On the top of each sat a stone eagle.

"We're here, we're here!" shouted Jeffery, remembering the eagles from his last visit.

The car ran up a winding drive and stopped before a lovely old house. It was long and rather low, with very tall chimneys. The windows shone with leaded panes, and the sides of the house came out to form a sunny courtyard, in which walked some white fantail pigeons.

With a flutter of snowy wings the pigeons flew to the roof, and sat there cooing. "Rookity-coo," they said, peering down at the visitors in surprise. "Rookity-coo!"

"Isn't it lovely!" said Susan, jumping out of the car. The old house glowed red in the sunshine, and seemed to welcome the children. It had known many children's feet in the years it had stood, and had heard many children's voices. Now here were more children of the same family, and the house was glad to welcome their pattering feet and to hear their happy calls.

"Granny! There's Granny!" cried Jeffery, and he ran to meet the pretty old lady who stood on the steps to greet them. She was small and round and smiling, and she wore a funny little cap on her white hair.

Granpa came up behind her. He wore a pointed white beard, and had a thick mop of silvery hair. He ran down the steps to kiss Mother.

"Welcome to Greylings Manor!" he said to them all. "It may be the last time we shall welcome you here—but we hope it will be the happiest!"

The children hugged their grandmother and kissed their grandfather. They knew them very well, for the two old people had often been to stay at the children's home. They were fond of them, and were very glad to see them again.

"Isn't it a lovely place, John?" said Jeffery, as he took his brother and sister up to their rooms. "We have been given the two little rooms up in the roof—good! I had one before, and it's so exciting there."

He opened a door. The others went in. They found themselves in a low-roofed room, with latticed windows that looked out on to the sunny garden at the back of the house. The walls of the room were crooked, the ceiling was crooked, and the big beams that ran here and there were crooked too! "It's like a room in a fairy-tale!" said Susan, delighted. "I love the whitewashed walls and the uneven floor. Is this my room or yours?"

"It's our room," said Jeffery. "John and I sleep here, and you have the little room that leads off it. Open that low door there in the corner and you'll see your room, Susan.

Susan opened a low door that came no higher than her shoulder. She stooped and went through it. She came into a small room that seemed like a doll's room! It was almost round, had a ceiling that sloped right down to the floor at one side, and two tiny windows that let in the sun. A white pigeon sat on a small slanting roof outside one window, and cooed softly.

"It's simply lovely!" said Susan. "Oh, I know what you mean when you say this is a house where things might happen, Jeffery! It's like the beginning of a story!"

Susan spoke more truly than she knew. It *was* the beginning of a story—but the children didn't know it yet!

They washed, and then went downstairs. Mother and Daddy were talking out in the garden with Granny and Granpa.

"They don't want to be disturbed," said Jeffery, "I'll show you the rest of the house!"

The other two followed him. It was the most exciting house in the world. For one thing there were three separate staircases! One was the main one, a wide, winding stair that went from the big landing to the hall. Another led from the kitchens to the servants' rooms, and a third, most mysterious, led from a door in the dining-room, behind the wall, and up to the children's room, entering Susan's room unexpectedly from a cupboard!

"How simply thrilling!" said Susan, as she went up the tiny stairway, so narrow and dark, and came out of the little cupboard in her room!

There were old family pictures to see—there was great-grandfather, looking rather stern. Great-great-grandmother, looking very pretty indeed in a blue bonnet, stared at them from her frame.

"She's like *you*, Susan," said Jeffery. So she was. She had just the same deep-blue eyes and curly golden hair.

They were still looking at the pictures when Granny called them.

"Mother and Daddy are leaving now!" she called. "Come and say good-bye."

The children ran downstairs. They hugged their parents, wished them a lovely holiday, and then watched them get back into the car. Daddy started the engine and called to them.

"Be good now! We'll write to you!"

"Good-bye, dears!" cried Mother, and she waved her hand. The car swept down the drive and disappeared out of the eagle-gates. They were gone!

"Our holiday has begun!" cried Susan, and she jumped up and down the steps. The boys turned to Granny.

"Where is Rags? Is he still here with you?" they asked.

"He's out with one of the maids," said Granny. "Look—here he comes! My goodness, he'll be delighted to see so many children to play with!"

He was! He was a rough-haired fox terrier, with bright eyes, a wagging tail, and a black spot on his white back. He tore up to the children, barked loudly, flung himself on each of them in turn, and licked whatever leg or hand he could find.

"You're just the same darling old dog!" said Jeffery, pleased. He patted him hard. "We'll go for some good walks together, Rags, old boy!"

"Woof!" said Rags, in delight, and rolled over on his back with all four paws in the air.

"Ridiculous dog!" said Granpa, tickling him with his foot. "I suppose you'll forget all about the old people, now you've got three youngsters to tear about with! Ah—there's the dinner-bell! I'm sure we could all do with something to eat!"

Indoors they all went, and took their places in the long, low dining-room. Rags lay down on Jeffery's foot. He was just as happy as the children!

CHAPTER TWO

THE GREYLINGS TREASURE

FOR the next few days the children and Rags had
a fine time, tearing round the garden, going into
all the sheds and out-buildings, eating peas in the
kitchen garden, and hunting for ripening strawberries.

When Rags was not with them, Whiskers, the
big black cat, sauntered along beside them. The

fantail pigeons disappeared like a cloud of snow-flakes when they saw Whiskers—but at other times they were very tame and would come flying down on the children's shoulders and hands.

"This is such a lovely place," said Susan, looking back at the old house, as she went out of the little white gate that led to the kitchen garden. "How I wish that Granny and Granpa could go on living here, and that it would be Daddy's later on—and ours too, when we are grown up."

"Look—there is a car coming up the drive!" said Jeffery. The three children watched to see who would get out of the car. It might be someone they knew. But it wasn't.

The chauffeur got out and opened the door of the car. A very grandly dressed lady appeared, followed by a tall man. They went up the steps to the front door.

The children went into the kitchen garden as soon as the visitors disappeared into the house. They thought no more about them at all—until later on in the morning.

Jeffery was playing hide-and-seek with the others. He had gone into a little hedged garden that Granny called her own. In it she had planted all her very favourite flowers, and here her pigeons came to be fed each day from her hands.

Jeffery pushed his way into the middle of the thick yew hedge. He was sure that the others would never find him there! He stayed there, quite still, and waited for the other two to hunt for him.

Whilst he was there Granny came into her garden. She sat down on her white seat, and looked into her little pond, where white water-lilies were showing.

Jeffery thought at first that Granny's footsteps were those of Susan or John, and he kept as still as could be. But when the footsteps stopped, and nobody spoke or called, he carefully parted the green boughs and peeped to see who was there.

"Oh! It's only Granny!" he thought. And then he got a shock!

Granny was crying! Tears ran down her apple-cheeks, and she mopped them up with a tiny lace handkerchief. Jeffery stared in horror. He had never seen a grown-up cry before, and it was dreadful to see tears rolling down Granny's cheeks. Whatever could be making her so unhappy?

He struggled out of the hedge at once. Granny heard him, wiped her eyes quickly, and then looked round in surprise. She tried to smile when she saw the hot, dirty face peeping out of the hedge.

"Oh, Jeffery dear!" she said. "You did make me jump! Are you playing hide-and-seek?"

"Yes," said Jeffery. He ran up to his grandmother.

"What's the matter?" he asked. "Why are you crying? Has somebody been unkind to you? Just wait till I see them, that's all!"

He looked so fierce that Granny couldn't help laughing, though she still had tears in her eyes.

"No," she said. "Nobody's been unkind. But— did you see those visitors this morning, Jeffery?"

"Yes," said Jeffery. "Did *they* make you cry?"

"In a way they did," said Granny. "You see— they came to look over Greylings Manor—to buy it—and it made me feel sad to think that Granpa and I will have to go. It has always belonged to the Greyling family—and now it must go to strangers. Poor old house—it will not like that!"

"But Granny, have you lost all your money, or something?" asked Jeffery. "Why must you suddenly go?"

"We haven't *suddenly* lost our money," said Granny. "The family has been unlucky, as the years went by. First, the Greylings Treasure was lost."

"The Greylings Treasure!" cried Jeffery, excited. "What's that? I haven't heard of that!"

"Here he is!" suddenly cried Susan's voice and she came running into Granny's hedged garden. "He isn't even hiding. Catch him!"

"No, Susan, don't," said Jeffery. "I'm not play-

ing now. Granny is telling me something marvellous—about the Greylings Treasure!"

"Whatever's that?" said Susan and John in surprise. They came to sit beside Granny on the white
seat. The old lady went on with her story.

"Well," she said, "the Greylings Treasure was
brought back from India two hundred and fifty
years ago by an adventurous Greyling—Hugh
Greyling. He had done a good turn to an Indian
Prince, and the Prince gave him some wonderful
presents."

"What were they?" asked Susan.

"There were strings of pearls, diamonds set in
marvellous metals, a golden cup studded with
rubies and sapphires, and other smaller things,"
said Granny. "There is a book all about this
Treasure in the library."

"I shall read it!" said Jeffery, thrilled.

"Well," said Granny, "this treasure was in the
Greyling family for some years, and then civil war
broke out. You know what civil war is, don't you?"

"It's a war when a country fights against itself,"
said Jeffery. "Families against families. Daddy
says it's the worst of all wars."

"It is," said Granny. "Well, in this civil war the
Greyling family was afraid that their enemies would
steal the Treasure. So Jeffery Greyling—yes, he had

your name Jeffery, and he was very like you to look at—well, this old Jeffery of long ago took the Treasure to hide it away safely. He left the house with it—and never came back!"

"What happened to him?" asked John, in surprise.

"Nobody knows," said Granny. "We think he was killed by his enemies. But anyway, the Treasure was never found or heard of again."

"What do you think happened to it?" asked Jeffery.

"Either Jeffery Greyling hid it somewhere in safety, where it was never found again—and then died before he could tell anyone about it, or else his enemies took it and kept it for themselves," said Granny. "But I don't think that is so because somebody would have been sure to have seen the Treasure, and sooner or later it would have been talked about."

"Oh, Granny! Do you mean to say that you think it's still hidden somewhere?" asked Jeffery, in astonishment.

"I sometimes think so," said Granny. "When the Indian Prince gave your great-great-great-great-great-grandfather the Treasure he told him that as long as the golden cup was drunk out of by the Greyling family once a year, good fortune, health, and happiness would remain with the family. But if the cup passed out of the family, and was not used by them, these gifts would pass away too."

"It sounds like a fairy-tale," said Susan, who loved magic and mystery. "Granny, did the tale come true?"

"Well, in a way it did," said Granny. "I don't believe in these old sayings of good and bad luck, you know—but ever since the Treasure went, the Greylings have been unlucky. They have lost their money through the years, they have had illness and sorrow—and now, alas, Granpa and I have so little money left that we must give up the old Manor House, and go to live somewhere else."

"Wait a little longer till I'm grown-up, and I'll earn heaps of money and give it to you!" cried John.

"I'm afraid we can't wait as long as that, John!" said Granny, putting her arm round him. "We shall have to go before Christmas. Those people who came to-day have offered to buy the house at a good price, and to take the two farms, as well, that go with it."

"Dear old Greylings," said Jeffery, looking at the old house, with its tall chimneys. "I'd hate to think it wouldn't be Greylings any more. If only we had that Treasure now, Granny! You could stay here then, and needn't worry."

"I'd like to see that book that tells us about the Treasure," said Susan.

"I'll show it to you when you go indoors," said Granny. So, that evening, the three children pored over an old book, in which were rough pictures of the Indian Treasure. The golden lucky-cup was clearly drawn and the children looked at it in wonder. It had precious stones set around the middle, and all down the handle. Someone had coloured the picture, and the cup shone as if the stones were real!

The children could not understand the reading in the book, for the lettering was very old, and had faded with the years. They looked at the pictures of great brooches and necklaces and pins, and how they wished they all belonged to the family now!

"It's the most exciting tale I've heard," said Susan. "Granny, I feel as if I must go hunting for the lost Treasure straight away!"

"Many people have hunted," said Granny, with a smile. "But nobody has found it. No—I'm afraid it was captured by enemies all those years ago, smuggled away, and then sold. It's gone for ever now."

But Susan wouldn't let herself think that. She loved to imagine all kinds of things. "I shall pretend it can be found!" she said. "I shall pretend to go hunting for it every day! I shall be a Treasure Hunter!"

"We will, too," said the boys, who liked Susan's pretends.

"My three Treasure Hunters!" said Granny, with a laugh. "Well, hunt all you like—but don't get into *too* much mischief!"

CHAPTER THREE

ADVENTURE IN THE WOODS

THE boys did not really take the treasure hunt seriously, but Susan did. You should have seen her hunting the next day! She tapped the walls of the old house to see if she could find hollow places, behind which treasure might be hidden. She went into the attics and got herself covered with dust and cobwebs, hunting everywhere in the corners.

"You're silly," said John at last. "All these places have been hunted in for years and years. Granny says there only was one secret passage, and that was the staircase to your room, which was found and opened long ago, and isn't secret any more."

"Children, you really *must* go out of doors," called Granny. "It is far too lovely a day for you to spend in the house."

"But, Granny, we're Treasure-Hunting!" cried Susan.

"Well, you must hunt outside," said Granny. "Go along—out of the house you go, all of you!"

So the three hunters had to go out of the house, and they wandered over to the gate of the kitchen garden. Tipps, the gardener, was there and he waved them away.

"Don't you come in here this morning!" he shouted. "You ate half a row of my best peas yesterday and you'll just keep out to-day!"

"Bother!" said John. "I felt just like a few peas. What shall we do?"

"Let's go treasure-hunting in the wood!" said Susan eagerly. "We haven't been there yet. We could follow one of those little paths, couldn't we, and see where it leads to."

"We shall get lost," said Jeffery.

"Well, we can take Rags with us," said Susan.

"Rags always knows the way home. Come on, Rags. We're going hunting! Hunting! Treasure-hunting, Rags!"

"Woof, woof!" said Rags, thinking that Susan meant rabbit-hunting. So all four of them set off for the woods. They went down the drive and out of the eagle-gates. They turned to the left and soon came to the wood.

They went in under the trees. There was a green light in the wood, very cool and lovely. The trees were so thick overhead that only tiny specks of sunlight got through and these lay like specks of gold on the ground below.

Rabbit-paths ran everywhere. Rags rushed excitedly about, following first one and then another. The children followed quite a wide rabbit-path, thinking it was a real path.

But it wasn't. It stopped at a big rabbit-hole and Rags almost disappeared down it, barking in excitement. The children had to pull him out.

"Well, we can't go down the hole," said John, laughing. "That's where the path leads to. Where shall we go now?"

"Let's go deeper into the wood," said Susan. "It feels mysterious and exciting. You don't know what we might find!"

"Well, you won't find fairies or witches, if that is what you're thinking of," said Jeffery, laughing.

"Listen—what's that noise?" said Susan, stopping suddenly. They all stopped. There was a rushing noise that was not the sound of the wind in the trees.

"It sounds like water," said Jeffery, puzzled. "Oh —of course! I told you there was a river that ran through the wood, didn't I? It wanders in and out, and we must be quite near it."

He led the way between the tall trees. The ground became rather wet and marshy, and the children had to tread carefully.

"There it is!" said Jeffery at last. He pointed to where a dark green stream flowed swiftly along between tree-grown banks. The children went to it.

It was deep, and flowed quickly. Susan thought it looked queer.

"Let's follow the banks," she said. "I'd like to see where it goes."

So they followed the stream. It was difficult, because bushes grew so thickly on the bank in some places that they had to leave the stream, go a good way round the bushes and then come back to the water.

It grew wider and shallower as they followed its banks deeper into the wood. It lost its deep green

"Look, Jeffery! They are steps!"

colour and became brown. It bubbled and gurgled, and in its depths quick fishes darted about.

Then suddenly the stream widened out into a large round pool, like a small lake. At one end of the pool the stream flowed in, at the other it flowed out.

"Isn't it lovely!" said Susan, in surprise. "I wonder how it made itself into a pond. It looks so round that it seems as if someone made it."

"Whoever would make a lake in the middle of a wood?" said John scornfully. "Ooh look—what a marvellous water-lily that is!"

Water-lilies covered the pond. They were of many colours. The wild yellow one grew there, but deep red and paler pink ones lay on the water also.

"I wish I could pick that deep red lily and take it back for Granny," said Jeffery, looking at the one that John had pointed to.

"It's deep," said Susan, looking into the water. "You couldn't paddle out to get it."

Jeffery made his way round the pond, looking to see if there was any shallower place. "There's a big flat rock here," he said. "And another under the water. I might be able to stand on that, and reach it."

The flat rock was green with slime. Jeffery stood carefully on it, barefooted, and then stepped to the flat stone below—and then he felt about with his foot and said, "I do believe there's another flat stone below this one as well. It's just like steps!"

"They *are* steps!" said Susan, in surprise. She had scraped the green slime off with a stone, and below the slime was white marble! "Look, Jeffery—they are real steps. Steps that somebody put here for the pond."

Jeffery stared down in surprise. Susan was right. Jeffery forgot all about the red water-lily and began to scrape the steps.

"Well, why should anyone build steps here?" he said. "You only put marble steps by a pond if you want to feed swans—or go boating—or if you have a house nearby that you sit in to look over the water."

"Swans wouldn't come here," said Susan. "They like more open water. And there aren't any boats."

"No—but there might have been once," said Jeffery. "I say—I wonder if there ever was a summer-house—or boating-house, or something, near here. After all, if somebody took the trouble to build marble steps here, they might have built a little summer-house for themselves as well!"

"Let's look!" said Susan. So the three children began to hunt around the pond. The trees and bushes were so thick that it was difficult to make their way here and there.

Suddenly Susan gave a shout. "I say! Look here! What do you think this is?"

The boys scrambled over to where Susan was standing. She was pulling at some thick ivy.

"Look," she said. "There's brick under this ivy. I believe the ivy, the brambles, and the honeysuckle have grown all together here, and hidden a building of some sort!"

The boys excitedly looked about. It certainly seemed as if the great bramble and ivy cluster might be growing over something. They peeped here and there, but they could find no proper building.

"It's like the Castle of the Sleeping Beauty," said Susan, "all overgrown with thorns. Oh, Jeffery, look, look!"

Jeffery and John looked. Rags had gone after a rabbit, and had scraped hard at the bottom of the great ivy tangle. Where he had scraped, stone steps showed—steps that must lead down to the pond!

"So there *must* be some sort of a building beneath this tangle of bushes!" cried Jeffery. "There must! Steps wouldn't lead down from nothing. There must have been a tiny house of some sort here, with steps leading down to the pool. However can we find out?"

"We'll have to borrow an axe from Tipps," said Susan, thrilled. "Then we can chop away the ivy and the other creepers, and see if there's a house underneath."

"Well, there won't be a Sleeping Beauty inside, so don't hope for that, Susan!" said Jeffery, grinning. "I expect it's just a tumbledown hut built by somebody long ago who loved to come and dream in the wood."

"Jeffery, let's go back and get an axe now, this very minute," begged Susan. "Look—when I pull away the ivy here, there is more stone or brick underneath. I *know* there's a secret house here."

"All right," said Jeffery, who was longing to find out more himself. "We'll go back now, this very minute."

So back they went, making their way over the marshy ground. They would never have taken the right path if Rags had not shown them the way! But he trotted ahead, sniffing, and soon led them to the rabbit-path they had first followed.

When they were at last out of the dark, green wood, they scampered along at top speed, up the drive and into Tipps's garden-shed. He was there, potting plants.

"Tipps! Would you please lend us your axe?" asked Jeffery. "The one you chop wood with."

B

"Indeed no," said Tipps. "I'll not lend you something to chop off your fingers!"

"Oh, Tipps! We aren't as silly as that!" said Susan. "Please do lend us the axe. It's for something secret and important—something we found in the wood."

"Oh, well—I suppose you want to chop up a dead tree," said Tipps. "Listen now—I'll lend the axe to Jeffery because he's the oldest and biggest—but none of you are to use it except him. See?"

"All right, Tipps," said Susan and John. Jeffery took the axe, and they made their way out of the shed. But just as they turned their steps towards the front gate, a bell rang.

"Bother!" said John. "That's for dinner."

"Let's miss dinner and go and chop," said Susan, who was always ready to do mad things.

"Don't be silly," said Jeffery, putting the axe carefully into the middle of the yew hedge to hide it. "We don't want to have Granny and Granpa hunting all over the place for us, and Tipps telling them he's lent us the chopper. No—we'll go in and have our dinner—and then we'll spend the afternoon in the wood, chopping!"

So they went in to their dinner. It was stew, and treacle tart, and the three children ate hungrily. It was exciting to think of the axe hidden in the hedge, waiting to chop away creepers that had grown around a secret house.

"How you do gobble to-day!" said Granpa, in astonishment. "Now, now, eat properly, or you'll be ill!"

"Granny, we found a pond in the middle of the wood this morning," said Susan, who could never keep quiet about anything.

"Did you?" said Granny. "Well, there did use to be one, I believe. There was supposed to be a summer-house there too long years ago, but that seems to have disappeared now. The river has made the wood so marshy that it is no longer a pleasure to walk there, as it used to be years and years ago. Be careful if you go into the wood very far—it is very boggy."

"We'll put Wellingtons on," said Jeffery. He frowned at Susan to stop her saying any more. So often she said too much, and then their adventures were stopped by the grown-ups before they had even begun!

They slipped away from the dining-room as soon as they could. "I'm going to have a quiet nap," said Granny. "So keep away from the house, won't you?"

"Oh, yes, we'll be far away from Greylings this afternoon!" said Susan. She ran to join the boys.

Jeffery was taking the axe from the hedge. It shone bright and sharp.

"Come on," he said. "We've got plenty of time this afternoon. We'll see what we can find!"

So off they went again with Rags, who was delighted to go hunting rabbits once more. The children did not find it very easy to make their way to the river, but once they found it, it was easy to follow.

"Look! There's the pool again!" said Susan, jumping for joy, and landing in such a boggy patch that the boys had to pull her out. "Come on! Do some chopping, Jeffery!"

CHAPTER FOUR

THE LITTLE SECRET HOUSE

JEFFERY went to the overgrown clump and began to chop away at the ivy stems. Some of them were very thick. He chopped hard above the steps where Rags had found a rabbit-hole.

He hadn't chopped for long before he gave a shout. "Yes! Look—there *is* a house of some sort under all this ivy. I'm chopping by the door. Come and pull away the stems for me."

Susan and John went to help Jeffery. He had chopped so hard that he was very hot, and his face was wet. He took out his handkerchief and mopped his forehead.

Susan and John began to tear away the broken stems of ivy. They were more careful with the blackberry sprays, because they were prickly. The honeysuckle came away more easily, for its stems were thin and brittle.

"Yes!" said Susan, excited. "There *is* a door behind here. Oh, Jeffery! Fancy there being a little secret house hidden under all this ivy and creeper—a house forgotten long ago and never used except by the rabbits."

Jeffery laughed. He took up his axe again. "Well, the rabbits must be getting a shock now," he said. "Stand away, you two. I don't want to chop your heads off!"

"Let *me* have a turn!" begged Susan, who was simply longing to chop too. But Jeffery shook his head firmly.

"Certainly not, Susan," he said. "You know quite well that we promised Tipps I would be the only one to chop. I'm the oldest and the biggest, and I know how to use an axe. Goodness knows what *you* might do, Susan, if you began chopping!"

Jeffery chopped hard. Some of the ivy stems were as thick as the trunks of small trees. The roots that these stems had put out held firmly to the door underneath—but once Jeffery had chopped the stems in half, it was easy to pull away the brown roots that clung everywhere.

"Jeffery, we've made quite a hole already!" said Susan, dancing about in excitement. "Oh, Jeffery, hurry! Soon there will be enough room for us to creep through."

"Well, I'm hurrying as much as I can," said Jeffery. "But it's jolly hard work."

Crash! Crash! The axe cut through one stem after another, and at last there was a hole big enough for anyone to crawl through, about the middle of the doorway. Jeffery twisted a handkerchief round his hand and bent back some of the more prickly sprays that the others couldn't manage.

He poked the axe in through the hole. There was a wooden door behind. "I can see the handle!" said Jeffery, in excitement.

He slipped his hand along the door and tried the handle. It would not even turn!

"It won't move," said Jeffery.

"Let *me* try," said John. "My wrist is very strong —perhaps *I* can turn the handle."

But none of them could. It was stiff with the

rust of many many years, and would not move. The three children were terribly disappointed.

"Let's see if we can find a window and chop the ivy away from that," said John. "We could get in through a window."

So they tried to find a window—but the creeping ivy and brambles were so thick that it was quite impossible to guess where a window might be.

Scratched and pricked all over their arms and legs, the children looked at one another and wondered what to do.

"There *must* be some way we can get in!" said John.

"Yes—there *is*!" cried Susan. "I know what to do!"

"What?" asked the boys.

"Chop down the door, of course!" shouted Susan, in excitement. "Can't you chop a big enough hole in the door for us to squeeze through, Jeffery?"

"But do you think we *ought* to do that?" said Jeffery. "I mean—after all, it's a door, and it isn't right to chop holes in doors."

"It can't matter with *this* door," said John, eager to try Susan's idea. "It must be nearly falling to pieces as it is! Go on, Jeffery—chop a hole in it! We'll never get in if you don't. I simply can't wait any longer!"

Jeffery didn't want to wait either. He lifted the axe and chopped at the door with it. The wood was quite rotten and gave way easily. The axe went through it at once. A few strokes, and there was a large hole in the door, through which the children could easily squeeze!

"Good!" said Jeffery, panting. "I say—doesn't it look dark inside there?"

"I guess it's full of spiders and earwigs!" said Susan, staring at the dark hole in the door. "It's a good thing we none of us mind them. Who's going in first?"

Nobody seemed quite so keen on going in after all! It really did look dark and mysterious through the hole in the door. It smelt a bit funny too.

"I believe I've got a candle-end somewhere in my pocket!" said Jeffery suddenly. He always carried a strange collection of things about with him. "You never know when any of them may come in useful," he would say, when the others teased him about them. He felt in first one pocket and then another—and then brought out a candle-end—about two inches of red candle.

"I've got some matches somewhere too," he said.

"Oh, do hurry, Jeffery!" said Susan, always the impatient one. "I want to see inside this strange, secret little house. Fancy finding a house all hidden and covered with creeper, that nobody has been inside for years and years and years!"

Jeffery found his matches, and lighted the candle-end. He held the candle inside the hole in the door. The three children pressed round it to see inside the queer woodland house.

It did indeed look very mysterious. It was full of dark shadows. It looked small, high and round. A bench ran round it, and there was a small fireplace or hearth at the back. A table was against the wall at one side, with something on it. The children could not see what it was.

"Let's go in!" whispered Susan.

"What are you whispering for?" whispered back John.

"I don't know—but it seems funny to talk out loud now!" said Susan, still in a whisper.

Jeffery squeezed in through the hole first. He said "Oh! What's that!" and quickly climbed out again.

"What do you mean? What's the matter?" asked John, half-frightened.

"Something touched my face," said Jeffery. "I didn't like it!"

"It was a spider's web, you silly!" said Susan. She laughed, and the sound seemed to make things bright and ordinary again. "You baby, Jeffery! Fancy being frightened of a spider's web!"

"Well, it didn't feel nice touching my cheek like that," said Jeffery. "You go in first, Susan, if you think a spider's web is so funny! Take the candle!"

So Susan climbed in through the hole in the door, brushing aside the hanging spiders' webs with her hand. She held the candle up and looked round the queer little house.

It had had two windows, but both these were blocked up with ivy and other creepers. The bench round the wall was thick with the dust of many, many years. So was the table. Susan held the candle up and looked to see what was on the table.

"Jeffery, the people who were here last drank out of these glasses!" she said. "There are two here—all dirty and dusty. Oh, isn't it strange to come here and find glasses still on the table!"

By this time the two boys had crept into the little house too, and were staring round in excitement.

"Those glasses are like the very old ones that Granny keeps in the cupboard in the drawing-room!" said Jeffery, picking one up. "She won't use them because she says they are old and rare—how pleased she will be to have two more!"

"Look at the fireplace," said Susan, holding the

candle to it. "There are the remains of a fire there. What fun it must have been to come to this house on a cold day, light a fire, and sit here in the middle of the wood, with that lovely pool gleaming below!"

"Yes, mustn't it," said Jeffery. "I'd like it myself! I'd love a little secret house like this. The squirrels would come to it—and the robins. The rabbits would peep inside, and perhaps a hedgehog would walk in, and sniff around."

"That does sound lovely," said Susan, delighted. "Poor little house—hidden away and forgotten all these years. Let's make it ours!"

"Oh, yes!" cried the boys, thrilled with the idea.

"We'll clear away the ivy from the windows, and let the light through," said Susan, busy planning as she loved to do. "We'll bring a brush and sweep the dust away. We'll clean up the whole house— and we'll make a fire here one day, and boil a kettle for tea!"

"What fun!" shouted Jeffery, and he jumped for joy. A long spider's thread caught his ear, and he rubbed it away. "I'd like to clear away these clinging cobwebs," he said. "I really don't like them!"

"Let's go home again now," said Susan. "The candle won't last any more. It's running down on my fingers now and the wax is very hot. We'll bring candles here when we come, and keep them on the mantelpiece. Let's take the two old glasses with us."

Off they went back home, carrying the two glasses carefully. They whistled to Rags, who had been chasing rabbits the whole of the time, and then made their way through the dim wood. What an exciting day they had had!

CHAPTER FIVE

THE HOUSE GETS A SPRING-CLEAN

GRANNY and Granpa were thrilled to hear about the secret house in the woods, but Granny was not at all pleased to hear of the axe.

"You are not allowed to use such dangerous things," she said to Jeffery. "Tipps is foolish to let you have an axe. You must not use that again, Jeffery."

"All right, Granny," said Jeffery. "But I am really very careful, you know, and after all, I shall soon be twelve!"

"Look, Granny, here are the glasses," said Susan—and she put them on the table. She had carefully washed them, and polished them with a clean cloth. They shone beautifully. Granny gave a cry of delight and picked them up.

"Look, Thomas!" she said to Granpa. "Two of those beautiful, heavy old glasses that we have in my cupboard over there. How lovely! These are rare, now, children, and I am delighted to have them. They are over a hundred years old!"

She put them proudly in her glass-fronted cupboard in the corner of the drawing-room. They were fat glasses, short and very heavy—the children wished they could use them each day for their lemonade but Granny wouldn't hear of it!

"Granny, we are going to make that little secret house our very own," said Jeffery. "We are going to clean it up, and keep a few books and things there. We shall clean up the steps that lead down to the pond—and then, when it is all ready, you must come and have tea with us there!"

"We can boil a kettle on the little hearth," said Susan, jumping round like a grasshopper. "We can make a fire! There's a table there too, and a bench round the wall. Oh, it really is a most exciting little house!"

"Well, I can't see why you shouldn't make it your own house if you want to," said Granny. "Greylings Wood is ours, and the house was ours too—so you can have it for a playhouse, if you like."

For the next few days the children spent all their time in the wood, going to and from their new house, carrying brooms and pans and cloths! Jane the housemaid was quite cross at the disappearance of so many of her cleaning things, and the children had to promise to bring them all back safely when they had finished with them.

Susan took charge of the cleaning, as she was the girl. They all went to the house the next day, and climbed in through the door again. This time they had plenty of candles and two candlesticks. They put two candles into the stands and stood them on the little mantelpiece. They lighted the house up well.

"You two boys had better see what you can do about the windows," said Susan. "It would be a good thing to let some light and air into the house. It still smells old and musty."

"We mustn't have the axe this time," said Jeffery, staring at the windows. "But I could borrow

Tipps' little saw, and saw through the ivy-stems.
It wouldn't take long."

So Jeffery ran back to Greylings and borrowed the
saw. He and John took it in turns to saw the thick
stems, and soon they were able to pull the ivy and
brambles away from the window, and to let in
air and light.

There was no glass in the windows—they were
simply round holes in the rather thick wall. Whilst
the boys were clearing the two windows Susan got
busy with the cleaning. She tied a handkerchief
round her hair and put on an old overall. The
house was dustier than anywhere she had ever
seen!

Rags was thrilled with the house. He jumped in
and out of the hole in the door a dozen times in an
hour, and trotted all round the house, sniffing
everywhere. He would have liked to live there
always, surrounded by rabbits!

Susan removed all the cobwebs first. They hung
down from the roof, they stretched here and there,
and were grey with dust. They were soon down!
Big spiders scuttled away. A robin hopped in at
the hole in the door, and flew to the mantelpiece.
He carolled a tiny song as if to say, "I'll help with
the spiders!"

But he didn't. He flew out again, and sat on a

branch outside, watching the children with his bright black eyes.

Susan swept down the walls with her broom. She swept the mantelpiece, the bench, and table. When she had got all the dust on to the floor, she began to sweep that into her pan.

The dust made the children sneeze. They blew their noses, and then settled down to their work again. It was fun.

"Get me some water from the pool, John, will you?" asked Susan, when she had swept up all the dust she could find. "I want to do a little scrubbing now!"

"I'll help you," said John, who liked to scrub.

"Well, I've got two scrubbing brushes here, so you can have one," said Susan happily. It was lovely having a secret house like this, making it their very own.

John fetched a pail of water from the pond. The children had found that there was a complete flight of overgrown steps leading down from the little house to the pool. Jeffery was determined to clean them and uncover them all as soon as he had finished the windows.

There was a lot to do, but the children enjoyed every minute. The sun was very hot in the garden of Greylings, but here in the wood, it was cool and green. The children had brought lemonade with them, and they drank it when they felt too hot.

Susan scrubbed the floor, the bench, and the table. The floor was of brightly-coloured tiles, set in a pattern, and at some time had had a rug over it, for Susan found threads of it still left.

"I say! What a lovely floor!" said Jeffery, looking in from one of the window-holes. "It looks beautiful now! Who would have thought there was a floor like that!"

It took the children three days to get the little house really nice. At the end of that time it was lovely!

Jeffery had managed to get the door to open now, and had cleared away all the creepers over the doorway, so that light came in there as well as in at the windows. Tipps' saw was not so quick at clearing ivy as the axe, but that couldn't be helped.

John had cleared the steps that led down to the pool. He had torn away the creeping roots that hid them, and had cleared them of earth and moss. They were of white marble and shone beautifully. John was proud of them.

Susan had made the house look really lovely. Everything was clean there now. The brightly-coloured tiles shone on the floor. The table and bench were quite clean, and the fireplace was cleared too, and was neatly laid ready for a fire, with paper, twigs, and old wood that the boys had found outside.

They begged an old rug from Granny for the floor. They brought along a little vase which they filled with flowers for the middle of the table. Susan even brought an old clock that she had found in a cupboard. It had belonged to Granpa, and one of its legs was broken. It had not been worth mending and had been put away in a cupboard.

John mended its leg. Susan wound it up and it went. So to the secret house it was carried, and there it stood on the mantelpiece, ticking away cheerfully!

"I always think a clock makes a house feel cosy and lived-in," said Susan happily. "Doesn't it all look nice? Let's have tea here to-morrow! We won't ask Granny and Granpa yet. We'll wait till we're sure the fire goes all right, and the chimney doesn't smoke. We'll try to-morrow!"

Rags was most interested in the house. He ran in and out, and Susan did wish he could be taught to wipe his feet. He seemed to take a delight in running in the muddiest places he could find, and then walking over the clean floor of the little house!

The next day the children brought along the things for tea at the house. Susan carried a kettle of water to boil for tea. The boys brought a picnic basket full of food. Inside there were unbreakable cups and plates which Granny had given them to keep in their house.

"Isn't this fun!" said Susan, as she put a gay little cloth on the table. "Jeffery, do let *me* light the fire, please, to boil the kettle! After all, I did lay it ready."

Everybody wanted to light the fire, but Susan was allowed to do it. She knelt down and put a lighted match to the paper. It flared up at once. The twigs began to crackle. The wood soon caught fire, and a lovely glow filled the hearth.

But it wasn't so lovely after a little while. Smoke began to pour out from the fireplace, and filled the little house. The children coughed.

"Oh dear! It's smoking!" said Susan. "What a nuisance! Do you suppose we ought to have swept the chimney?"

"Well, I shouldn't have thought the fire was used often enough to make the chimney really sooty," said Jeffery.

Susan poked the lighted wood to the back of the fireplace, hoping that the smoke would soon go up the chimney. But it didn't. It went pouring out into the room. Soon the children's eyes began to smart, and they choked with the stinging smoke.

"Wood smoke is always horrid," said Jeffery,

going outside to wipe his streaming eyes. "This won't do, Susan. We'll have to put out the fire. We can't boil water for tea to-day. We'll have to do that when we've put the chimney right."

"I expect it's stuffed up with ivy stems and leaves," said John. He kicked the fire out, and soon only a few wisps of smoke rose from the hearth.

But it was impossible to have tea in the smoky house. Susan was very disappointed about it. She took the tea outside, and they sat on the steps, looking down to the little pond, and ate their egg sandwiches, ginger cake, and chocolate biscuits there. They drank the water out of the kettle, pouring it into their cups.

"This is really a lovely place!" said Susan. "Look how the sun comes slanting through the trees just there, and lights up the pond. What a lot of water-lilies there are out to-day!"

"There's a red squirrel watching us," said John in a low voice. "Don't move. He's in that hazel tree over there."

The children watched the big-eyed creature. He sat on the branch, his bushy tail curled up behind him. Then with a light bound he leapt to the ground and scampered up the steps to them. Rags saw him and would have pounced on him, but Jeffery had him by the collar.

Susan held out a bit of chocolate biscuit. The squirrel took it in a tiny paw and then bounded into the trees, carrying it in his mouth.

"He likes chocolate!" said Susan. "Oh, isn't he sweet! I'd like to tell him to live in our little house when we are not there. He can be our caretaker!"

As the shadows began to grow longer, one or two rabbits came slipping out of their holes. They sat not far off, washing their big ears, bending them down as they cleaned them. The children watched, keeping quite still. Rags whined, and longed to chase them, but they would not let him.

"We *are* lucky to have a little house all to ourselves in the wood," said John. "All the animals and birds will soon be tame for us, and we can feed them and make friends with them!"

The robin was already very tame. It took crumbs from Susan's hand, and did not seem at all afraid. A big freckled thrush sat nearby and eyed the children warily, turning its head first to one side and then another.

"It looks at us first out of one eye and then out of the other!" said Jeffery, with a laugh. He threw the thrush a bit of bread—but the robin flew down and got it before the thrush stirred from the branch.

"I could stay here all evening," said Susan. "But I'd really like to see what's the matter with that chimney, Jeffery. I'd like to put it right before Granny and Granpa come to tea!"

"Well, we'll have a look at it now," said Jeffery, getting up. The squirrel bounded up a tree as he moved, and the rabbits shot into their holes, showing white bobtails. Rags raced after them at once, and began to scrape earth into the air in a great shower!

"Have you got the brush here that you had yesterday, Susan?" said Jeffery. "The one with a long handle, I mean. I could put that up the chimney to see if there is anything stopping it up."

"Yes, there it is," said Susan. "In the corner."

Jeffery took it. He went to the fireplace and knelt down beside it. "I expect there is a bird's nest or something stopping it up," he said. "It is a very short chimney, and it should be quite easy to clear."

He put the broom up—and at once a shower of twigs and moss and leaves came down. It all fell into the fireplace. "A bird's nest," said Jeffery. He pushed the brush up as high as he could. Another shower of twigs and moss came down.

"Go outside and see if the brush is sticking out of the chimney," said Jeffery to John. John went out and looked. He came back.

"Yes," he said. "I can just see it. The chimney should be clear now."

"Right," said Jeffery. He pulled the brush down—but the end of it stuck against something in the chimney. Jeffery tugged hard, but the brush-end would not come.

"Blow!" he said. "What's the matter with it?" He put his head up the chimney and felt about with his hand. To his surprise he found something sticking out halfway across the chimney. This was what the brush had caught on.

Jeffery felt round it. It felt like a box or something. He grew excited.

"I say!" he called. "There's a sort of opening in the side of this chimney—a kind of hidey-hole, I should think! And there's something been stuffed into it—something too big for the hole—so that it sticks out half across the chimney!"

"Oh, Jeffery! Get it down, quick, get it down!" shouted John and Susan.

"I'll try," said Jeffery. "It seems to have stuck. No—here it comes!"

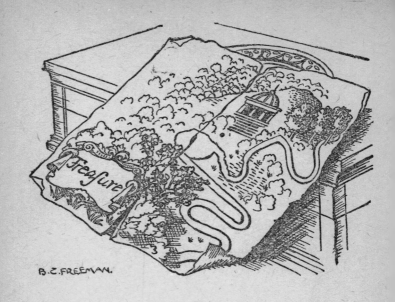

B. C. FREEMAN.

CHAPTER SIX

A MOST EXCITING DISCOVERY

He had tugged so hard at the box that it had moved from its place. He slid it out from the hole. It was heavy and Jeffery could not hold it in one hand. The box slid down the chimney and landed in the back of the fireplace with a crash.

"Gracious!" said Susan. "What a funny old box!"

"Isn't it exciting!" said John, almost beside himself with joy. "Is it the Treasure?"

"Of course not!" said Jeffery. "The box is too small to hold the Treasure! But it may hold something exciting, all the same."

It was an iron box, with a stiff clasp in front. On the top of the box was a raised letter—G.

"G for Greylings," said Susan, tracing the letter with her finger. "This is an old Greylings box. Open it Jeffery, quickly! Whatever can be inside it?"

It was not easy to open. The years had made the clasp very stiff, and Jeffery had to get a knife from the picnic basket to force it open.

"Shake it, John, and see it if rattles," said Susan eagerly. "Perhaps it might have a few old brooches inside."

John shook it—but it did not rattle.

"It sounds empty!" he said. "Oh dear—I do hope it isn't!"

Jeffery took the box from John, and began to work at the stiff fastening. It suddenly gave way, and Jeffery opened the lid. The three children peered inside in excitement.

"There's nothing inside it at all!" said Jeffery in the greatest disappointment. "Look—it is empty!"

So it was. Nothing was to be seen except the sides and bottom of the box itself.

John was puzzled. "But Jeffery," he said, "why should anyone want to hide a box in a secret chimney-hole, if there was nothing in it?"

"How should *I* know?" said Jeffery gloomily. "It must have been hidden there over a hundred years ago. Perhaps more. A silly joke, perhaps."

"It couldn't have been a joke," said Susan, taking the box from Jeffery. "Nobody sticks things up chimneys for a joke! Do you suppose there *was* something in the box—and somebody found it—and put the box back again after taking out the things inside?"

"Well, that's an idea," said Jeffery. "But how disappointing for us!"

Then Susan made a discovery. "Look, Jeffery," she said, holding up the box. "Doesn't it seem to you as if the box ought to be bigger inside than it is?"

"Whatever do you mean?" asked the boys.

"Well," said Susan, "if you look at the outside of the box it seems quite big—but if you look, *inside*, it doesn't look *big enough*!"

"You mean—there might be a secret bottom to it!" cried Jeffery, and he snatched the box from Susan. He examined it very carefully—and then he

The box slid down the chimney.

nodded. "Yes—there *is* a false bottom to it. You're right, Susan. How clever of you!"

"How can we open the secret part?" cried John, going red with excitement.

"I don't know," said Jeffery, busy pressing and tapping to see if he could open it. "My goodness! Suppose there is something really thrilling here after all!"

Susan and John could hardly keep their hands off the box as Jeffery tried to open the bottom part. It was no good—he couldn't do it.

He gave it to John, and John tried. Then Susan had a try. But no matter what they did they couldn't open the bottom of the box.

"It's some clever little trick, I'm sure," said Jeffery, in despair. "Oh, I *do* wish we could find it."

Susan grew impatient. She turned the box upside down and banged it with her fist. It slipped from her knee and fell on to the floor.

"Susan, be careful!" cried Jeffery—and then he stopped, and stared at the box. It had fallen upside down, and as Jeffery stared, he saw that the bottom of the box had slid crooked! Somehow or other in its fall, the secret spring had been touched, and the bottom was now loose!

Jeffery grabbed the box. He pressed on the bottom of it, as he held it upside down. The bottom slid away neatly, and the three children saw a small narrow space inside, hidden between the false bottom and the real one.

And this time there was something inside! Yes, there really was!

It wasn't brooches or anything like that—it was a sheet of thick parchment-like paper, doubled over. Just that and nothing more.

"A bit of paper," said Jeffery, taking it out very carefully. It fell in two as he touched it, breaking at the fold. It was very, very old.

"What does it say?" asked Susan, bending over to see it.

"It's a map," said John. "What a funny old map!"

"So it is," said Jeffery. "But what's it a map *of*?"

"Goodness knows!" said Susan. "And what's this one word on the map—just here? It's such old, old printing that I can't even read it!"

"What's that first letter?" said Jeffery, trying to make it out. "It's a J, I think. J—and that's an R, I believe. J—R—there's no word beginning with Jr."

"J—R—is that an E?" wondered Susan. "It's a funny one! And the next letter is certainly an A. Jrea—worse than ever!"

"And then comes an F," said Jeffery. "Jr—eaf—it must be some foreign language!"

"There are some more letters after that," said John. "I give it up! But I know what we'll do—we'll ask someone who can read old writing, and see if they can tell us what the word is. Perhaps if we know what the word is, we should know what the map means."

"Gracious! Look at the time!" said Susan. "Granny will be wondering whatever has happened to us! We'd better pack up and go home."

So they packed up their things, and, leaving the kettle behind for another day, they went to Greylings, carrying the old box with them. What a find they had had!

When they got to Greylings, they found a car in the drive. "It's the same one that came the other day," said Jeffery, looking at it. "It belongs to those people who want to buy the house."

"Well, Granny and Granpa will be busy with them, then," said Susan. "We'd better go into the study and wait till the visitors have gone."

So into the study they went—and, of course, they got out the strange map, pieced it together once more—and tried to find out what the word said.

"If only we could find out!" sighed Susan. And

then a voice behind her said, "And what do you want to find out, little girl?"

The children looked round. They saw that Granny had brought a gentleman into the room—the man who wanted to buy the house. She was showing him the study once more, and the children had not heard the door open.

Jeffery did not want to say anything about the map. He tried to take it off the table—but as it was in half, he only managed to get one piece before the man leaned over the table to look.

"I want to know what that word says," said Susan, in her clear voice. "We've been puzzling and puzzling over it. It's an old map we found to-day, hidden in this old iron box, up the chimney of our secret house in the woods."

Granny looked surprised. So did the man. He bent over the piece of parchment at once. "Where's the word?" he said. "Ah—well, let me see. That first letter is a T."

"T! We thought it was a J," said Susan.

"T—R—E—A—S——" read the man.

"S!" said Susan scornfully. That's not S, it's F."

"In the old days the letter S was written like an F," said the man. Then he jumped, because Jeffery gave a shout. He didn't mean to shout, but he couldn't help it. If the first letter was a T—and the fifth was an S—then he knew what the word was!

But he didn't say it. He tried to take the paper out of the man's hand—but the man held on to it. "Wait, wait," he said, "I haven't finished. T-R-E-A-S-U-R-E. The word is Treasure! How very interesting!"

The three children's faces went red with excitement and joy. "So it's a map showing where the Treasure was hidden!" thought Jeffery to himself. "We can puzzle it out—and perhaps find the Treasure for Granny!"

"May I take this old piece of paper to a friend of mine who is extremely clever at puzzling out old papers?" said the gentleman, suddenly, turning politely to Granny. "I could perhaps find out a good deal more for you, Mrs. Greyling, and it might be most interesting."

"Well—it's kind of you," said Granny, not knowing quite what to do. "But I'd rather like to keep the paper and show it to my husband."

"Very well," said the man, "I'll take it with me now, show it to my friend at once, and send it back to you to-night, with a note telling you what he says about it."

But Jeffery did not want the precious paper to go

out of his sight. "Please, it's mine," he said. "I want it. We found it ourselves."

"Of course, of course, my dear boy," said the man, smiling at Jeffery. "I quite understand your feelings. I will only keep the paper an hour—my friend is staying at a hotel nearby, and will tell me at once his opinion of it—whether it is genuinely old or not—and if it contains anything of importance to you. Your grandmother has been so kind to me that I would like to do her this little service, if I may."

Poor Granny could do nothing but smile and thank him. She did indeed think it was kind of him, but she was sorry because she guessed that the children wanted to show her their find and talk about it as soon as the man had gone. But as she hoped he would buy Greylings, she did not like to offend him.

"Take it, by all means," said Granny politely. "It would be kind of you to find out exactly what the paper means—if it *does* mean anything!"

The man patted Jeffery on the shoulder. The boy was angry, and looked it. What right had this man to go off with their precious paper?

He went almost at once, carrying the parchment carefully in his hand.

The children clustered together as soon as Granny

took the man out of the room to his car.

"What did you want to go and tell our secret to a stranger for, you stupid, silly girl?" said Jeffery to Susan. "Now see what you've done! He's guessed it's something to do with the long-lost Greylings Treasure—and he's got the map. At least—he's only got half of it, thank goodness! I was quick enough to get the other half, and hide it behind my back before he saw it. So he won't be able to tell much from *his* half!"

"That was quick of you, Jeffery," said John. "But really, Susan *is* an idiot to go and blurt out our secret like that."

"I'm sorry," said Susan, looking ready to cry. "I didn't think. I really felt so excited."

"Well, Susan, if that's a map showing where the Treasure was hidden, we don't want strangers going after it and finding it," said Jeffery. "I should have thought you would have been sharp enough to keep your tongue quiet."

"Don't grumble at me so, Jeffery," said Susan, who hated her big brother to think she was silly. "I'm very, very sorry, really I am."

"Well, don't say a word another time," said Jeffery. "We must just wait and see what happens now—I hope the man brings back our paper all right."

CHAPTER SEVEN

MR. POTS OF MONEY

GRANNY was told all about the finding of the box, and she called Granpa to hear about it when he came in. They looked at the old iron box with the big letter G on it. They exclaimed over the secret bottom, where the paper had been hidden. And Granpa longed for the man to bring back the parchment so that he might see the map himself.

"I shan't tell *any*one that we've got the other half

of the map," said Jeffery to the others, when they were alone once more. "Not *any*one. This is *our* secret—and if there's going to be any finding of the Treasure, *we're* going to do it. See?"

The others saw quite well and they agreed heartily with Jeffery. They waited impatiently for the man to come back.

"Supposing he doesn't?" said Susan. "Supposing he keeps the paper for himself, and tries to get the Treasure?"

"Oh, don't be so silly, Susan," said Jeffery, who still felt cross with her. "How can he find anything if *we've* got one half of the map? Do use your brains."

"I *am* using them," said Susan indignantly. "He might be able to make out enough, just by using his half. It looked to me to be the most important half."

"Here he is again!" cried John, from the window. "And he's got the map. Good!"

The man was shown into the study again, and Granny and Granpa came too, eager to hear what was said.

"I've taken the paper to my friend to puzzle out," said the man, whose name was Mr. Potts. "He says there is no doubt at all that it is an old map, which shows the whereabouts of some Treasure."

"Really!" said Granny, thrilled.

"Yes," said Mr. Potts, his big moustaches seeming to bristle with excitement too. "But my friend, who is used to dealing with old documents like this, says that there is only half of the real map here. He says there should be another half."

"Dear dear," said Granny, looking round the room as if she expected the other half to come floating down to her. "Now where can that be? In the box, do you think?"

"Quite likely," said the man eagerly. "May I look and see?"

Jeffery gave a secret wink at the others. He handed Mr. Potts the box. He felt quite safe in doing that because he knew quite well that there was nothing in the box at all! The other half of the old map was at that moment in the top drawer of the desk in the corner! Jeffery had slipped it there as soon as he had seen Mr. Potts coming up the steps again.

Mr. Potts shook the box. He opened and shut the false bottom. He peered into the secret hiding-place and scraped round it with a pencil. There was nothing there at all.

"No," he said. "It's quite empty. But I am perfectly certain there must be another half to this old map. Until it is found, no one will be able to hunt for the Treasure. Do *you* know where it is?" he said very suddenly, wheeling round on Susan.

Susan had no idea where Jeffery had put the map. She shook her head. "No," she said, "I don't know where it is at all."

"Do *you*?" asked the man, staring at John. John went very red. Like Susan, he had no idea where the half was but he couldn't help blushing.

"I don't know at all where it is," he said.

Mr. Potts turned to ask Jeffery—but that sharp boy had guessed he would be asked, and he had slipped out of the room. He wasn't going to tell an untruth—but he was jolly sure he wasn't going to tell the truth to Mr. Potts either!

"I wonder if you children are telling the truth," said Mr. Potts, looking at the blushing John.

That made Granny angry. "Mr. Potts," she said, "I think you forget that they are my grandchildren. They are all truthful children, I can assure you."

"Sorry, Mrs. Greyling," said the man, with a laugh. "This boy went so red I thought he wasn't telling the truth."

"May we have our map back, please," asked Susan, trying to make Mr. Potts stop staring at John, who was looking more and more uncomfortable.

"Certainly," said Mr. Potts. "Here it is. But it isn't much use to you or to anybody unless the other half can be found."

He gave the map to Susan. "That word is certainly 'Treasure,'" he said. "And I should think that if we could find the other half of the map, and piece it together, there's a good chance of coming across the Greylings Treasure. You were good enough to tell me the old story the other day, Mrs. Greyling, and I was *most* interested in it!"

"Well, thank you for your help," said Granpa.

"May I ask a favour?" said Mr. Potts, smiling very charmingly at Granpa. "If you *should* come across the other half of the map, let me show it to my friend, and he will work it out for you, and help you to find the Treasure. It needs someone very learned in old documents to trace out the meaning of them—and I should be delighted to help you if I could, by getting my friend to do his best for you."

"Thank you," said Granpa again. "We will certainly promise to let you see the other half, if we find it."

"Where did you say you found the box?" asked Mr. Potts, turning to Susan.

Susan told him, rather sulkily. She didn't want to tell him any more than she could help, after Jeffery's scolding—but if she didn't tell him, Granny would —so she didn't see that it mattered.

"Very interesting, very, very interesting," said Mr. Potts, when he heard about the secret house, and the hole in the chimney. "You are very lucky children! Well—don't forget to let me know if you find the other half of the map, will you?"

He patted Susan on the shoulder, smiled at her most beautifully, and then said good-bye. As soon as he was gone Susan stamped her foot.

"Horrid man! Patting me and smiling at me with a nasty treacly smile! He'd like to get the treasure himself, I know he would!"

Jeffery slipped into the room, grinning.

"Hallo!" he said. "He's just gone! Isn't he dreadful? Fancy Greylings Manor being *his*! I just simply couldn't bear it!"

"He's frightfully rich, Granny says," said John.

"Well, Potts is a good name for him then," said Jeffery, grinning again. "Mr. Pots of Money!"

The others laughed. "You were clever to slip out of the room before you could be asked if you knew where the other half was," said Susan. "John went awfully red. I really thought Mr. Pots of Money would guess that he knew about the other bit of map."

"Where's the half he brought?" asked Jeffery.

John gave it to him. "Oh, good—well now we'll be able to fit the pieces together and see what *we* can puzzle out. We may not be clever and learned, like Mr. Potts's friend is—but I hope we're smart enough to see what this map means!"

"Let's go up to our room to look at it," said John. "If dear Mr. Potts comes back suddenly, he might see we have two bits. And I say—suppose Granpa sees them! He has promised to let Mr. Potts see the other half."

"Well, we mustn't let him or Granma see the half then," said Jeffery. "Now remember, Susan—don't you go and give the game away!"

"Of course I shan't!" said Susan crossly. "Don't keep saying things like that, Jeffery."

"Come on. Let's go up to our room and have a good look at the map again," said John. So they set out to go upstairs—but Granny and Granpa were in the hall, near the stairs. Suppose they stopped the children and asked them about the other half of the map, whilst they still thought of it?

"Susan! We'll go up to our rooms by that secret staircase that leads into your room," said Jeffery. "Quick! Come into the dining-room before we're seen."

They slipped unseen into the dining-room and went up the funny, narrow stairs that wound up to Susan's room. All three children stepped out of Susan's cupboard, laughing.

"It's fun to come up those old stairs!" said Susan. "There's a table in your room, Jeffery. Let's go and put the map there and really study it hard. Now that we know it may be a map of where the Treasure was hidden, it is much, much more exciting!"

Soon the three children were bending over the funny old document. Jeffery hurriedly stuck the back of the halves together with gummed paper, so that they could see everything better.

"Look!" he said suddenly. "Do you see this half that Mr. Potts took away? Compare it with the other half—and you'll see that every line on Mr. Potts's piece looks dented—as if someone had run a pencil over every bit of the map! Do you know what has been done!"

"No, what?" asked Susan, puzzled.

"Somebody has traced the map," said Jeffery. "They wanted a copy of it—so they laid tracing paper over it, and pencilled a copy! The lines would show through the tracing paper quite clearly. It's like when we trace maps at school. Mr. Potts has got a copy of this! No wonder he was willing to bring it back so quickly!"

"That means he thinks it's a proper map, showing where the Treasure *is*," said John slowly.

"It shows something else too," said Jeffery. "It shows that he means to try and find it! Why would he take a copy of it if he didn't want to find it! No—he believes in Greylings Treasure—and he believes in our map. Thank *goodness* he only saw half!"

"Do you think he may try to get the other half?" asked John solemnly.

"I hope not!" said Jeffery. "But you never know. Do you know what I'm going to do? I'm going to take a tracing of the map myself—and then put the real map into some good safe place so that we don't need to use it. We'll hide the tracing too, except when we use it."

"Do the copy now," said John. "I can see Granny and Granpa in the garden, and Mr. Potts has gone. Then we can hide the real map away."

Jeffery got some tracing paper and sharpened a pencil.

In ten minutes he had carefully traced the map on the paper, which he folded and put into his pocket.

"Now we'll hide the *real* map!" he said.

"Where?" asked Susan.

"It had better be somewhere quite simple," said Jeffery. "Difficult places are always searched. *I* know! We'll put the map in your dolls' house,

Susan! I'm sure no one would think of looking there!"

Jeffery got some seccotine, and knelt down on the floor. He carefully stuck the two halves of the map on to two ceilings in Susan's dolls' house—on the bedroom ceiling, and on the kitchen ceiling!

"Nobody, nobody would *ever* think of looking there!" said Susan, in delight. And, indeed, it was a clever place.

The bell rang for supper.

"Now we shan't have any time to work out the map!" said Jeffery. "Bother! We'll do it afterwards, when we're in bed! You can come into our room, Susan, and we'll see if we can work out the map. We'd better wash now, and change into something clean. Hurry!"

CHAPTER EIGHT

WHERE IS THE WINDING ROAD ?

AT supper that night Granny and Granpa asked
the children all kinds of questions about the secret
house and the iron box. They were really just as
excited as the three children.

Jeffery said nothing at all about the other half
of the map. Granpa wanted to see the piece that

Mr. Potts had had, and Jeffery took out his copy of it.

"I've put the map in a safe place," said the boy. "You see, Granpa, if people keep handling it, it will fall to pieces, it's so old!"

"Quite right, my boy," said Granpa, taking the tracing. "Very sensible of you."

The children went early up to bed that evening, for they all so badly wanted to study the complete map and see if they could puzzle it out. As soon as Susan was undressed and had her dressing-gown on, she slipped into the boys' room.

They were already in bed. They had lighted their bedside lamp, and their two heads were close together, looking hard at the map.

Susan climbed into bed beside them and looked too.

"It's an odd sort of map," said Jeffery. "Look at this curving snake thing—it must be a road! And then there are three big trees. Well, those trees are probably dead by now and fallen down. But it's possible they may still be standing in a row somewhere."

"And look at this funny hump-shaped thing" said John, pointing with his finger. "Is it a hill? There aren't any hills like that round here, are there?"

"There might be," said Jeffery. "We haven't

explored everywhere yet, you know. And goodness knows what might be in that deep wood of ours! It's almost a forest, it's so thick and so big."

"Then what's this funny little drawing down here?" said Susan, pointing to what looked like a roughly drawn church. "It's got a row of queer little lines beneath it— steps up to it, I suppose."

"It's very odd," said Jeffery, his face red with trying to make out the map. "I read it like this— first we have to go down a winding road or lane. Then we come somewhere where there are three big trees in a line. Then we come to a hump-backed hill. Near there we shall find a little church or building of some sort—and perhaps the Treasure is hidden somewhere about there."

"That sounds splendid, Jeffery!" said Susan, her eyes shining with excitement. "I wonder where the winding road is?"

"We'll get a map of the district," said Jeffery. "It will show us all the winding roads there are. We should come to the three big trees at the fourth bend in the road. If you count, you'll see there are four bends in the drawing."

"Yes. So there are," said Susan. "You are clever, Jeffery! Oh, I'm longing to go exploring now. Where can we get a map to see if there are any winding roads round here?"

"I believe there's one in Granpa's study," said John. "I saw Granpa looking at it the other day. Shall I slip down and fetch it?"

"Yes," said Jeffery. "Go down Susan's little staircase, John. You won't be seen then, perhaps."

John slipped out of bed. He ran into Susan's room, opened her cupboard door, and went down the curious little stair. He stopped at the bottom to listen if there was anyone in the dining-room. He could hear nothing. He stepped into the dining-room, ran to the door and then crept into the study, which was nearby. He could hear the wireless murmuring in the drawing-room.

"Good!" thought John. "If I do make a bit of a noise, no one will hear me if the wireless is on!"

He opened the glass front of the bookcase. It made a click as it ran back. But nobody heard. John hurriedly looked down the row of books. He was sure the map had been put back there.

It had. There it was. "Map of the Greylings Lands."

He took it out of the bookcase, shut the glass front, which made a most alarming click again, and then ran back to the staircase. He was up it and into Susan's bedroom in a trice.

"Good boy!" said Jeffery, pleased, when John danced in, holding up the map. "You've been jolly quick. But what a row you made! We heard the click of the bookcase up here!"

"Yes, I know—I couldn't help it," said John. "But the wireless is on, so Granny won't hear anything. Come on, let's see if we can find this winding road."

They opened the big folding-map. It showed the whole of the land held by the Greylings family. There were the two farms, the Manor House and its grounds, the Greylings Wood, and the roads around and through the property.

"It's jolly big," said Jeffery. "I hate to think of it all going to Mr. Pots of Money. He's not the right person to have it. I bet he'd turn the people out of the farms, and cut down all that lovely wood to sell for timber!"

"Look—would you call *that* a winding road?" asked Susan, pointing to a place called Cuckoo Lane.

"It's not *very* winding," said Jeffery. "And it only seems to have three bends, not four. Let's see if there's a road that winds more than that."

They studied the Greylings map from end to end. They looked at every road, every lane. They even studied the field-paths that were shown running here and there.

"Well, it's funny, but Cuckoo Lane seems to be absolutely the only road or lane that winds at all," said Jeffery at last. "Maybe we shall find that it has more bends than the map shows. The other roads are either straight, or just sort of wavy—no proper bends."

"Well, you see, it's very flat ground around here," said John. "People can walk straight from place to place. When there are hills, the roads wind a bit."

"What shall we do to-morrow?" said Susan. "Shall we go to Cuckoo Lane, and see if we can find four bends in it—and maybe three enormous trees, and a hill somewhere?"

"Yes—that's what we'll do," said Jeffery. "We'll go to-morrow morning—and in the afternoon we'll ask Granny and Granpa to have tea at the secret house with us. It will be fun!"

There was the sound of someone coming up the stairs to the landing outside. "Quick, Susan—it's Granny!" whispered John. "Get back to bed!"

Susan almost fell out of bed, in her hurry. She shot across the room, slipped into her bedroom and jumped into bed as Granny opened the boys' door.

"I heard you talking, my dears," said Granny. "It's quite time you put out your light and went to sleep. You will wake Susan if you talk like this."

Jeffery giggled. He knew quite well that he wouldn't wake Susan—she was wide enough awake already! He snuggled down under the clothes with

John. Granny bent over them and kissed them good night.

Then she tiptoed into Susan's room, and softly kissed her too. Susan didn't make a sound. But you should have heard those three children giggling as soon as Granny went downstairs!

"Susan, I hope we don't keep you awake with our talking!" called John.

"Be quiet, John," said Jeffery. "You'll have Granny back again, if you shout like that. We'd better go to sleep. Well, good night, Susan. I expect we'll all dream of the winding lane and the Treasure!"

B. C. FREEMAN.

CHAPTER NINE

A VISIT TO TIMBLES' FARM

THE next day the children asked their Granny and
Granpa if they would go to tea at the little house.

"Yes, we'd love to," said Granny. "We're longing
to see it! We'll all have tea there at four. What
are you going to do this morning?"

"We're going for a walk, Granny," said Jeffery.
"Unless you want us to do anything for you?"

"No," said Granny. "It would be nice for you to go for a walk. Where are you going?"

"Along Cuckoo Lane, I think," said Jeffery. "We'll take old Rags—that is, if he can walk after such a huge breakfast!"

"You shouldn't feed him at meal times," said Granny. "He gets so many scraps now that he's getting quite fat. Aren't you, Rags?"

"Woof!" said Rags, leaping about the room like a kangaroo, excited because he had heard the wonderful word "walk"!

"You will pass near Farmer Timbles' house," said Granpa, looking up from his paper. "Go in and see Mrs. Timbles. She will be delighted to welcome you."

The children set off as soon after breakfast as they could. Rags pranced ahead of them, barking at the sparrows in the roadway. Jeffery had with him the copy of his map.

They went down the drive, out through the gates. The stone eagles sat on the gate-posts, looking over the road as they had done for three or four hundred years. They were so old that they had begun to crumble away here and there.

Down the road went the children, followed by Rags, till they came to a stile. They climbed over it and went across a large field. There was a stile at the other end, and then a narrow path that ran between two tall hedges.

"We come into Cuckoo Lane at the end of this path," said Jeffery, looking at the big map.

They were soon in Cuckoo Lane. It began at two cottages nearby and then wandered away across a common to Farmer Timbles' house.

"Now, it begins *here*," said Jeffery, standing at the cottage gates. "We'll follow it carefully and count the bends."

They set off down the lane. On one side was a low hedge of hawthorn. On the other there was nothing—the common stretched away, soft and heathery.

"Here's *one* bend," said Susan, as they rounded a corner. "Good! But oh dear—the lane looks awfully straight now, doesn't it, Jeffery? It looks straight almost as far as Farmer Timbles' house."

"Well, maybe it goes past his house, after all," said Jeffery. "There may be a few bends we can't see."

Down the lane they went again, passing a duck-pond and Jeffery thought they might call that another bend. Then, just as it came to Farmer Timbles' house, it wound round to his front gate.

"That's three bends, anyway," said Susan, pleased.

"Jeffery, let's just see if the path goes on, before we go and call on Mrs. Timbles."

So they went to see if the lane went on anywhere, or whether it stopped at the farm.

To their great disappointment it seemed to stop at the farm gate! Only field-paths were to be seen after that.

"Isn't it tiresome?" said Susan. "But perhaps, Jeffery, the old map is wrong—maybe there should have been only *three* bends shown?"

"Perhaps so," said Jeffery. "But what I'd like to see is some big trees! It's rather wild land here—too much common—and I can't see any big tree except that one over there by the farmhouse—and that's not really very big."

"And where's the hill?" asked John, looking all round. "The land is so flat here. I can't see a hill anywhere!"

"It's very disappointing," said Jeffery. "But let's go in and see if Mrs. Timbles is anywhere about. She may be able to tell us if the lane ever went any farther than this. After all, this map is very, very old, you know, and lanes can disappear easily enough, if they are not used."

They went into the farmyard. It was a lovely place. Cows lowed in a shed nearby. Pigs grunted in a big sty. Hens clucked all over the place, and from somewhere not far off came the curious sounds of turkeys gobbling.

"There's Mrs. Timbles, with the turkeys!" said Jeffrey. "Hallo, Mrs. Timbles! We've all come to see you!"

Mrs. Timbles shut the door of the turkey-house. She beamed at the three children, who liked her at once. She was fat and round, and her face shone like a large, red, polished apple.

"Well, I never!" she said. "The three little Grey-lings! Welcome, my dears—I'm right glad to see you all! I was wondering when I'd get a sight of your merry faces. How like your father you all are! Ah, I remember him here as a boy—and a monkey he was too! Let all my turkeys out one day, he did, and such a time we had getting them back."

"Did Daddy really do that?" said Jeffery, in the greatest surprise. He couldn't imagine his father doing anything so naughty. "Oh, I must ask him about it!"

"Yes, you ask him if he remembers Mrs. Timbles' turkeys!" said the farmer's wife, with a laugh. "It was this very house he let them out of! The rascal!"

"Why don't you let them loose like the hens and the ducks?" asked Susan, who felt sorry for the big birds shut up in the house. There was wire-netting round two sides, but they did look very crowded together inside, she thought.

"You mustn't let turkeys touch the ground," said Mrs. Timbles. "If they get wet feet, they're done for! But come along, we don't want to stand here talking about my greedy turkeys! You come along in and I'll see if I can find a few cakes for you, and something to drink!"

They followed her into the sunny farmhouse. They sat down in a great kitchen, whose floor was tiled with old red bricks, so clean that it seemed a shame to tread on them. At one end burned a cheerful wood fire. Bright red geraniums flowered on the window-sill, and cups and saucers with a bright red pattern seemed to flower on the dresser!

"It's a lovely kitchen," said Susan, looking round it. "When I'm grown up I shall have a kitchen like this, and I shall live in it like you do. It's nicer than drawing-rooms and dining-rooms."

Mrs. Timbles disappeared into a larder as big as Granny's study. She brought out some ginger buns, some tarts that were so full of home-made jam that they ran over, and a great jug of something that looked a little like lemonade, but wasn't.

"It's nettle beer, my dears," said Mrs. Timbles. "Nettle lemonade! Made of the youngest leaves of the hedgerow nettles, according to an old, old recipe that my great-grandmother had from Greylings Manor when she was cook there a hundred years ago!"

The children tasted the nettle drink and thought it was simply lovely. They ate all the buns and the tarts and were very sorry when they were finished. They were too polite to ask for any more. Rags sat beside them, licking up any crumbs that were dropped!

"I'll not give you more to eat," said Mrs. Timbles, who knew quite well what the children were thinking. "I've plenty to offer you—but I know you'll not be eating any dinner if you have too much now! And what will your Granny say to me then?"

The children laughed. They loved being in the old kitchen and having such a feast. The farmhouse felt as old as the Manor House.

"*Is* it very old?" asked Susan, looking up at the enormous black beams that ran across the ceiling and in the walls of the kitchen.

"Very, very old," said Mrs. Timbles. "As old as Greylings Manor. Ah, children, I'm grieved to hear that the old mistress is going, and the old master. We've belonged to Greylings, we Timbles, as long as anyone knows. We don't want to belong to strangers!"

"Isn't it a pity that the Greylings Treasure can't

be found?" said Jeffery. "Then Granpa would be rich."

"The Greylings Treasure has been lost this many years," said Mrs. Timbles, gathering up the dirty plates. "Many a man has hunted for that, my dears. But it's my belief it went years and years ago. It will never be found now."

"Is the lane old that goes to your house, Mrs. Timbles?" asked Jeffery.

"As old as the house, I guess," said the farmer's wife.

"Did it ever go farther than the house?" asked Jeffrey.

"No, never," said Mrs. Timbles. "It had no need to. There's no house beyond this one. It only runs between the two cottages down the way, and our farm."

The children were disappointed to hear that. But they did not tell Mrs. Timbles why they wanted to know. They got up to see the young chicks and ducklings at the back of the farm, and to look at the lambs frisking in the fields beyond.

"What's that old place just there?" asked Susan, pointing to a tumble-down stone hut, with no roof, not far off. Lambs were playing in and out of it.

"No one knows," said Mrs. Timbles. "It's been like that for years. I did hear say that there was something funny about it, but I never found out what. There's not much left of it now."

"Let's go and look at it," said Susan. But there was no time.

"We must hurry back," said Jeffery. "We've been all the morning! Rags, Rags! Stop sniffing about, and come along home!"

They said good-bye to Mrs. Timbles, who begged them to come again soon. They hurried down the lane, counting the bends again.

"It's no good, there are only three," said Jeffery. "And one of those isn't much of a bend really. And there aren't any big trees about and I didn't see any hill at all, did you? I looked and looked everywhere, when we went round the farm."

"So did I," said John, looking gloomy. "I'm afraid this lane isn't the right one. Well, we'll have to think again, that's all!"

CHAPTER TEN

SOMEBODY ELSE IS TREASURE-HUNTING!

THAT AFTERNOON the three children and their grandparents went to picnic in the little house.

Granny didn't at all like the marshy ground she
had to cross, and John had to keep putting down
handfuls of twigs on the muddiest bits for Granny
to walk on.

Rags came with them, of course, quite beside himself with joy at chasing rabbits again. His tail wagged the whole time, and his tongue hung out of his mouth.

"We'll make a fire again this afternoon," said Susan happily. She loved making fires. "I hope the chimney won't smoke this time."

"It shouldn't smoke now," said Jeffery. "It was the birds' nests and the iron box that make it smoke, because they stopped up the chimney."

Granny and Granpa were amazed when they saw the secret house, and looked at the doorway and windows which the children had cleared by chopping and sawing away the ivy and brambles.

"I *had* heard of this place," said Granpa. "But even when *I* was a boy it had disappeared. I remember looking for it, and thinking it must have fallen to pieces. But it must have been overgrown like this, even then, and I didn't see it."

Susan went to lay the fire—and then she stopped and stared. The fireplace was not as she had left it! It had been full of birds'-nest twigs and leaves and moss. But now it wasn't! The mess had been cleared out of the fireplace, and was all over the floor.

"Look," said Susan to the boys. "Somebody has been here!"

The boys stared at the fireplace. They, too, remem-

Granny and Granpa visited the secret house.

bered that it had not been cleared when they had left the day before. How strange!

"Why should all that mess have been moved away from the hearth!" wondered Jeffery. "Well—for one reason only!"

"What?" asked John.

"Because *some*body was hunting all around for something!" said Jeffery. "Somebody has been looking for the other half of the map! Yes—that's what happened. They've looked up the chimney—and cleared the hearth to hunt for it, too. And look—they've caught their sleeve on this old nail!"

The nail stuck out from the mantelpiece and on this hung a small piece of blue cloth.

"Mr. Potts wore a blue suit yesterday," said Jeffery. "And I guess he's been here hunting—and tore his suit! Serve him right!"

"Well, he didn't find much!" said John. "I wish I'd caught him."

"I don't," said Jeffery. "He might be rather unpleasant! I don't like him!"

The children didn't tell their grandparents what they had discovered. They quickly cleared away the mess, and Susan laid and lighted a fire in the hearth. This time it burnt beautifully and didn't smoke at all. The children were very pleased. Susan put the kettle on the fire to boil.

They had a lovely picnic, except that Rags discovered the chocolate buns, which John had stupidly put on the floor for a moment. Rags quite thought the plate was meant for him, and he ate six of the buns before he was noticed! Then he was driven out of the house in disgrace, and spent his time pawing in the pool at a big fish he could see below the water.

"I know he'll fall in," said Susan. But he didn't. He wasn't fond enough of water for that!

"Well," said Granny, when the picnic was over, "that was a real treat. I think you've cleaned the house beautifully, Susan darling. You will be able to have it as your own hidey-hole whilst you are at Greylings!"

"The pool is very pretty from here," said Granpa, sitting on a step and looking down at the lilies. "I like the bit of the stream you can see too. It winds in and out beautifully between the trees."

"Yes, doesn't it," said Susan—and then a thought struck her.

It was such a wonderful thought that she went red at once. She beckoned to Jeffery and took him behind the little house. He was puzzled at her excited face.

"Jeffery! Did you hear what Granpa said?" whispered Susan.

"Of course," said Jeffery. "But I didn't see anything in it!"

"But, Jeffery! When he said the stream *winds in and out beautifully*, didn't you think of anything!" cried Susan, forgetting to whisper. "Don't you see? We've been looking for a winding lane—but it's a river in the map, not a lane!"

"Gracious! I believe you're right!" said Jeffery, thrilled. "Yes—why didn't we think of that before? The river, of course. At its fourth bend—goodness, we'll have some more exploring to do to-morrow!"

They told John, who came up to see what the excitement was. He glowed with delight. "Of course, of course!" he said. "We *are* idiots not to have thought of that. Good old Granpa! He gave us the right idea and didn't know it!"

Granny was puzzled to know why the children seemed so excited when they went home that evening. But they didn't say a word! No—this was their own secret, and they meant to do their exploring without anyone knowing.

"And now that we know somebody else is doing a bit of exploring too, we'll keep our secret all the tighter!" said Jeffery, remembering the fireplace in the little house. "Mr. Potts has been to our little house—but he doesn't know any more than he did before!"

"Well," said Granny, when they reached home, "that was a very pleasant outing. You were clever to discover that hidden house, children—it is really most exciting. I can imagine how thrilled you were to find the iron box in the chimney too—and the old map. It is a great pity that there is only half of it."

"Well, the other half may turn up," said Granpa. "If so, we'll let that fellow Potts have it and see if his learned friend can make out what it all means. *I'm* afraid it doesn't mean anything."

The children looked at one another, but they said nothing. Susan longed to tell everything, but she knew she mustn't.

They went up to their rooms—and Susan made a queer discovery! She opened one of her drawers to get a clean handkerchief—and to her great surprise she found that the drawer was most untidy!

"Which of you boys has been untidying my drawers?" she shouted to the two in the next room.

Neither of the boys had even been in the room. Susan opened the other drawers—they were none of them as neat as she had left them. She was puzzled.

"I only tidied them this morning," she said. "Granny scolded me yesterday because they were untidy, and I spent ages putting them nice—now they're all higgledy-piggledy again."

Jeffery came to see. Then he went to the big chest of drawers that the boys shared in their room, and opened the top drawer, and then the next one.

"Look here!" he said. "Someone has been through my drawers too. This is pretty queer."

Susan went into the boys' room and they looked at one another. They each thought the same thing.

"It's Mr. Potts, or somebody belonging to him," said John slowly. "They've been looking for the other half of the map. They guessed we've got it, because I went so red yesterday when they questioned me about it."

"So they came and hunted through our things whilst we were out," said Jeffery. "The burglars!"

"Jeffery! You don't think they've found the halves of the map, do you?" said Susan suddenly.

"Good gracious! I hope not!" said Jeffery. He rushed to the dolls' house and knelt down. He switched on the little electric lamps that lighted the house and looked inside. He gave a sigh of relief.

"No, it's all right," he said. "They're here, safe on the ceilings. It's a good thing we thought of such a good place!"

"Let's go downstairs and find out if Mr. Potts called," said John. So they went down. In the hall they found Jane, the housemaid, arranging some flowers.

"Hallo, Jane," said Jeffery. "Did anyone call whilst we were out this afternoon?"

"Yes, Master Jeffery. Mr. Potts came, and another gentleman," said Jane. "They said they would like to see you children. They were sorry you were out."

"Did they come into the house?" asked Jeffery. "Or did they go off straightaway in their car?"

"Mr. Potts asked if his friend might use the telephone," said Jane. "So I showed Mr. Potts into the dining-room and took his friend to the hall telephone. He was there such a time!"

"Was Mr. Potts waiting in the dining-room all that time?" asked John.

"I expect so," said Jane.

The children ran off. "I bet he *didn't* wait in the dining-room all that time!" said Jeffery. "He slipped up the little staircase to Susan's room and had a good hunt round while his friend was pretending to telephone. He's a clever one, is Mr. Potts!"

"Jeffery, I don't think you ought to carry the map-tracing about with you," said Susan seriously.

"Suppose he caught you and searched you. He'd find it!"

"You're right, Susan," said Jeffery. "Well, I know something to trick dear Mr. Potts! I shall make up a false map, and keep it in my pocket! Then, if he does catch me and search me for the map, he'll get on the wrong track—because he'll have a false map to follow!"

"That's clever, Jeffery," said Susan. "You had better do it to-night—and we'll burn the tracing you made, after looking at it very carefully and learning it by heart! We can always turn the dolls' house upside down and study the map on the ceilings, if we forget anything!"

So that night Jeffery made a false map. At least, half of it was quite correct, because Mr. Potts had seen the half with the words "Treasure" on it—but the other half was a real muddle!

Jeffery drew four more bends in the river instead of two, on the first half. He drew six more trees, a few small bushes, and then something that looked like a piece of bread-and-butter with a bite out of it!

"Whatever's that?" asked Susan in surprise.

"I don't know!" said Jeffery with a laugh. "Just something to puzzle Mr. Potts, that's all!"

He burnt the other tracing, after the three of them

had studied it very carefully indeed, and had learnt it so well that anyone of them could have drawn it correctly from memory. Then Jeffery slipped the false map into his pocket.

"Now, Mr. Potts can find it if he likes!" he said.

"Jeffery, can we go and find the four bends of the river to-morrow?" asked Susan. "I'm longing to do some more exploring."

"Yes, rather!" said Jeffery. "We'll go treasure-hunting again for all we're worth!"

CHAPTER ELEVEN

THE CHILDREN FOLLOW THE MAP

THE NEXT day the three children set off once more with Rags. They had wanted to stay out to a picnic lunch but Granny had said no.

"Mr. and Mrs. Potts have kindly asked you all to tea this afternoon," said Granny. "So I will take you in the car. I want you home for lunch, so that you can tidy yourselves and change into something nice afterwards."

"Oh, what a nuisance!" said Susan. "I don't like Mr. Potts."

"Well, you may like his house and grounds!" said Granny. "He has a wonderful lake, so he tells me, and four boats. He says you can go out in one."

"Oh, good," said John, who loved boating. "That won't be so bad."

"All the same, it's a waste of time when we have so much exploring to do," said Jeffery, as they got ready to go to Greylings Wood.

Rags knew the way very well to the secret house now, and set off on the usual path at once. But Jeffery called him back. "Hie, Rags, old boy! We're not going that way to-day!"

"Which way are we going then?" asked Susan, surprised.

"We want to find out where the river enters the wood," said Jeffery. "I think we must count the bends from when it enters the trees. I asked Tipps this morning where it went into the wood, and he said we had to go down the road for about a mile —then we'd see it under a bridge."

So Rags and the children went down the road in the sunshine. After about twenty minutes' walk they came to a small stone bridge that spanned the little river.

"Here it is," said Jeffery. "Come on—we'll leave the road here and go into the wood."

There was no hedge, and no railing. The children simply walked among the trees and followed the stream. It ran quite straight for a little way and then curved slightly.

"Is this one of the bends, do you think?" asked Susan excitedly.

Jeffery shook his head.

"No," he said. "We must look for fairly big bends, I think. They were very curved ones in the map."

A pleasant path ran by the bank of the stream for some way. Then the path stopped at an old wooden seat, and the children had to scramble along through an overgrown part of the wood for some time.

Just after the wooden seat the stream took a great turn to the left, almost doubling over on it itself.

"The first bend!" said Jeffery, pleased. They followed the curve as best they could, and almost at once the river curved again, this time to the right.

"The second bend!" said Susan. "We're getting on, boys!"

They were in a part of the wood that they did not know—but after they had followed the stream for a little while longer they suddenly came to the piece they knew, that led to the pond by their secret house!

Susan was very surprised. The boys laughed at her. "But, Susan, you must have known that we would come to it some time," said Jeffery. "After all, it's the same river!"

"Yes, I know," said Susan. "But I just didn't think we'd arrive here somehow. Well, there's a fine bend just beyond the pond, Jeffery—that's the third one!"

They scrambled round the pond, and tried to follow the third bend. But it was quite impossible because the ground was so marshy just there that they sank almost up to their knees. Rags hated it. He stood and barked loudly at the children.

"He thinks we're quite mad!" said John. "Come on, Rags, old fellow. Don't get left behind."

Rags ran off round the trees. "We'd better follow him," said Jeffery, pulling his foot out of a muddy hole. "We can't possibly go this way. We shall come to the river another way, and perhaps miss this marshy bit."

So they followed Rags between the trees on drier ground. The dog seemed to know that they did not want to go very far from the water, for, as soon as possible, he led them back to it.

Jeffery stood on the bank and looked up the river, the way they had come. It was almost straight after the third big curve.

"Only one more bend, and then we should come to the three big trees or the humpy hill," said Jeffery. "Come on. It's drier here."

They were now able to follow the stream better. Great beeches grew all around, and the undergrowth was scarce. Some of the beech trees were so old and knotted that they seemed to have queer faces in their wrinkles.

At last the children came to the fourth bend. This was a good one. The river swung round to the right and then the children saw before them a marvellous avenue of trees, planted in two straight rows, with what must once have been a grassy lane between them.

Now the space between them was no longer a lane but was completely overgrown with bushes and undergrowths of all kinds. But it was easy to see what a fine avenue it must have been, for the trees still stood there in their places, swaying in their two long rows.

"Somebody planted this avenue a long time ago," said Jeffery. "Perhaps they liked to ride here—or maybe it was a proper roadway at one time, leading to somewhere."

"The only difficulty is—where are our three big trees?" said John. "With so many trees it's difficult to know which are the right three!"

Jeffery stared at the trees. He noticed that they were not so big as some of the others they had passed on their way through the wood.

"I don't think these trees are more than a hundred years old," he said at last. "So they couldn't have been planted at the time that map was drawn. It's three much bigger, much older trees we must look for—more like those enormous old beeches we passed a little time back."

"Do you think it might be three of those that we want?" said Susan.

"Of course not," said Jeffery. "We want three trees *after* the fourth bend in the stream, not before. We must hunt about the place for three enormous old trees. I only hope they haven't died or been cut down."

They made their way through the trees, looking for three together. Susan came across a great old tree, with such a thick trunk that she felt sure the tree must be about three hundred years old! It had a knotty, wrinkled trunk.

"Here's a very, very old tree," called Susan. "Oh, and look—here's another not far off. They are two of the oldest trees we've seen."

"Where's the third?" said Jeffery, looking around. "These two are certainly enormous—and look, Susan, look, John, there's the stump of a third old tree! In between these two we've found—see? There were *three* trees here once—but one must have died and been cut down. Thank goodness its stump was left to show us where it grew!"

The children stared at the two gnarled old giants and the stump of the third. They were in a slanting line, just as the map had shown.

"There are no other trees in a slanting line as far as I can see," said Jeffery, hunting around. "They are either in straight lines, like those in the avenue, or they are just growing anywhere. These must be the three!"

"Well, now we must look for the humpy hill," said John. "How will these trees help us? Do we have to follow the direction in which they are pointing?"

"Either that—or we climb one of the trees and see what we can find!" said Jeffery.

"Climb up the biggest one!" said Susan.

"I'll climb this one and you climb that one," said John to Jeffery. So each boy climbed up one of the old, old trees. They had to be careful because the twigs were brittle, and some of the boughs were quite dead.

But at last they got to the top. And then Jeffery gave a shout.

"I can see something!"

"*I can see something!*" called *Jeffery.*

"What?" shouted Susan, at the bottom.

"A humpy hill!" cried Jeffery.

"Oooh!" said Susan, almost beside herself with excitement. "Where is it?"

"It's in the very thickest part of the wood, I should think!" said Jeffery. "Wait a minute—I've got my compass. I'll set it so that I know exactly in which direction the hill is."

John could see nothing from his tree. His view towards the hill was hidden by Jeffery's enormous tree. He climbed down quickly. Jeffery climbed down too, slipping on one bough, and grazing his knee rather badly.

But he was too excited to do any more than mop his knee with his handkerchief. "It's funny," he said. "The hill sticks just above the top of the trees—and it's not got any trees on it at all, as far as I could see. It's just a grassy hill. It's buried so deep in the wood that no one would ever find it unless they knew it was there. Oh, I say, aren't we getting on!"

"Have we got time to go and find the hill?" asked Susan, leaping round in joy. She could never keep still when she was excited.

"Stop, Susan," said Jeffery. "You make me feel giddy. Well, I don't think we really *have* got time! But all the same, we'll *make* time! We'll have a *look* at the humpy hill, even if we can do no more than that to-day!"

He showed the others his compass. "I've got to keep the needle pointing exactly *there*," he said, showing them the little swinging needle in its round glass case. "If I do, and we follow the direction, we are bound to come to the humpy hill. I say—isn't this thrilling!"

They set off in the direction to which the needle pointed—due north. It was difficult going, for the wood grew very thick indeed, and the children had to force their way through. The beech trees had given way to oak, hazel, and birch, and the undergrowth, untrimmed for years, had grown thick and matted.

Soon their legs were scratched, and their clothes were torn. But they would not stop. It was far too exciting!

After forcing their way through the wood for about twenty minutes they came suddenly to the hill. It was very queer, for it had no trees on it at all, and yet there seemed no reason why trees should not grow there. It rose very steeply from the ground of the wood, covered with grass and bracken.

"Well—there's the hill!" said Jeffery in delight. "We *are* reading the map well!"

CHAPTER TWELVE

RAGS IS A GREAT HELP!

THE THREE children looked at the queer, humpy hill.
A rabbit peeped out of a burrow and popped back.
Rags was up the hill like a flash of lightning and
put his head down the hole.

"Shall we climb the hill?" asked Susan.

"Well, we shall be awfully late for lunch," said
Jeffery, looking at his wrist-watch. "But we simply

must go on a bit farther and see if we can find that church-like place!"

So they climbed up the hill, seeing little rabbit-paths here and there. When they got to the top they exclaimed in surprise. They were level with the tops of the trees, and they looked over the top of the wood, seeing the swaying branches for miles! It was a lovely sight.

They could see no sign of any little church anywhere. They looked on all sides of the hill, but there was no building of any sort or kind. It was really disappointing.

"I say, I hope we're not going to lose the trail just as we've followed the map so well," said Jeffery. "But I can't see any building, can you, John?"

"No, I can't," said John gloomily. "Let's go down the other side of the hill and hunt around a bit, Jeffery. Perhaps the church was built among the trees, and is hidden from us."

So down the other side of the steep, humpy hill they went, and spied around to see what they could find. They found nothing at all.

It was Rags who found something! He shot after a rabbit that had ventured too near him, and when it rushed under a bush, he rushed after it and began to scrape there for it, thinking it had gone into the ground! Jeffery pulled him out—and then called to the others.

"Come and look here—Rags has scraped out a big old stone, as grey as our gate-posts!"

They crowded round to look. They scraped away more of the moss and creeper, and sure, enough, it was an old stone.

"I guess that was once part of a wall," said Jeffery. "What *sillies* we are! That old building shown in the map must have fallen down long, long ago! All we shall find will be the great squares of stone, like this one, that it was built of. Let's look."

They began to hunt, scraping away moss here and there, and pulling away brambles—and at last they found enough stones to show where some building had been. It could not have been a very large building, for the children found a rough outline of the shape, guided by the great stones they had unearthed round about.

"Well, this was the building all right," said Jeffery. "The thing is now—*where* is the flight of steps that led up to it? You remember the lines that looked like steps in the picture, don't you, you two?"

They remembered quite well. "I don't see how there could possibly have been any steps to this building," said Susan, puzzled. "It's built flat on the ground. If it had been built on the hill, there might have been steps leading up to it, as there are to our secret house, from the pond—but you can't have a flight of steps if you build on the ground itself!"

Jeffery was puzzled and disappointed. It was too bad that they had found everything except the steps! He looked at his watch and gave a shout. "Goodness! It's one o'clock already—and lunch is at one. We *shall* get into a row! Come on—we must go at once. We'll come back to-morrow."

"Isn't there a shorter way home?" asked John, thinking with dismay of the very thick wood they would once more have to force their way through.

"Well, if there is, we don't know it!" said Jeffery. "Hie, Rags! Where are you going? Come back, sir! Here, Rags, come back!"

Rags was trotting off in another direction. He took no notice of Jeffery at all.

"RAGS!" yelled Jeffery angrily. "Don't pretend to be deaf. Come here! You'll be lost if you go wandering off by yourself when we're so far from home!"

Rags stopped and looked back at the others. He cocked his ears up, and put on a most cheeky expression. But he didn't come back.

"I'll go after him and get him," said Jeffery, angry. "He'll make us later than ever."

So he ran after Rags—who at once began trotting off again in the opposite direction. It was most annoying. Jeffery called and shouted, and ran after the little dog, but he still would not come.

Then Jeffery noticed that Rags really did seem to know the way he was going, and he stopped and thought. "I say, you others!" he called. "I think old Rags knows another way home! After all, he's lived here all his life and gone rabbiting in the woods hundreds of times. I expect he knows all the shortest ways home. Shall we follow him?"

"Yes," said Susan. So all three children followed Rags, who wagged his tail, very pleased. He led them through the wood, leaving behind the very thick part, and then, most unexpectedly, came out at the field behind Farmer Timbles' house! It was most astonishing.

"Good gracious!" said Jeffery, amazed. "Who would have thought we were so near the farm? Well, that's jolly good, I must say—we can run home all the way from here, instead of scrambling through the wood. It will be a shorter way to come to-morrow too."

They set off home at a trot, and arrived at a

quarter to two, dirty, tired, hungry and with their clothes torn and scratched. Granny was very cross indeed.

"You naughty children!" she said, coming out of the dining-room and catching them just as they were creeping upstairs to change and wash. "Three-quarters of an hour late! You don't deserve any dinner at all! And just look at your clothes—and what *have* you done to your knee, Jeffery?"

"Oh, nothing much, Granny," said Jeffery, looking down at his badly-grazed knee, which he had forgotten all about. "I climbed a tree and slipped as I was climbing down again. Really it's nothing."

"I give you five minutes to wash and put on something clean," said Granny. "If you are not down by then I shall send out the dinner and you can have bread and butter instead."

They all shot upstairs, and soon taps were running and clothes were being hurriedly changed. They rushed into the dining-room just in time!

"Now I don't want you to speak a word," said Granny, still very cross with them. "Eat your dinners, and try to make up for your bad behaviour."

So they ate hungrily, and didn't say a word. Granpa had had his dinner and was in the garden, smoking.

"You will be ready at three o'clock to go with me in the car to Mr. Potts' house," said Granny, when they had finished. "It is nearly half-past two now. Wash again, a little more carefully, bind up that awful knee, Jeffery, do your hairs properly, put on your best things, and be down in time. You had better begin to get ready now—it is nearly half-past two."

"Bother Mr. Potts," grumbled Susan, as they went upstairs. She was very tired with her exciting morning, and would have liked to take a book and go and read in the hammock.

At three o'clock they were all ready, looking very clean, neat and well-dressed. Jeffery had bandaged his knee with a clean handkerchief.

"Now, are we all ready?" said Granny, appearing down the stairs. "Yes—you look nice, all of you. Now please behave yourselves, and don't climb trees or anything this afternoon!"

The children were glad to see that Granny was smiling again. She was never cross for very long, for she was very sweet-tempered. They all got into the car and set off.

Mr. Potts' house was more like a mansion. It was simply enormous, and the grounds were marvellously laid out. There was the lake that Granny had told them about, and a few small boats moored at the bank.

Mr. and Mrs. Potts greeted them all very heartily. Mrs. Potts was rather fat, and had more rings on her fingers than Susan had ever seen anyone wear before. She had six ropes of pearls round her neck, and bright ear-rings dangled in her ears.

"They must be very rich people," said John to Susan, in a low voice. "I wonder what they want to buy Greylings for, when they've got an enormous place like this?"

The children were told that they might go out in the boat, with Mr. Potts to help them to row. They would much rather have gone by themselves, but it would not have been polite to say so.

They all got into the little boat. It was painted red, and was very pretty. There were two pairs of oars. Jeffery took one pair and Mr. Potts took the other.

"It's quite a way, to row round the lake," said Mr. Potts. "I'll show you some ducks' nests, and a little waterfall we've made."

It certainly was quite a long way round the lake! John took the oars after a bit, and then Susan had a turn. They saw three ducks' nests, all with eggs in, and came to the little waterfall, which was very pretty.

Mr. Potts talked a lot. He tried to be very nice to

them indeed. He noticed Jeffery's bandage, and spoke to him about it.

"Hurt yourself, Jeffery?" he asked.

"Nothing much," said Jeffery.

"He did it this morning," said Susan, who always liked to talk when she could. "He was climbing a most enormous tree—right to the very top he went —and when he came down, he slipped and grazed his knee badly."

"A most enormous tree?" said Mr. Potts. "And where was that? In the wood?"

"Yes," said Susan. "Ever so far in the wood. We followed . . ."

She stopped and gave a cry of pain. John had punched her in the back to stop her saying any more. He knew what Susan was like once she began talking. She never knew when to stop!

"Dear me, why did you stop your sister telling me about your adventures this morning?" asked Mr. Potts. "I am most interested. Do go on, my dear."

But Susan would say no more. She bit her lip and hoped that Jeffery wouldn't scold her afterwards. Why was she so silly as to tell things she had much better say nothing about?

"Well, we'd better be getting back," said Mr. Potts, seeing that none of the children was going to say any more about their morning adventures. "I'm afraid this is rather a dull afternoon for you, after all your tree-climbing this morning!"

But it wasn't so dull after all—because something most unexpected suddenly happened!

CHAPTER THIRTEEN

MR. POTTS IS CLEVER

MR. POTTS and Jeffery rowed back to the bank.
Susan got out first, and then John. Then Jeffery
stood up—but suddenly the boat wobbled violently
—and Jeffery fell straight over the side into the
water!

It wasn't at all deep—Jeffery could stand quite
easily. But he got a shock, and came up gasping

and spluttering. Mr. Potts looked *most* alarmed and grabbed him at once. He pulled him into the boat and then helped him to the bank.

"Oh, Jeffery, are you all right?" cried Susan, who had been really frightened.

"Of *course* I'm all right!" said Jeffery, half cross at the fuss. "I can't imagine how I fell in. The boat rocked like anything and I lost my balance, that's all."

Granny and Mrs. Potts came hurrying up when they saw what had happened. Mrs. Potts was dreadfully upset.

"Oh, my dear boy, you are so wet!" she cried. "Come along in at once and take your wet things off. Mr. Potts has some shorts you can have, and a vest and pullover. Dear, dear, I *am* sorry this has happened."

"Now don't get upset, my dear," said Mr. Potts to his wife. "*I'll* see to the boy. He won't be any the worse for his wetting, and I can easily get him dry clothing. Come along, Jeffery—we'll see what we can do for you."

Susan and John went with Jeffery. Mrs. Potts sank down on a garden-seat, looking quite pale. Granny found that she had to comfort her, because she really looked as if she would burst into tears!

"Such a thing to happen!" she kept saying. "Such a thing to happen!"

Mr. Potts took the children into an enormous kitchen, where three maids were at work. They were astonished to see the children with Mr. Potts, but at once saw what had happened.

"I'll take his wet clothes off, sir," said a kindly faced cook, bustling forward.

"No thank you," said Jeffery firmly. "I can take them off myself. I hope I shan't make your kitchen floor too wet, though."

He stripped off his wet clothes, and took the big warm towel that Mr. Potts offered him. It wasn't long before he was quite dry. Mr. Potts picked up the wet clothes and went through the door with them. "I'll get you some dry ones," he said.

"Oh, sir! Let *me* take the clothes!" cried the house-parlourmaid, running after him. "I'll dry them and press them."

But Mr. Potts took no notice of her and disappeared quickly. The cook went to the scullery, and the third maid went into the garden. The house-parlourmaid followed Mr. Potts after a minute, and the children found themselves alone.

"Jeffery! You *were* a silly!" whispered Susan. "It's the first time you've ever fallen out of a boat!"

"And so would *you* fall out if the boat was rocked violently just as you were standing on one foot, ready to step out," answered Jeffery crossly. "That boat was rocked on purpose—by Mr. Potts. He *wanted* me to fall in the water!"

"Oh, Jeffery! But why?" asked Susan, horrified.

"So that I would have to change my wet clothes under his eyes—and he could take them away—and run through my pockets to see if he could find any signs of the *map*!" said Jeffery.

The other two stared at him in silence. They hadn't for one moment thought of such a thing—but now they saw that it was very likely to be true. After all, the clothes had been whisked off by Mr. Potts, although it was the maid's job to take them and dry them.

"But, Jeffery——" said John, beginning to giggle, "you had the false map in your pocket—the one we made up!"

"I know that," said Jeffery with a laugh. He pulled the big towel round him more closely. "Old Pots of Money will have to use his brains to work out *that* map, won't he!"

"What a good thing you didn't have the proper tracing in your pocket," began Susan. But Jeffery nudged her, for he had heard footsteps. The house-parlourmaid came back with some dry clothes—

some rather big shorts belonging to Mr. Potts, a
vest, and a yellow pullover.

"Has Mr. Potts got my wet clothes?" asked
Jeffery.

"Yes, he has," said the maid rather indignantly
"He won't let me hang them out, he's doing them
himself!"

Jeffery winked at the others. "Well, I've no
doubt he has some good reason for seeing to them
himself," he said. The others giggled. They knew
what Jeffery meant. But the maid didn't, and she
looked annoyed. She tossed her head, sniffed, and
went to join the cook in the scullery.

Jeffery felt rather odd in his big clothes. Granny
laughed when she saw him. Mrs. Potts patted him
kindly and said, "Well, I expect you'd all like some
tea now. I can see Edith bringing it out on the
terrace. Come along."

They went to the magnificent terrace that over-
looked the lake—and there, set out on low tables
was the most scrumptious tea that the children
had ever seen.

There were great ripe strawberries, and rich
cream. There were the most exciting sandwiches
imaginable, honey in the comb, looking like golden
syrup, a chocolate cake as big as a Christmas cake
little iced cakes of all kinds, a jam sandwich stuffed

with cream as well, and a dish of the most exciting biscuits. And, to end up with, the maid brought out a tray full of strawberry and vanilla ice-creams.

"Well, this was worth falling into the pond for," said Jeffery, as he ate his second ice-cream, and wished that he could manage a third.

"I'm so glad you enjoyed your tea," said Mrs. Potts, who had eaten just as much as the children. Susan thought it wasn't surprising that she was so fat, if she ate gorgeous teas like this every day. She wished she could have tea like that every day herself—but Granny would say it wasn't good for her, she knew!

The car came round for them after tea and they said good-bye and thank you, and got into it. Mr. Potts promised to send Jeffrey's clothes back the next day.

"That will just give him nice time to dry our false map and copy it out!" said Jeffery, with a grin, as they sat in the car waiting for Granny to finish saying good-bye.

They drove home, feeling rather full up. Granny gave a sigh as they turned in at their stone gateposts. "Dear old Greylings Manor!" she said, as the beautiful old house came in sight. "I am sorry to think you will soon no longer be ours. Mr. Potts will be your master instead!"

"What does old Pots of Money want to buy your house for, Granny?" asked Jeffery. "His own is far bigger and grander."

"Jeffery! Don't call him that!" said Granny, looking half-shocked and half-amused. "You must call people by their right names."

"Well it *is* his right name," said Jeffery. "He *has* got pots of money, hasn't he?"

"Yes—I suppose he has," said Granny. "He doesn't want Greylings Manor for himself though—he wants it for his daughter, who is soon getting married."

They swept up to the steps and jumped out. "Now you'd better go and do something quiet," said Granny. "After that enormous tea you won't want to climb trees or run races, I hope. And if you don't come to supper, I shall quite understand. I am sure you can't possibly manage any more to eat to-day!"

But, dear me, by the time that supper was on the table, the children were quite ready for it! Granny seemed very surprised indeed, but she gave them just as big helpings as usual.

The next day a parcel arrived for Jeffery from Mr. Potts. It was his clothes, all dry now, and neatly pressed. He ran his hands through his pockets. Everything was there—string, handkerchief, two bits of toffee, an unusual stone he had picked up, a pencil stump, a broken rubber, a notebook— and the map! Yes, that was there as well.

"Carefully copied, I'm quite sure!" said Jeffery, putting it back again with a grin. "Well, Mr. Potts may be smart—but we're smarter! I didn't guess he'd get me into the lake—but we were ready for him, anyway. We did that map just in time for him!"

"I wish to-morrow would come quickly," said Susan. "I do want to hunt round that ruined building again—what's left of it! I simply can't *think* why there are those steps shown on the map, if there are none to be seen by the building."

"Perhaps they are not steps," said Jeffery.

"Well, what else can they be?" asked John.

"I can't think!" said Jeffery, frowning. "No— they *must* be steps. But yet there never, never could have been steps there, if the building was set on the level ground, as it seems to have been."

John was thinking hard. He looked up. "I suppose, Jeffery, there couldn't have been steps leading underground from the building, could there?" he asked. "You know—steps going down to a cellar, or something, from *in*side the building?"

Susan and Jeffery stared at John in surprise. Then Jeffery smacked his hand down on a nearby table.

"Of course!" he said. "Of course! *That's* what we've got to look for! Steps going *down* from the building—not steps going *up* to it! Good for you, John!"

"To-morrow we'll take forks and spades, said John excitedly. "We'll probe all over the ground and see if we can uncover a floor of some sort. And then we'll see if there are any signs of steps going underground!"

"Now I shan't be able to go to sleep to-night!" said Susan, her eyes shining. "I shall keep on and on thinking of to-morrow!"

But she did go to sleep, and she dreamt of finding a wonderful place where beautiful treasures were stored—but just as she was going to take what she wanted, Mr. Potts popped up and drove her away! Susan woke up with a jump, feeling very angry with Mr. Potts.

CHAPTER FOURTEEN

A THRILLING MORNING

THE next morning Jeffery went to ask Tipps to lend him a garden fork and two spades.

"I got into trouble over lending you the axe," said Tipps. "I don't think I'd better lend you anything else."

"Oh, go on, Tipps, please do," begged John. He saw Granny in the distance and called to her.

"Granny! May we borrow some gardening tools, please? Tipps says he had better not lend them to us."

"Well, so long as it's not an axe or a scythe," said Granny. "I'm glad to hear you want to do some gardening!"

"Dear old Granny's got remarkable hearing," said Jeffery. "Nobody said a word about doing any gardening! Anyway, Tipps, let us have the things we want, now that Granny says we can."

They marched off with the tools, hoping that Granny wouldn't call them and ask where they were going to garden. Jeffery slipped indoors for his torch. He thought that if they *did* find steps going underground, they would want a little light to see them!

"We'll go the short way," said Jeffery. "We won't scramble all through the wood again. Where's Rags? Hie, Rags, come on—you can take us the way you took us yesterday!"

As they marched down the drive to the gates, Mr. Potts's car came in. Mr. Potts saw the children and stopped the car.

"I just came to ask if Jeffery was all right after him wetting yesterday," he called, showing all his white teeth in a wide smile. "But I see you are, Jeffery. Dear me, wherever are you going with those spades and forks?"

The children couldn't think what to say. Then Jeffery spoke up.

"We're going to the farm," he said. This was quite true. They had to pass the farm—and they meant to call in for a moment to see Mrs. Timbles.

"Oh! You're going to help the farmer, are you?" said Mr. Potts. This wasn't exactly a question, so nobody answered it. But John, of course, went as red as a tomato. He always did if he felt awkward or guilty about anything. Mr. Potts noticed his red face at once.

"Have you found the other piece of that map?" he said suddenly.

Now this was a very difficult question to answer. If Jeffery said yes, Mr. Potts would ask him for it and would see that it was different from the copy he had found in Jeffery's pocket. If he said no, it was an untruth, and Jeffery, like the others, hated untruths.

The three stared at Mr. Potts, quite tongue-tied— and then Rags saved them! He suddenly saw a stray hen and barked loudly at it. He rushed at it, and the frightened creature fluttered into the hedge.

"Excuse us, sir—we must rescue the hen!" cried Jeffery gladly, and he darted off. The others went too and left Mr. Potts in his car, looking annoyed.

"Quick, Rags, scare the old hen through the

hedge," whispered John, "then we can squeeze through after it and disappear!"

Rags was delighted to find that for a change the children were encouraging him to bark at a hen, instead of scolding him for it. He went completely mad, barked his head almost off, leapt round like a kangaroo, and made the hen almost faint with fear. The children made as much noise as they could, too, shouting to the hen and to one another, as they pretended to shoo away Rags and catch the poor hen.

They squeezed through the hedge, and although they could hear Mr. Potts calling to them, they took no notice and shouted all the more loudly. At last they began to giggle. Jeffery hurriedly picked up the hen, and tore off with it, afraid that Mr. Potts would leave the car and come after them.

But he didn't. They heard the car going up the drive. Jeffery set the hen down when he came to the hen-run, and it ran to join the others, squawking out its adventures at the top of its voice. Rags barked joyfully. He had had a wonderful time.

"Poor old hen!" said Susan, sorry for the clucking bird. "But it did save us from a very awkward moment, Jeffery."

"It did," said Jeffery. "Come on. We'd better slip off quickly before old Pots of Money catches us again."

So once more they set off, this time without anyone stopping them. They came to Farmer Timbles' house, and stopped for a few minutes to talk to Mrs. Timbles. She was most astonished to see their spades and forks.

"What in the world are you going to do?" she asked.

"It's a secret, Mrs. Timbles!" said John. "We'll tell you all about it one day."

"All right, I'll wait till then!" said the farmer's wife. "Would you like some of my new cakes?"

"Well, if you'd let us take a few with us, we'd be *very* pleased," said Jeffery. "But we can't stop long to-day, because we have a busy morning in front of us!"

"I'll pop some into a bag for you," said Mrs. Timbles kindly, and she did. The children were thrilled when they saw her put at least twelve cakes into the bag for them.

They set off again with Rags, who was very much interested in the bag of cakes. Jeffery sent him on in front, hoping that he would be sensible enough to take them the way they had come yesterday.

He did take them the right way. He was a very clever dog, and loved trying to read the children's thoughts. He trotted ahead, and it was not long before the children came to the humpy hill, and found the place where they had uncovered so many old grey stones the day before.

"Now the thing to do is to jab about with the fork and see what we can feel underneath all this moss and stuff growing on what must have been the floor of the building," said Jeffery. So, taking the long-pronged fork, he began to jab strongly here and there.

Each time he jabbed, the fork struck something hard. He stopped, and looked at the others. "There must be a proper floor all underneath here," he said. "A tiled floor perhaps, like our secret house has. We'll clear it if we can."

Jeffery was right. Under the moss, the grass and the bracken was a tiled floor. The tiles were small, and even after so many years were still bright in colour. Rags helped as much as he could, scraping away with his feet in excitement.

After a great deal of hard work the children had most of the floor uncovered. Many of the tiles were broken. Some were missing altogether.

Then John uncovered a flat slab of stone, quite different from the coloured tiles.

"Look!" he said. "Here's something different. A big slab of stone—and it's got some old pattern on it."

Susan and Jeffery came beside John to see what the pattern was. Jeffery gave a shout.

"Don't you know what the pattern is, sillies? It's the Greylings eagle—just like the ones on the gate-posts, only flat instead of rounded. That shows this was a Greylings building."

"Why do you suppose they laid a flat stone here suddenly, in the middle of the coloured tiles?" asked John. "It seems odd to me."

"It *is* odd," said Jeffery, "But I bet I can explain the oddness! I guess there's the flight of steps underneath that slab!"

"Oooh, really?" said Susan and John in delight. "Goody!"

"The thing is—how are we going to get it up to see?" wondered Jeffery. "It looks jolly heavy. I wonder if there's an iron ring or anything that we can pull it up by? Let's clear the whole slab properly and see."

They cleared it from end to end—but not a sign of any iron ring was to be seen. Jeffery stood on the slab and jumped on it to see if he could make it move.

The slab moved at once. There was a creaking, cracking noise as if something underneath was breaking, and Jeffery leapt off the slab in alarm. The children stared at it. Something below the slab of stone had given way, and it was lying all crooked, a little below the surface of the ground.

"Now what did it do that for?" said Jeffery. "It did give me a shock when it moved like that—and did you hear that funny breaking noise?"

"Perhaps, Jeffery, the stone is placed on wooden supports or something," said John. "And maybe they have rotted with the years, and when you jumped on the stone, the wood cracked and gave way."

"I think you're right," said Jeffery, kicking at the stone with his foot. "I don't like to tread on it again. I wonder how we could move it?"

"There's a big stone over there, that was once part of the wall," said John. "I think we could all three carry it between us—then we could drop it down on the slab and see if that would move it!"

"Good idea," said Jeffery. They went to the big square stone and with great difficulty lifted it up. They staggered with it to the slab, and then, at a word from Jeffery, dropped it right on to the flat stone.

The result was most startling. The heavy stone struck the slab, which at once gave way, and, with a crash, it disappeared entirely, taking the heavy stone with it! The children found themselves staring into a big black hole!

"Golly!" said Jeffery, in the greatest astonishment. "Look at that!"

"The flight of steps must be down there," said John excitedly. He bent over to see. Jeffery took out his little torch and flashed it downwards into the hole.

It was a deep hole, with an old stairway leading downwards. "So we were right!" said Jeffery, in delight. "John! Susan! Down there is where the Greylings Treasure is hidden! I'm sure of it!"

Susan was so excited that she almost fell down the hole. Jeffery pulled her back. "Don't be silly," he said. "The whole place is rotten with age—if you miss your step you'll crash down there and hurt yourself. Look—can you see the slab of stone right down there, on the floor and the other stone beside it?"

Yes, they could see them both. They examined the entrance too, where the slab had been, and saw that the flat stone had rested on wood, which, as John had said, had become rotten, and had given way when Jeffery jumped on the stone.

"I want to go down the steps," said Susan. "Jeffery, do let me be the first one."

"Certainly not," said Jeffery. "Those steps may look all right, but they may be quite rotten too. I shall try them first."

"Well, be careful, then, Jeff," said John anxiously. Jeffery stuck his torch in his pocket and sat down at the entrance to the hole. He tried the top step with his foot. With a crack it broke away at once, and the splinters went down below. Jeffery tried the next step." That broke too. The steps were as rotten as deadwood in a tree struck by lightning.

"Blow! The steps are no use at all," said Jeffery. "They wouldn't bear the weight of a mouse!"

"Well, how shall we get down then?" asked Susan, so anxious to explore underground that she simply could not keep still.

"We'll have to get a rope," said Jeffery. Both the others looked most disappointed at once. They couldn't bear the thought of going home and leaving the exciting hole even for an hour!

"Couldn't we jump down and chance it?" said John.

"Don't be so stupid," said Jeffery. "You'd break your leg to start with, and you'd never climb out again! Rags, go away. You'll fall in."

"Well, let's go home quickly and get the rope," said John impatiently. "Anyway, it's almost dinner-time. We'd better not be late again—though I'm sure we shall. We can come back after dinner."

"Come on, then," said Jeffery, and he turned to go. "Gracious! We *are* late again! Run!"

CHAPTER FIFTEEN

AN UNEXPECTED PUNISHMENT

THEY hadn't gone very far before a thought came into John's head. "I say," he said, stopping, " do you think we ought to leave that hole open like that? Suppose anyone came along and saw it—and got down before we did?"

"Yes—you're right, John," said Jeffery. "We ought to have thrown bracken and branches over it to hide it. Let's go back and do it quickly—it won't take a minute!"

But a great surprise awaited them as they made their way back through the trees. The sound of voices came to them!

Jeffery put his hand on Rags' collar at once, in case he should bark.

"Sh!" he said to the others. "Don't make a sound. Take Rags, John, and I'll creep up and see who it is."

Jeffery crept silently from bush to bush, keeping himself completely hidden—and at last he came in sight of the ruined building. He had a dreadful shock! Mr. Potts was there, with another man! They were looking in the hole and talking in excitement.

"Those children are smart!" said Mr. Potts. "They've found the very place. That map in the boy's pocket was wrong. We've been on a regular wild goose chase this morning, following goodness knows how many bends in the river! It's a good thing we heard their voices, and came to see what they were doing!"

"We'd never have found this by ourselves," said the second man. "This little hill is well-hidden, and the old building is fallen to pieces. Those are the steps shown in the map, Potts—no doubt of it.

But they're quite rotten. We'd better come back again with a rope."

"Well, those kids will be back after lunch," said Mr. Potts, rubbing his chin and thinking. "Let me see—how can we stop them? I know! I'll get my wife to phone up the old lady and invite the children to go for a picnic somewhere! Then they will be out of the way. I can't come back here after lunch, as I've business to see to—but we'll be here early in the morning before those kids are about."

"Well, come on then," said the other man. "I wish we knew a short way back—I hate wading in that marshy bit! I'm soaked to the knees!"

Jeffery couldn't help grinning. He wasn't going to show them the other way back! He waited until the men had disappeared round the humpy hill and then he shot back to the others. He told them all he had heard. They listened in rage.

"*Well!*" said Susan. "So he thinks he'll get the Treasure before we do, does he? He thinks he'll get us nicely out of the way for the rest of the day! Well, he won't. We'll refuse to go to the picnic!"

"Quite right," said John. "We've simply *got* to get here this afternoon. Then, when he arrives early to-morrow morning, he'll find nothing at all!"

"I say, we *must* go!" said Jeffery. "It's five to one! You know what a row we got into yesterday!"

They simply raced home, carrying the spades and fork, hoping that Granny wouldn't be too cross.

But she was. She was very angry indeed, and worse, still, Granpa was in a rage too.

"Half-past one! said Granpa, as they trooped into the hall. "Is that what you call being punctual? Two days running! Disgraceful! Really disgraceful!"

"We're awfully sorry, Granpa," said Jeffery.

"Being sorry isn't enough," said Granpa, looking really fierce. "Your Granny orders nice meals for you and then you keep the whole household waiting like this."

"It is really very naughty of you all," said Granny. "I've a good mind to send the dinner out and make you have bread and butter—but I'm sure you are all very hungry, and I don't like to do that."

"But you'll be punished all the same!" said Granpa, looking very fierce still. "Oh yes! You'll go up to your rooms after lunch and there you'll stay for the rest of the day. You'll have your tea up there and no supper! Bad children! I'm angry with you!"

Granpa stalked out of the hall and the children stared after him in dismay. What! Spend the rest of the day in their bedrooms, when they had such important work to do after lunch? They couldn't !

"Granpa!" called Jeffery. "Please forgive us. Just this once. You see . . ."

"I never listen to excuses," said Granpa. "You'll just do as you are told and say no more."

Susan began to cry with tiredness and disappointment. She stamped her foot. "It's too bad, it's too bad!" she shouted. "Granpa, you're unkind! You ought to listen to Jeffery."

"*Susan!*" said Granpa, in a shocked voice. "Don't be rude. I shall send you all up to your rooms immediately if I have any more nonsense."

Susan didn't want to make the boys lose their lunch, so she wiped her eyes and said no more. They went meekly into the dining-room and sat down.

"You mustn't make Granpa angry by arguing with him, Susan," said Granny, serving out big helpings of cold meat, potatoes, and salad. "You have really been very thoughtless, coming in late again like this, and you deserve to be punished. Now I don't want to hear a word from any of you. Eat up your dinner quietly."

Granny took up the paper and sat down. The children were very hungry indeed, and they ate quickly. Just as Granny had finished ladling out the raspberries and cream for pudding, the telephone bell rang.

The maid came into the room after a minute.

"Mr. Potts on the telephone, Madam," she said. Granny got up and went into the hall. The telephone was in the hall cloakroom. Granny left the door open, and the children could hear every word she said.

"Good afternoon, Mr. Potts," she said. Then she listened. "Oh, it's very kind of Mrs. Potts to offer to take the children for such a lovely picnic, but I'm sorry to say they can't come. No, they really can't Mr. Potts. . . . No, they are not ill . . . as a matter of fact, they have been rather naughty, and they have been told to keep to their rooms for the rest of the day. What? Yes—I'm afraid they will be indoors—they will not be allowed out at all . . . so you see they can't possibly go to the picnic—but please thank Mrs. Potts for me. Another day perhaps."

Then Granny listened again as Mr. Potts spoke for some time.

"Well, I'm glad you have really decided to buy Greylings," said Granny. "Yes—the papers will be ready for us to sign to-morrow. Our lawyer will be here, and if you like to come to-morrow morning at ten o'clock, the whole matter can be finally settled. Yes . . . yes . . . good-bye."

Granny put back the receiver. The children longed to speak to one another and say what they thought, but they had been told not to talk. Oh dear! So everything was to be settled at ten o'clock to-morrow morning. It was dreadful. Tears trickled down poor Susan's face and fell into her raspberry juice.

Granny came back. "Mrs. Potts wanted to know if you could go for a picnic with her this afternoon," she said. "Now you see what you have missed by being so silly!"

"I don't want to go picnicking with Mrs. Potts," said Susan. "I'm glad we're not going! I don't like Mr. and Mrs. Pots of Money!"

"Susan! Don't talk like that!" said Granny sharply. "Mr. Potts is buying Greylings Manor, and you will have to be polite to him if you ever want to come and see the old place again."

"Granny! Please don't let him buy it!" said Jeffery. "Granny, we're going to find the Treasure for you, really we are!"

"Don't talk nonsense, dear," said Granny. "I suppose you are thinking of that old map? Well, I'm sure it doesn't mean anything at all."

"Oh, but, Granny, really we . . ." began Jeffery, but Granny wouldn't let him say any more.

"That's quite enough, Jeffery," she said. "Have you all finished? Well, go up to your rooms then. And remember that you are to stay there for the rest of the day. Tea will be sent up to you, but you'll have to go without supper—and I do hope you will remember that when you are guests in somebody's house the least you can do is to be punctual for meals!"

"We're very sorry, Granny," said John humbly, hoping that Granny would change her mind. "Couldn't we just stay in our rooms till tea-time and then take Rags for a walk?"

"Certainly not," said Granpa, who had come in at that moment. "I never heard of such a thing! Go along now—and can I trust you not to leave your rooms—or must you be locked in?"

"You can trust us," said Jeffery, his cheeks going red. "We promise to stay in our rooms for the rest of the day."

"Very well," said Granpa. "I trust you. The Greylings never break their word."

The children went upstairs slowly and sadly. They sat in the boys' room and looked at one another dolefully.

"This is the worst bit of luck that could happen!" said Jeffery. "Who would have thought that Granpa would be so fierce?"

"Well, what about Granny?" said John. "She was fierce too. And all the time we're trying so hard to find the Treasure for them."

"Yes, but grown-ups don't think of things like that," said Jeffery. "Oh, do stop crying, Susan. I can't think where you get all your tears from. I really can't!"

There was a scraping at the door, and Rags whined outside.

"The dear old dog!" said John, jumping up. "He wants to share our punishment too! Good old Rags."

Rags came in and jumped up on to Jeffery's knee. He licked the boy's chin.

"Jeffery, I suppose we can't possibly go to the woods?" said John, in a timid voice. "I feel as if we *must*—don't you think Granpa would understand, once we had got the Treasure?"

"I know enough of Granpa to know that he would rather lose the Treasure than have any of us breaking our word," said Jeffery. "We've given our word of honour, John, and we can't possibly break it. Don't even think of it! It would be an awful thing to do, and I'd hate myself for it."

"Yes—you're right," said John, in a miserable voice. "Oh, how I wish Mr. Potts was at the bottom of his own silly lake!"

That made Jeffery laugh. "That's where he tried to put *me* yesterday!" he said. "Well, old Pots of Money knows *we* are safely out of the way now, picnic or no picnic—so he's safe to attend to his business this afternoon. If only we could have borrowed a rope and gone down that hole—we'd have been down it by now if it hadn't been for this silly punishment!"

"I'm tired," said Susan. "I'm going to lie on my bed and have a nap."

But no sooner had she laid herself down than an idea came to her. She jumped off her bed and ran to the boys.

"I've got an idea!" she said.

B.C. FREEMAN.

CHAPTER SIXTEEN

AN UNDERGROUND ADVENTURE

THE boys looked at Susan. "What is it?" asked Jeffery doubtfully. He didn't think there *could* be any good ideas just at the moment.

"Well, listen, Jeff," said Susan, "We've promised to stay in our rooms for the rest of the day, haven't we?"

"Yes," said the boys.

"But we haven't promised to stay in them all night long!" cried Susan. "Mr. Potts is going to explore that underground place early in the morning—well, why can't we go *to-night*? We can take torches. We shall be quite all right. It would be just as dark down in that hole in the daytime as in the night, so it won't make a bit of difference, really."

"Well! That *is* an idea!" said Jeffery, really thrilled. "Why didn't we think of it before? Of course—we shan't be breaking any promise if we go there to-night. We'll go!"

"We'll go!" shouted John, and he banged his eiderdown so hard that the feathers flew out of it.

"We'll creep down Susan's secret stairs so that no one will hear us!" said Jeffery.

"We'll take our torches! We'll find a strong rope! We'll get the Treasure before old Pots of Money!" shouted John.

"Sh!" said Susan, delighted that her idea was thought so much of. "You'll tell everyone in the house what we're going to do if you shout like that!"

"I feel much happier, now," said John. "What shall we do till tea-time, Jeffery?"

"I think we'd better try and have a nap," said Jeffery. "It looks as if we shall be up half the night!"

So they all three lay on their beds and shut their eyes. The smell of the early roses outside the window came in. Bees hummed loudly. Everything was peaceful, and soon the children, happy again now, were fast asleep. They had worked so hard that morning, digging and scraping that they were really tired out.

They did not awake until Jane, the housemaid, came knocking at the boys' door with their tea. She came in and set the tray down on the table.

"And what have *you* been doing to get sent to your rooms like this?" she said. "Late for lunch, I suppose. There's nothing that makes your granpa crosser than that!"

"Oooh, what a nice tea you have brought us, Jane!" said Susan, looking at the tray of things. "Egg sandwiches—my very favourite ones! And what are these—potted meat. Thank you, Jane!"

"And ginger biscuits and seed cake!" said John. "Well, I shan't mind going without my supper now."

"You'll never be able to eat all this," said Jane. "Ring when you've finished and I'll fetch your tray."

"Thanks, Jane," said Jeffery. Jane left the room, and the three children drew up their chairs and began their tea.

They enjoyed it. They talked about what they were going to do that night. It was very exciting.

"I think we'd better keep slices of that seed-cake for to-night," said John. "We shall be awfully hungry if we go exploring at midnight!"

So they cut three enormous slices and put them in the top drawer of the chest. Then they rang for Jane.

"Good gracious!" she said, when she came in and saw what a lot they had eaten. "Nearly everything gone! *You* won't miss your suppers!"

She went, carrying the tray. The children found some cards and played Happy Families until seven o'clock. Then Granny came in.

"Well," she said, "I'm very sorry to have had to punish you like this—but you will please remember in future not to be late for meals, won't you?"

"Yes, Granny," they all said.

"You had better go to bed now," said Granny. "You are not coming down to supper. I will say good night—and I hope to-morrow you will turn over a new leaf, and we shall all be happy together again. It upsets me to have to treat you like this—but I promised your mother I wouldn't spoil you. You are usually such *very* good children!"

They kissed their Granny good night and listened to her going down the stairs to the hall.

"It's not worth while getting undressed," said Susan.

"Yes, we'd better," said Jeffery. "Granny may come up again for something—or even Granpa—and we don't want to get into any more trouble. We can easily dress again about midnight."

So they undressed and got into bed. But none of them could go to sleep! They talked to one another and listened to the hall clock chiming the hours and the half-hours.

"Granny's gone to bed now," said Susan. "I heard her door click. It must be eleven o'clock."

It was. The clock struck eleven almost at once. The children talked again until midnight—and then, when the hall clock chimed, they slipped out of bed.

"Don't make a sound," said Jeffery. "If we drop anything on the floor it may waken Granny or Granpa."

So they were very quiet indeed. They were soon dressed. Jeffery took the slices of cake out of the drawer and they all ate them. The cake tasted delicious at that time of night!

"We had some supper after all, said John, with a grin.

They took their torches, and opened Susan's cupboard. The top of her secret stair was there, and one by one they crept down the tiny winding stairway to the dining-room. They crept out of the dining-room and went to the garden door at the side of the house. It was locked. They unlocked it and stepped outside.

"Good! There's a bright moon," said Jeffery. That was lucky. The moonlight lay on the ground like pools of silvery water, and everywhere was bright.

"Where is Rags?" asked Jeffery. Jane had taken him down with her at tea-time, and he had not come back.

"In his kennel, I expect," said John. So they went to the kennel and there was Rags, staring at them in delighted astonishment. What! A walk at this time of night! Well, he was quite ready for it! He slipped out and joined the children.

"Now for a rope," said Jeffery. They went to Tipps' shed and shone their torches round. They soon found that there was quite a big coil in one corner. It was thick and strong, just what they wanted.

Jeffery picked it up. It was heavy. He flung it over his shoulder, and thought he could carry it quite easily like that. Then, with Rags at their heels, they set off for Timbles' Farm, for that was the shortest way to the ruined building.

They had to use their torches in the wood for it was dark there. They arrived at the hole, and pulled away the branches and bracken that covered it. Mr. Potts had put them back, for he did not want anyone else to find the hole.

"I'll go down first," said Jeffery. He tied the rope to a tree-trunk nearby, and then let the other end fall down the hole. Then he let himself carefully down the rope, swung on it, and slid down slowly to the ground below.

"Come on!" he shouted to the others, flashing his torch around. "There's a passage here. It smells a bit musty, but it's all right—not blocked up, or anything."

The other two slid down the rope. Jeffery helped Susan, who was so excited that she might have fallen. They all three switched on their torches and looked around.

In front of them was a narrow passage, with the roof just above their heads.

"I believe it leads into that hill!" said Jeffery. "You know—the little humpy hill."

He was right—it did! The children followed the passage, which was very narrow in parts, and at last came out into a curious oblong room, hewn out of the very heart of the hill!

It was strange to stand there in the light of their

torches, and look round at a room where no or
had been for many, many years.

"This must have been a hiding-place for th
Greylings at some time or other," said Jeffery. "I
the old days people were often ill-treated because o
their religion, and maybe this room was a hide
hole for long-ago Greylings. It's a marvellou
place—right in the heart of a wood—and in th
heart of a hill!"

"Where is the Treasure, do you suppose?" aske
John, looking round. They flashed their torche
everywhere. The room was furnished very plainl
with strong wooden benches and an old narro
table. On a shelf old plates and mugs still stoo
dusty and cobwebby. The floor was tiled like th
floor above. There was no fireplace at all.

"I can't see anywhere for Treasure to be hidden
said Jeffery. "I say! Wouldn't it be too disappoin
ing to have come all this way, to the very end o
the map, and find that the Treasure wasn't he
after all!"

"Jeff, look—there's an old wooden door in th
corner," said Susan suddenly. She shone her torc
there and the boys saw what she meant. They ha
not noticed the door before, because the walls wer
of earth and the door was as brown as the earth.

"I say! I wonder if that's a cupboard or an

hing!" said Jeffery, in excitement. He went over to
he door. It was fast shut, and seemed to be bolted
n the other side.

"Funny!" said Jeffery. How could it be bolted
he *other* side. People wouldn't bolt themselves
n a cupboard surely!"

"The door is as rotten as those steps were," said
ohn. He aimed a kick at the lower part of the old
loor. It gave way and the wood broke at once.
ohn kicked again, and soon there was an enormous
ole in the door!

Jeffery put his hand in at the hole and felt about
or bolts. He found them but they were too stiff
o undo. So he and John kicked at the door until
t had almost been kicked away, and the three
hildren could easily squeeze through the hole.

It wasn't a cupboard. It was the entrance to
nother passage, a little wider than the first one,
nd leading in the opposite direction.

"Come in—let's see if we can find anything here,"
aid Jeffery. He walked a few steps and then came
o a stop. In his way, stopping up the passage, lay
 great wooden box, with bands of iron round it.
he lock had rusted, and the lid was loose.

The children shone their torches on it and looked
t one another, very thrilled. Was it—could it be—
he Treasure, at last?

CHAPTER SEVENTEEN

THE TREASURE AT LAST !

"I HARDLY dare to lift up the lid in case the box
is empty!" said Jeffery, in a whisper. Nobody
knew why he whispered, but it seemed the right
thing to do. He lifted up the lid—and then, oh,
what a marvellous sight!

The Greylings Treasure lay in an old box! Somehow or other the dust and the damp had kept away

rom the box, and the Treasure shone undimmed.
Great brooches, wonderful necklaces, jewelled pins—
nd loveliest of all, the wonderful Greylings cup
made of pure gold, with its handle and the middle
tudded with precious stones! Jeffery lifted it out.

"Look!" he said. "Oh, look! The very cup that
we saw pictured in that old book. The lucky-cup!
It's been here for years and years and years. Oh,
what will Granny say? She'll be rich! She won't
need to sell Greylings after all!"

Susan began to jump up and down in excitement.
She forgot that the roof was so near her head and
she jumped right into it. But she was so happy that
she didn't even feel the bump. She knelt down by
the box and put her fingers among the jewels.

"Pearls for Granny! Brooches for Mummy! Lots
of lovely things for everyone," she said. "Oooh!
This is wonderful! How clever we are, aren't we,
Jeffery?"

"I think we are rather," said Jeffery. "After all,
people have been hunting for this lost Treasure for
years and years—and now three children have
found it!"

"Won't Mr. Potts be angry when he hears that we
got here first and found everything!" said John.
"And he'll be angrier still when he finds that Granny
won't need to sell her dear old house to him after

all! Oh! I'm longing to get home and wake u
Granny and Granpa and tell them everything!"

"Listen," said Jeffery suddenly. "What's tha
noise?"

They all listened. "It's Rags barking," said John
in surprise. "What's he barking at?"

"Suppose somebody is coming through th
woods," said Susan, clutching Jeffery. "Suppos
it's Mr. Potts and the other man, coming at night
What will he say when he finds us here?"

Jeffery ran back into the oblong room, and the
made his way down the first passage. He shone hi
torch up to the top of the entrance hole. Rag
looked down, wagging his tail. He gave a sho
yelp.

"Is there somebody coming, Rags, old boy?" sai
Jeffery. "Come on down with me. Jump!"

Rags jumped into Jeffery's arms. He was ver
glad to be with his little master. Jeffery listene
and at last heard something. It was the sound o
people scrambling through the wood! In the siler
night the sound could be heard very clearly.

Jeffery thought quickly. There was no time t
get out. Was there any good hiding-place up th
second passage for them? Could they take th
Treasure with them and hide it? But how coul
they carry that heavy box?

"Oh, look! The lucky-cup!"

He took out his pocket-knife and cut a good piece of loose rope from the rope that hung through the hole. It might be useful. Then, hearing voices coming nearer, he shot back to the others.

"Sounds like Potts and one or two more," he said. "Come on. Let's see if this passage has got any sort of hiding-place for us."

"How are we going to take the Treasure with us?" asked John.

Jeffery quickly tied the rope round the big box. He knotted it at the top, leaving two long ends which he looped firmly. He gave one loop to John and took the other himself.

"We can carry the box between us," he said. "It's too heavy for one person—but we can easily carry it like this, swung on the rope."

"Good idea," said John. "Get out of the way, Rags, old boy. You don't want this box on your head!"

Susan had crept to the old room and had listened to see what was happening. She heard somebody at the entrance to the hole.

"Hallo! Look here!" came Mr. Potts' voice. "Somebody's dropped a rope down. I didn't see it this morning, did you?"

"No," said another voice. "I suppose those kids aren't down there now, are they?"

"They'll be sorry for themselves if they are!" said Mr. Potts, in an angry voice. "Making false maps and trying to throw us off the trail—stupid little idiots!"

Susan waited to hear no more. She fled up the second passage to tell the boys.

"Oh, here you are," said Jeffery impatiently. "We wondered where you were. Don't go disappearing like that just when we've got to escape."

Susan told the boys what she had heard. The three of them set off up the second passage, the boys carrying the box between them.

"I only hope this passage *leads* somewhere!" said Jeffery. The underground way ran straight for some time then turned to the left. It was dark, musty, and low. The three torches threw a bright light in the dark tunnel.

The passage suddenly split into two ways—one to the right and one going straight on.

"Blow!" said Jeffery. "Which way ought we to go, I wonder?"

John anxiously shone his torch up first one way and then the other. "The right-hand way seems a bit wider," he said. "Let's go that way."

"Right," said Jeffery. "Susan, have you a handkerchief? Well, throw it down on the ground just a little way up the *other* passage, will you?"

"Whatever for?" asked Susan, in surprise.

"So that old Pots of Money will think we've gone up that way, and follow the wrong path," said Jeffery.

Susan laughed. "You *are* clever, Jeffery!" she said. She threw her little white handkerchief down on the ground a little way up the passage. Then the three of them, with Rags nuzzling against their legs, took the right-hand tunnel.

It went on for ages. Once they came to where part of the roof had fallen in, and had to climb over a heap of stones and earth.

"I feel like a rabbit running through a burrow," said Susan.

"With foxes behind us," said John.

"Oh, don't!" said Susan. "I hope Mr. Potts has gone up the wrong passage."

Mr. Potts had! He and his friends—there were two of them this time—had jumped down the hole, found the strange underground room, and squeezed through the broken door that led up the second passage. But when they came to the splitting of the ways, they caught sight of Susan's handkerchief, just as Jeffery had hoped they would.

"They've gone up there," said Mr. Potts. And up the wrong passage they had gone! But before they had gone very far the passage came to an end in a small cupboard-like room, whose walls were of stone. It was quite empty, though, hundreds of years before it had been used for storing and hiding many things.

By the time that Mr. Potts and his friends had turned back and gone to follow the children's passage, the three treasure-finders had got a long way ahead.

"I simply can't *imagine* where this is leading us to," said Jeffery, putting down the box for a moment. It was really very heavy, and though the two boys were strong, their arms were aching badly.

They went on again after a bit. Rags ran ahead, thinking that all this was a fine adventure! Every time he turned round his eyes gleamed like the head-lamps of a small car, in the light of their torches.

Suddenly the passage came to an end—and facing the children were a few rough steps of stone.

"Hallo—look at this!" said Jeffery. "We've come somewhere at last."

John shone his torch overhead. The stone steps led to a square stone slab that lay flat in the earthy roof above their heads.

" Why, it looks as if there's a slab of stone at the entrance here, just like the one we moved," said Jeffery.

"But not nearly so big," said John. "Get up the steps, Jeff, and try to heave up the stone with me."

Both boys went up the steps. They bent double and heaved with their backs against the slab. It seemed to move a little.

"Jeffery! John! They're coming! I can hear them!" suddenly cried Susan. "We shall be caught. Oh, do hurry!"

There was the sound of voices and footsteps to be heard a good way along the passage. Jeffery and John pushed at the stone slab with all their strength. Rags ran back along the passage, barking loudly and fiercely.

"That's right, Rags! Keep them there! Don't let them pass!" shouted Susan. Rags felt grand. He tore down the passage till he saw Mr. Potts and his friend and then the plucky little dog stood in front of them, barking, growling, and showing his teeth. He would *not* let them pass!

The children heard Mr. Potts' voice shouting to them.

"You naughty children! What are you doing here at this time of night? Call your dog off. He's making himself a nuisance!"

The children didn't say a word. Jeffery heaved up with all his might—and the roots of the grasses that had been clinging to the stone slab and keeping it tightly in place, all gave way. The stone lifted up—and Jeffery put his head out into the cool night air!

"Golly! It's open!" said John, thrilled. "Just in time too! Come on, Jeff—hand out the box. Susan, come along. Leave Rags there to bark and give us a start!"

The children all climbed out of the hole. They stood there in the bright moonlight for a moment, wondering where they were. And then Jeffery suddenly knew!

"We're near Timbles' Farm!" he cried. "Look—there it is, down there, beyond the field-gate. Do you know where we are—we've come up inside that funny little ruined stone hut we saw the other day in the field. We wondered what it was! Fancy! There's an underground way between the old building in the wood and this one—and we've found it!"

"Oh, do come on," said John, who was very much afraid of being caught. "Let's go down to the farm and wake Mrs. Timbles up. She'll look after us!"

"Come on then," said Jeffery, thinking it would be very nice to see plump Mrs. Timbles. They half-stumbled, half-ran down the slope of the field, the boys still carrying the box between them.

When they came to the pig-sty, Jeffery put the box

down. "Let's hide the Treasure here," he said. "Nobody would guess it was in a pig-sty!"

The others giggled. It seemed funny to hide treasure with the pigs—but as Jeffery said, no one would ever think of looking there!

So under the straw of the pig-sty went the old box. The pigs grunted sleepily in surprise. Jeffery stood up and stretched his tired back.

"Look! There are Mr. Potts and friends," he said. "Let's go and wake the farmer! I feel as if I'd like a grown-up on our side now!"

CHAPTER EIGHTEEN

SAFE AT TIMBLES' FARM

In the bright moonlight the children could see the
three men running over the sloping field. What the
men were going to do the children couldn't imagine
—perhaps they would take away the Treasure—
perhaps they would be very angry indeed—they
might march them all the way home, and tell some
dreadful story to Granny and Granpa.

175

"Come on, let's bang on the farm door," said Jeffery. "No one will find the Treasure in the pig-sty."

They ran round the farmhouse, and Jeffery banged on the big knocker there. The sound thundered through the night. Crash! Crash! Crash!

A window was flung up and the farmer looked out in astonishment.

"Who's there?" he shouted.

"It's us!" shouted back Jeffery. "We're in trouble —somebody is chasing us. Let us in!"

"Good gracious—it's the Greylings children!" said Mrs. Timbles' voice, and her head appeared by the side of the farmer's. "I'll go down and let them in, Fred."

In half a minute the big bolts were being drawn back, and the great wooden door was opened. The children pressed inside and Jeffery banged the door. He could see the three men coming up the path.

"Now, my dears, what is all this?" said Mrs. Timbles, in the greatest astonishment. She looked very queer because she had on an enormous white nightgown, with a pink shawl thrown over it, and her hair was done up in four tight plaits that stuck out round her plump red face.

Before the children could answer there came

another knocking at the door. Mrs. Timbles jumped.

"Bless us all!" she said. "Who's that now?"

The farmer came into the hall; he had pulled on his breeches, and put on some bedroom slippers. He looked just as amazed as his wife.

"Fred! There's someone at the door again!" said Mrs. Timbles.

"Ay! I can hear them," said the farmer. "I'll open before they knock my door down."

The children went into the big kitchen with Mrs. Timbles. She lighted the oil lamp, and poked the fire which still showed red.

"Why, you're shivering!" she said, looking at them "You can't be cold this warm night."

"We're shivering with excitement," said Jeffery. "Oh, Mrs. Timbles, take care of us, won't you?"

"Of course, of course," said Mrs. Timbles, in still greater surprise. "You're safe here."

The farmer brought Mr. Potts and his two friends into the kitchen. Mr. Potts looked very angry. He glared at the three children, who stood close to fat Mrs. Timbles.

"Now what's all this about?" asked Farmer Timbles, looking sternly at the three men. "Have you been frightening these children?"

"Let me explain," said Mr. Potts. "I have bought Greylings Manor, and . . ."

"You haven't bought it yet!" said Jeffery.

"Don't interrupt, my boy!" said Mr. Potts. "The final papers are being signed to-morrow—but I regard myself as the owner of Greylings lands now. Everything is settled."

"Well, what's all that got to do with you being out at this time of night?" asked Farmer Timbles.

"My friends and I are interested in the old ruins belonging to Greylings," said Mr. Potts. "Naturally those belong to us, as well as the house and grounds. Well, we have beeen doing a little exploring, and these children have very strangely and rudely been trying to interfere with our affairs. My friend here is an authority on old books, china, jewellery, and so on, and I have promised to let him have any old Greylings property to examine."

"You're not telling the story truthfully," said Jeffery, boiling with rage.

"My dear boy, don't be rude," said Mr. Potts. "As you can see, Farmer, these children are quite out of hand. Well, we have been looking for some old things that belong to the property—and we have reason to believe that these children have stolen them to-night. This is a very serious matter, Farmer, as you will see—but if the children are willing to hand us back our property now, we will not make any more trouble about it."

"They didn't bring anything in here with them at all," said Mrs. Timbles. "And let me tell you, sir, that these children are not the sort to steal! I never heard of such a thing!"

"Mrs. Timbles! It was the Greylings Treasure we found!" said Jeffery. "It's Granny's and Granpa's! It doesn't belong to Mr. Potts. We found it to-night! They were after it too—these three men!"

"The Greylings Treasure!" said Mrs. Timbles, in the greatest surprise. "Well, I never did! The Greylings Treasure! Are you sure, Master Jeffery?"

"*Quite* sure," said Jeffery. "We looked it up in an old book, and saw the pictures of some of the things —and they were there, in the old box!"

"Well, my boy, you must let us have the box," said Mr. Potts. "I tell you, I have bought Greylings, and anything found on the property is mine. You will get into serious trouble over this, if you don't give me what belongs to me."

"That's so," said one of the men.

"I don't care!" Jeffery almost shouted. "You shan't have it!"

"Well, Jeffery, give us the box to put somewhere safe just for to-night," said Mr. Potts. "Then to-morrow we will all go into the matter with your

Granny and Grandfather. You will see that I am right. Now, be a sensible boy and tell us where you put the Treasure."

"Well, lad, I think maybe you'd better do that," said Farmer Timbles. "If this gentleman *has* bought the property, you'd better be careful."

"I will *not* give up the Treasure!" said Jeffery.

"No, we won't!" cried Susan and John. They were all quite certain about that.

"Then we shall find it ourselves," said Mr. Potts, looking furious. "And you will get into trouble, all three of you. I'll see that you do—you interfering little wretches!"

The men went into the hall and out of the front door. They began to hunt about in the moonlight for the box of Treasure. The children flew to the window of the front room and watched them. Would they look in the pig-sty?

They did go to it—but the sty smelt and the men didn't even open the gate. They did not think for one moment that the children would have chosen such a peculiar place!

Mr. Potts suddenly grew tired of the search. "Come on," he said to the others. "We'll have something to say about this to-morrow!"

To the children's great delight they saw the three men going away. Then, and not till then, did they pour out their extraordinary story to Mrs. Timbles and the astonished farmer.

Jeffery and John went out to the pig-sty to get the box. It was covered with straw, and did not smell very nice—but who cared for that! How the children enjoyed Farmer Timbles' surprise when they opened the box and displayed the marvellous things inside! Mrs. Timbles too, could not believe her eyes. She would not even touch the things— she just stared and stared at them, saying, "I never saw such a thing! Never in my life!" over and over again.

"So, you see, we've got the lost Treasure at last!" said Susan, jumping round the kitchen like a frog. "Isn't it awfully exciting, Mrs. Timbles?"

"I never heard of such a thing!" said Mrs. Timbles, and her plump face looked even redder than usual with the surprise and excitement.

"Well, I'm going to take you children back home," said Farmer Timbles, getting up.

"Oh, couldn't the little things stay here for the night?" said Mrs. Timbles. "They'll be tired out."

Jeffery did not at all like being called a little thing, but he was so delighted at the thought of staying the night at the farm, that he felt he didn't mind anything. The children looked at the farmer anxiously.

"Well, let them stay if you want to," said Farmer Timbles. "I'm not wanting to dress and go out at this time of night! We will telephone to the Manor early to-morrow morning, before the children are missed."

So that night the children cuddled down in soft goose-feather beds at Timbles' Farm. They were terribly excited and terribly tired—but very, very happy. They didn't care what Mr. Potts said—the Treasure was theirs!

CHAPTER NINETEEN

GOOD LUCK TO THE GREYLINGS!

THE children's grandparents were immensely
astonished when the telephone rang early the next
morning, and the news was told them. At first they
simply couldn't understand it—but when they
heard Jeffery's voice on the phone, telling them that
he had found the Treasure, the two old people sat
down and stared at one another in astonishment.

Farmer Timbles told his wife to give the children some breakfast, but for once in a way the three were really too excited to eat anything. They swallowed down the creamy coffee that kind Mrs. Timbles made, and then begged the farmer to take them home in his pony-cart.

They were afraid of meeting Mr. Potts on the way home! They wanted to get the Treasure safely to Greylings Manor. So Farmer Timbles put the fat brown pony in the little cart, and brought it round to the front door.

He and Jeffery put the box in the cart. Then they said good-bye to Mrs. Timbles and climbed into the little cart themselves. It was a bit of a squash but nobody minded.

"Gee up there!" said Farmer Timbles, and the pony trotted down the farm lane. "Clickitty-clack, clickitty-clack," went her hooves.

Granny and Granpa were waiting excitedly for the children. They really couldn't believe it was true! They had telephoned to a friend of Granpa's, an old man who was very wise about long-ago things, and knew whether they were real or not.

He had arrived just before the children came. His name was Mr. Frost, and his hair was as white as his name. He, too, was very excited, for if the children really had the old Greylings Treasure, it was very wonderful.

The pony-cart clattered up the drive. The children sprang out, and the farmer lifted the old box on to his shoulder. Granny opened the front door and the children rushed to meet her.

"Granny! We've got the Treasure!"

"Granny! We've had such an adventure!"

"We've found the Treasure, Granny!"

"What a noise!" said Granny, and she led the way to the study, where Mr. Frost sat talking to Granpa. Granpa had got out the old book that showed the Treasure, and he and Mr. Frost were examining the pictures carefully.

Farmer Timbles put the old wooden box gently down on the table. "It's been in the pig-sty," he said, with his large smile. "I'm afraid it doesn't smell very good."

Nobody minded that! Granpa flung back the lid and everyone looked inside. For a moment there wasn't a sound to be heard. Then, to everyone's surprise, Granny began to cry! She cried quite quietly, and the tears rolled down her soft pink cheeks one after another.

"What's the matter, Granny?" asked Susan, in alarm, putting her arms round the old lady.

"Nothing, dear—just tears of happiness," said

Granny. "It's so wonderful—just as we were thinking of selling Greylings, you find the Treasure!"

Mr. Frost looked quite amazed. With his long thin fingers he took first one thing and then another out of the box. Soon the table was covered with precious jewels, and the wonderful golden cup shone in the midst of them.

"Yes," said Mr. Frost, in a low voice, "yes! This is all old—very old. Wonderful stuff. Marvellous! And to think it has remained unspoilt and undiscovered all these years!"

"Is it worth a lot of money?" asked Susan.

"It is worth a fortune!" said Mr. Frost. "It is almost priceless! This cup alone is worth thousands of pounds."

"Ooooh!" said the children, and looked with wide eyes at the dull gold of the carved cup, with its precious rubies and sapphires shining and glowing around it.

"But I shan't sell this cup," said Granpa. "The famous Greylings cup, found after so many years! It is unbelievable! The lucky-cup is back where it belongs!"

"Granny, you won't have to sell Greylings now, will you?" asked John.

"No, we shan't said Granny. "We shan't have

to leave our dear old home—it will be your father's—
and yours—and your children's!"

"Mr. Potts said that it was his, last night," said
Jeffery. "I knew he wasn't telling the truth."

"Well, he almost was," said Granpa. "Except for
my signing one document, and Mr. Potts signing
another, the sale was completed. I'm not sure even
now that we shall not have some difficulty in
drawing back from the sale. We shall see what our
lawyers say. I have no doubt that we shall find
a way out all right."

"It seems to me that this man's strange behaviour
will not sound too good when it is told to your
lawyers," said Mr. Frost suddenly. He had listened
very carefully to all that the children had said. "I
think, my dear sir, that you will find Mr. Potts will
not want anything said about his behaviour, and
will not make any more trouble."

"He did make Jeffery fall into the lake," said
Susan. "We are sure of that."

"Yes. He is not a charming friend to have at all!"
said Mr. Frost. "I shall be interested to hear what
he has to say about all this."

Susan, who had been listening impatiently to all
the talk, suddenly went quite mad! "But we've got
the Treasure, the Treasure, the Treasure!" she
yelled, dancing round like a top. "Nobody can

take that away from us! It's ours, it belongs to the Greylings! Hurrah! Hurrah!"

She took up two pearl necklaces and hung them round her neck. She pinned two enormous brooches to the front of her frock. She put an enormous bracelet round her wrist, and took the golden cup into her hand.

Everyone watched her and laughed.

"*I've* got the Treasure! *I've* got the Treasure!" she sang, and danced round the room again. Just at that moment the door opened, and Jane showed in Mr. Potts and his lawyer! Susan almost bumped into them.

Mr. Potts stared at Susan in amazement when he saw all the jewellery she wore. "The Greylings Treasure!" he said. "So you *did* find it after all! I began to think last night, when we hunted round the farm for it, that you had made up the tale of finding it, just to annoy us!"

"It was in the pig-sty, the pig-sty, the pig-sty!" chanted Susan.

Mr. Potts suddenly remembered Granny and Granpa and bowed stiffly to them.

"I have brought my lawyer to hand you my cheque for Greylings," he said. "And, Mr. Greyling, as your property is now mine, I also claim the Greylings Treasure."

The children held their breath. What would Granpa say to that?

Granpa offered the box of cigarettes most politely to Mr. Potts. "I'm afraid," he said, "that there will be no sale. I can't accept your cheque, as now that the Treasure has been found, there is no need for me to part with Greylings Manor. I very much regret that you have been put to so much unnecessary trouble. I shall be pleased to pay you whatever sum our lawyers agree upon to make up for the trouble you have been put to."

"But this won't do, this won't do!" said Mr. Potts, in a rage. "You can't get away with things like that! I'll soon show you that you can't behave like this to me."

"Mr. Potts," said Granpa, in a voice like icy cold water, "if I have any nonsense from you, my lawyers will hear my grandchildren's tale of your very peculiar behaviour this last week—and I do not think you would want that make public. I quite understand your disappointment over the sale—and over the Treasure—but I do feel very glad that Greylings Manor is not going to belong to your family! I think, if I may say so, that it deserves a better fate!"

Mr. Potts listened to all this with a furious face. He went red—and then white—and then red again.

He tried to speak. He swallowed hard. He looked as if he were going to burst—and then, with a noise that sounded like the squawk of an angry hen, he stamped from the room. His lawyer followed him, looking worried.

The front door banged. There was the noise of a car being started up. It sounded as angry as Mr. Potts had looked.

Then the car drove off down the drive. Everyone heaved a sigh of relief.

"Horrid man!" said John.

"I feel rather guilty about him," said Granpa. "The sale *was* almost completed—and I would have considered myself bound to go on with it, if it had been any other man. But I have heard such strange tales about Mr. Potts lately that I feel he is not the right owner for Greylings—and now that I have heard how he has scared you children, and tried to get the Treasure for himself, before the sale was really completed, I am glad we have defeated him!"

"Oh, Granny! Oh, Granpa! Isn't everything lovely!" cried Susan, who was still wearing a great deal of jewellery. "Oh, I'm so happy! Greylings belongs to Greylings—and we can go on coming here as often as we like!"

"You certainly can!" said Granny, hugging the

excited little girl. "You all deserve a reward for being so clever!"

"We've got our reward," said Jeffery. "We've got the Treasure. Oh, Granny, it *was* such fun hunting for it! You nearly stopped us finding it yesterday, though, when you sent us to our rooms!"

"Poor children!" said Granny. "No wonder you were late for lunch! You should have told us all that you were doing, and then we would have understood!"

"Well—it was rather fun having a secret," said John.

"Woof!" said Rags, who had been quite bewildered by all the excitement. He had hidden under the table, and now he came out and licked Jeffery's legs.

"Rags was a *great* help, Granny!" said John, patting the little dog. "We simply couldn't have done without him."

"I think," said Granpa, beaming round at everyone, "I think that such an exciting day needs a celebration—what about going out to the ice-cream shop and ordering the largest and most delicious ices they have?"

"Oooh, good!" shouted the children—and off they all went in the car to eat chocolate, strawberry, and vanilla ices—and what do you think Granpa did?

He had taken with him the golden Greylings cup—and he had it filled with iced ginger-beer at the shop!

"Now we must all drink from the lucky-cup!" he said. "Just as the Greylings did long years ago. And each year we must all meet and drink from it again, and we'll hope that good fortune and happiness will come to everyone of the Greylings family!"

Then all of them drank from it and said the same words—"Good luck to Greylings—and may it always belong to—a Greyling!"

THE END

Harrap's Dictionary of
Law and Society

CONTRIBUTORS AND CONSULTANTS

Susan Deebank LLB

Annette Grogan CQSW

Roslyn Innocent, Solicitor

Roger Leng LLB

Howard Timms BA

EDITORS' NOTE

The laws described in *Harrap's Dictionary of Law and Society* are those of England and Wales at the time of printing. The Dictionary does *not* cover the law of Scotland, Northern Ireland, the Republic of Ireland, the Isle of Man and the Channel Islands, which are substantially different.

Harrap's Dictionary of
Law & Society

HARRAP'S *REFERENCE*

First published in Great Britain 1989
by Harrap Books Ltd
Chelsea House, 26 Market Square,
Bromley, Kent BR1 1NA

ISBN 0 245-54833-5 (cased edition)
ISBN 0 245-54835-1 (plastic edition)

Copy preparation: Clark Robinson Limited, London
Typesetting: Action Typesetting Limited, Gloucester
Printed in Great Britain by Richard Clay Ltd, Bungay, Suffolk

Preface

Law is a fundamental social institution – no society could exist without the rule of some kind of law. From the earliest times, people have tried to write down clearly the rules that govern their society. Of necessity, written law as it has evolved to the present day is complicated, and in many cases difficult for the uninitiated to understand, and the mechanism of law-making can be equally confusing.

Harrap's Dictionary of Law and Society is an accessible guide for the lay person – a businessman or woman confronted with a contract, or a consumer trying to decipher a credit agreement, for example. It is also an indispensable companion for the student of law, giving quick reminders of the meaning of words and phrases and making the important distinctions and connections between the different areas of the law and the ways in which they relate to our form of society.

The Dictionary provides clear and straightforward definitions of the most commonly-encountered legal terms and concepts, as well as concise explanations of frequently-used, but easily misunderstood sociological jargon. The application and often arcane intricacies of the law all too easily appear daunting and impenetrable to the layman. This Dictionary seeks to dispel much of the mystery that has surrounded the meaning and usage of both legal and sociological language. Cross-references are indicated in boldface, and these lead the reader to related articles or to places where further clarification of the root article can be found.

The body of law that is dealt with in this Dictionary is exclusively the law that applies to England and Wales. At the time of writing, there was profound and heated debate regarding the reform of the English legal system. The authors and editors have defined the law as it then stood, and have anticipated only the changes that were certain to occur.

S.A.M. - Clark Robinson Limited, London 1989

A

abandonment Relinquishment of a right to property or of a claim or legal action.

When goods are abandoned they are no longer in the possession of any particular person. Therefore they may be freely taken without committing theft.

abatement Reduction, termination, cessation or suspension.

abatement of action Termination or suspension of a legal action by operation of law or order of the court. Criminal proceedings abate on the death of the defendant, but not on the death of the prosecutor. Some civil actions abate on the death of the defendant or plaintiff; an action may also abate because of a procedural defect — for example, if a **writ** has not been properly served. An example of an action that does not abate on the death of either party is **defamation**.

abatement of nuisance Lawful termination of a **nuisance** by an aggrieved landowner — for example by smothering a bonfire to stop smoke blowing across the land. Except in an emergency, notice should be given of an intention to abate.

Under the Public Health Acts, local authorities may issue abatement notices to terminate statutory nuisances that are health hazards (for example, a leaking roof in rented accommodation). If an abatement notice is not complied with, a Magistrates' Court may issue a nuisance order to enforce compliance.

abdication Voluntary relinquishment of an office or status.

Under United Kingdom law the throne may be abdicated only by Act of Parliament, because succession to the throne is prescribed by law.

abduction Unlawful removal of a person.

Abduction of a child is an offence under the Child Abduction Act 1984 s.2. A parent or guardian cannot be liable for abduction, but may commit an offence of taking or sending a child out of the United Kingdom without consent of the other parent or any party entitled to custody of the child (1984 Act s.1).

The Sexual Offences Act 1956 contains three specific abduction offences: taking away a girl under 16 without consent of her parents or guardian; taking away a girl under 18 without consent with the intention that she should have unlawful sexual intercourse with men; and taking away a mentally defective woman without consent of her parent or guardian and with the same intention.

abet To participate in crime by assisting or encouraging the principal offender at the scene of the crime. Under the Accessories and Abettors Act 1861 s.8, an abettor may be liable for the offence as if he had been the principal. Typical means of abetting are acting as lookout, driving a vehicle involved in the crime or restraining the victim of the crime.

abettor Person who **abets** a crime. *See also* **aiding and abetting**.

abeyance State of being temporarily suspended. An estate in land is said to be in abeyance if for a period of time it is not held by a particular person.

ABH *See* **actual bodily harm.**

abjuration Renunciation of a legal right or privilege by oath.

abode Place in which a person habitually resides; a home. Right of abode refers to a person's right to reside in a particular country. Persons having a right of abode in the United Kingdom are British citizens and those **Commonwealth citizens** who are given such a right under the Immigration Act 1971 as amended by the British Nationality Act 1981.

The term is also used to refer to a person's home address. A person with no fixed abode is someone who has no permanent address.

abominable crime Euphemism for the offences of **sodomy** and **bestiality**, used in Offences Against the Person Act 1861 s.61. This provision was replaced by the offence of **buggery** in the Sexual Offences Act 1956 s.12 as amended by the Sexual Offences Act 1967.

abortion Miscarriage of a pregnant woman before the full period of gestation. Under the Offences Against the Person Act 1861 s.8 it is an offence to procure an abortion. Abortion may, however, be lawful under the Abortion Act 1967 if two medical practitioners certify that there is a substantial risk of severe handicap or abnormality to the child or that continuing the pregnancy would pose a risk to the life or health of the mother or her existing children. Procuring an abortion after 28 weeks of gestation amounts to the offence of child destruction under the Infant Life Preservation Act 1929 and is lawful only if the mother's life is threatened by continuing the pregnancy.

abrogate To repeal, nullify, cancel. A provision in a statute is abrogated, for example, if expressly or impliedly repealed by a later Act of Parliament. When a treaty is abrogated it means that it is brought to an end.

abscond To leave a place against the wishes of others or contrary to law. Absconding in order to avoid creditors may enable a creditor to present a petition to court to have a person declared bankrupt.

A person who is released on **bail** pending a criminal trial commits the offence of absconding under the Bail Act 1976 s.6 if he or she fails to appear at court to answer the charge without reasonable excuse.

absence State of not being found at a particular place.

Complete absence in the sense of not being seen or heard of for seven years may raise a presumption of death. When a person is presumed dead his or her estate may be distributed according to the normal laws of **succession,** and his or her spouse may marry again without committing **bigamy.**

absolute Unconditional, complete, final.

An absolute order is one that takes effect immediately and is not subject to the fulfilment of any conditions.

absolute discharge Sentence following the conviction of a person for a criminal offence (Powers of the Criminal Courts Act 1973 s.7) by which the convicted person suffers no adverse consequences whatsoever. Absolute discharge is appropriate when the crime does not merit punishment and the offender does not need supervision. It is commonly used when a technical offence has been committed but the behaviour was not morally wrong.

absolute offence Offence committed without proof of any guilty mind or other fault on the part of the offender. Generally criminal offences require proof of intent or guilty knowledge or other fault, such as **recklessness** or **negligence**. However, a large number of absolute offences have been created by statute to enforce compliance with schemes of statutory regulation, such as those dealing with pollution and factory safety.

absolute privilege Defence to an action for **defamation**. Absolute privilege applies in circumstances in which the public interest in allowing persons to speak openly and without inhibition outweighs the private interest in protecting reputation. Statements in judicial proceedings and in Parliament, for example, are absolutely privileged.

absolute title Title to land that is guaranteed as being without impediment by virtue of registration under the Land Registration Act 1925.

absolve To release from blame, guilt, punishment or responsibility.

abstracting electricity Criminal offence under the Theft Act 1968 s.13, committed when a person dishonestly uses, diverts or wastes electricity without authority. For instance, the offence is committed if a person tampers with the electricity meter in his or her home to make it look as though fewer units have been used, in order to avoid payment.

abstract of title Written summary of the history of a **title** to land. It must trace back at least 15 years to a root of the title. The vendor of land must supply an abstract to the purchaser except in the case of **registered land**.

abuse Language or demonstrative behaviour that is insulting to those present. Abuse of a person that is untrue and is communicated to a third party may amount to **defamation**.

Abuse of others that causes them to fear immediate violence, or that is intended or likely to provoke a **breach of the peace**, or that is likely to cause **harassment** or distress is an offence under the Public Order Act 1986 ss.4–5.

abuse of process Use of the processes of a court for an improper purpose. A court may set aside (refuse to hear) a civil action or dismiss a criminal charge on the ground that an abuse of process has occurred.

abusing children *See* **child abuse.**

abuttals Parts of a plot of land that are directly adjacent to neighbouring land.

academic lawyer Person with academic legal qualifications who is not qualified to practise law. Academic lawyers are normally engaged in teaching and research.

ACAS *See* **Advisory, Conciliation and Arbitration Service.**

acceptance Agreeing to be bound by the terms of an offer which when communicated to the party making the offer creates a **contract** binding both parties. If the party making the offer stipulates a mode of acceptance that does not involve immediate communication, then acceptance is made by doing what is stipulated. For instance, if a seller stipulates that his customer may accept an offer by posting a letter of acceptance, then the contract is complete when the letter is posted even if it is subsequently lost.

acceptance of service The receiving of legal papers by a solicitor on behalf of his client.

access Term with two applications.

First, access to a highway. Such access is a right vested in the owner of land adjoining the highway.

Second, the opportunity for a parent or grandparent to spend time with a child over whom he or she does not have custody and control. Upon separation or divorce, when one parent is granted custody and control of a child the other parent is normally granted reasonable access. However, the modern approach of courts is to regard access as a right vested in the child, not the parent, and access will be refused if it is deemed harmful to the child.

accession Succession to the throne by the next in line on the death or abdication of the reigning sovereign.

accessory Formerly, one who was a party to a **felony**, other than a principal offender. An accessory before the fact gave assistance before the offence (for example, by providing tools); an accessory after the fact gave assistance in concealing the crime or helping the felon to escape. Felony was abolished as a separate category of crime in 1967. Accessories before the fact are now liable as aiders, abettors, counsellors or procurers of the offence. Accessories after the fact are liable for assisting an arrestable offender under the Criminal Law Act 1967 s.4. *See also* **aiding and abetting**.

accident Unavoidable mishap causing harm or loss. Accident may be pleaded as a defence to any criminal charge that requires proof of **intention, recklessness** or **negligence**. It may also be pleaded as a defence to an action for **damages** in which the plaintiff claims that the defendant has caused harm by negligence.

accident book Record of all accidents at work in which injury is suffered. Employers are required to keep such a book under the Health and Safety at Work Act 1974.

accommodation agency Agency that finds rented accommodation for prospective tenants. The Accommodation Agencies Act 1953 provides that no fee may be charged unless accommodation is found and a lease entered into by the tenant.

accomplice Participant in crime with others. An accomplice may be a principal offender or an aider, abettor, counsellor or procurer of the crime. At a criminal trial, if the prosecution calls an accomplice of the defendant to give evidence against him or her, the judge must warn the jury that it may be dangerous to rely upon the accomplice's evidence without **corroboration**.

accord and satisfaction Satisfying a legal obligation by a means other than that originally contemplated, with the agreement of the person to whom the obligation is owed. If a debtor owes a creditor £100 payable in six months time, for example, it is accord and satisfaction if the creditor agrees to accept £50 immediately in full satisfaction of the debt.

Accountant-General Officer of the High Court who is responsible for funds paid to the court by the defendant.

accounting, false *See* **false accounting.**

accused Person who has been charged with a criminal offence. *See also* **defendant**.

acknowledgement of service Procedure and document by which the defendant in a civil action in the High Court acknowledges receipt of the **writ** and indicates whether he or she intends to defend the action. If the defendant fails to acknowledge receipt within 14 days, or does not signify his intention to defend the action, the plaintiff may have judgment entered in his or her favour without a hearing.

A petition for divorce, issued in a County Court, requires completion of an acknowledgement of service. If the **respondent** indicates an intention to defend, the case is heard in the High Court.

acknowledgement of wills Certification by two witnesses that a **will** was signed in their presence by the **testator**. A will that is not properly acknowledged is generally invalid under the Wills Act 1837 (as amended by the Administration of Justice Act 1982).

acquittal Discharge from guilt of a criminal offence following a verdict of not guilty by a jury or dismissal of the case by a Court. Acquittal by a jury is final and the prosecution may not appeal against it. The prosecution may appeal against acquittal by a Magistrates' Court on the grounds of **mistake** of law. If such an appeal is successful the case may be sent back to the Magistrates' Court for rehearing.

action Civil proceeding by which one person sues another for **damages** or some other remedy, usually commenced by **writ**.

action in personam Action to enforce or confirm a right, or to seek a remedy for a wrong, against a person. Examples are actions in **contract**, in which it is alleged that one party is in breach of a personal obligation, and actions for **negligence**, in which it is alleged that a person should be liable for loss arising from his or her personal fault.

action in rem Action to enforce a right over property. Historically, actions in rem were available for the recovery of land, but these were replaced by **actions in personam** in 1833. In modern times a ship or aircraft may be arrested by action in rem as security for a claim brought against the owner.

actionable per se Claim that may be enforced in the court without proof of any loss. For instance, if a person were forcibly tickled in public to the amusement of onlookers, he or she might bring an action for **trespass** to the person without proof of any loss or damage. If no loss has been suffered, the court may award **nominal damages** or provide other remedies, such as an **injunction**.

action, real *See* **real action**.

actions, successive *See* **successive actions**.

active partner *See* **partnership**.

act of God Unforeseen calamitous event by natural causes such as earthquake, flood or hurricane. Some insurance policies exempt liability for loss caused by act of God. Act of God is a defence to some **torts**.

act of indemnity Act of Parliament passed in order to ratify a prior illegal act and indemnify the perpetrators from either civil or criminal liability. Historically, it was used to indemnify illegal acts committed in war. In modern times, it may be used to indemnify local councillors who have ordered expenditure in good faith, although it was not, in fact, authorized by law.

Act of Parliament Legislative instrument of the Queen in Parliament. Draft legislation is put before Parliament as a **bill**. In order to become law it must be passed by a majority of those present in both the House of Lords and the House of Commons and receive the **Royal Assent**. By convention the Sovereign does not refuse assent to a bill that has passed both Houses.

act of state Act committed in a foreign country, on behalf of the government of the United Kingdom. For example, if the British army at war in a foreign country destroyed a factory to prevent it falling into enemy hands, this would be an act of state. In law, a person who suffers loss as a result of an act of state is barred from suing for **damages**.

actual bodily harm (ABH) Bruising or swelling, pain or discomfort, fractured bones, or physical symptoms such as persistent shaking brought about by shock. It is an offence to commit an **assault** that occasions actual bodily harm under the Offences Against the Person Act 1861 s.47.

actuary Person trained in statistics who calculates the risks involved in particular types of insurance and sets the premiums accordingly.

adaptation Process of changing, modifying or altering something. An adaptation is also the thing that has been changed, altered or modified. Solicitors frequently draft **contracts** for clients by adapting standard-form contracts.

address for service Address that the plaintiff or defendant in a civil action nominates as the address at which he or she may be served with court documents such as **writs, orders** and **summonses**. The address need not be the residence of the party, but it must be within the United Kingdom.

ademption Extinguishing of a specific **legacy** in a will because it has been implicitly revoked by the **testator**. For example, if in his will Brian leaves his violin to Cecil, but uses the violin as firewood before his death, the legacy to Cecil is thereby adeemed.

adjourned sine die Suspension of a legal proceeding by a court without fixing a date on which the proceeding would be recommenced.

adjournment Temporary suspension of court proceedings.

adjournment of the House Suspension of the sitting of either the House of Lords or House of Commons until the following day.

adjudication Process by which a court reaches a decision on the facts of law at issue in a legal proceeding.

adjustment Settlement of the amount of the loss between the insured (or third-party claimant) and the insurer in a claim on an insurance policy. In motor claims in which both parties to an accident are fully insured, the adjustment takes place between the two insurers. Loss adjusters are people who either settle claims on behalf of insurance companies or who negotiate with insurance companies on behalf of claimants.

administration of estates Management and distribution of the estate of a dead person. On death, the estate vests initially in the **personal representatives** of the deceased, who are under a duty to collect all debts due to the deceased, to pay all **creditors** and to distribute the property to the persons entitled to it. The personal representatives may be **executors**, if appointed under a will, or **administrators** if appointed by the court.

administration order Court order directing that the affairs, business and property of a company are to be managed by an **administrator** appointed by the court, for the duration of the order. An application for such an order can be made by the company directors or by the company's **creditors**. When a company is unable to pay its debts, an order may be granted if it is deemed that it may rescue the company, or, alternatively, realize more money from the company's assets than would be realized by an immediate **winding-up** of the company (Insolvency Act 1986).

administration pendente lite Administration while litigation is pending. The court may appoint a person to administer a will in circumstances in which there is a dispute as to the validity of the will and litigation is to take place in order to resolve the dispute.

administrative law Body of laws that govern the formation, powers and duties of public authorities such as the Crown, local authorities, the national industries and the BBC. There has been a considerable increase in the number and variety of administrative bodies in the 20th century and their powers and functions are wide-ranging − for example the provision of a social security system, the regulation of town and country planning, and the operation of a public education system. Legal supervision of the exercise of these powers is provided by **judicial review** in the High Court.

administrative tribunal Body established by statute, empowered to resolve disputes arising out of the exercise of the powers of public authorities under **administrative law**.

Administrative tribunals deal with a wide range of disputes, including, for example, those arising from the assessment of social security benefits, or compensation payable on the compulsory purchase of land. The purpose of the tribunal is to provide quick, cheap and informal justice and one of their main advantages is that the members of the tribunal are often specialists in the field of the dispute. A Council on Tribunals exists to keep under review the constitution and working of tribunals and to receive and investigate public complaints.

administrator Term with two applications.

First, a person appointed by the court to manage and settle the estate of a dead person. If a will names a specific person to carry out this function, he or she is designated the **executor** of the estate. If there is no will, or an executor is not named, the court appoints an administrator for this purpose. *See also* **administration of estates**.

Second, a person appointed under an **administration order** to manage the affairs, business and property of a company.

Admiralty Court Court, created by the Administration of Justice Act 1970, that forms part of the Queen's Bench Division of the High Court. It deals with matters such as claims for injury or loss through collision at sea and ownership of shipwrecked goods. The judge is often assisted by experienced laymen called lay **assessors**.

Admiralty law Law pertaining to navigable waters (the sea, ocean, great lakes and navigable rivers). It covers ship collisions, claims for salvage services, seamen's wages, damage to cargo and towage claims. Disputes are generally heard in the **Admiralty Court**.

admissibility of evidence Principle determining whether evidence should be considered by a court in legal proceedings. If one party to the proceedings challenges the admissibility of an item of evidence, the matter must be ruled upon by the judge. *See also* **character evidence; hearsay evidence**.

admission Term with two applications.

First, a statement made by a party against its own interest in legal proceedings. In civil cases an admission made in pretrial proceedings is thereafter binding on the party who makes it.

Second, admission to the Roll of Solicitors, the process by which a person is accepted into the solicitor's profession.

adoption Act of taking a child, not your offspring, to be your lawful child. Adoption was first introduced in England and Scotland by the Adoption of Children Act 1926. Present controls over adoption are governed by the Adoption Act 1976, which provides for the adoption of any unmarried person under the age of 18.

Arrangements for adoption can be made only by local authorities or adoption agencies registered with the local authority. Applications for an adoption order are made to a court, and the court when granting the order may impose any conditions it deems necessary. An adoption order transfers all rights, duties, obligations and liabilities in relation to the child from the natural parents to the adoptive parents.

adult Person of full age, who has attained the age of legal majority. Under the Family Law Reform Act 1969 full age is deemed to be 18. In criminal proceedings, a person under 17 is normally tried in a **juvenile court,** whereas a person aged 17 or over may be tried as an adult in a **Magistrates' Court.**

adulteration Addition of a substance to a food or medicine (or any other substance) so as to render it dangerous or otherwise adversely affect its quality, to the prejudice of the purchaser. Offences of adulteration are found in the Food Act 1984.

adultery Consensual sexual intercourse between a married person and a person of the opposite sex who is not the spouse. Adultery has never been an offence in English law. Under the Matrimonial Causes Act 1973, adultery may be evidence of **irretrievable breakdown of marriage,** which entitles a spouse to petition for divorce.

adverse possession Possession of land in a manner inconsistent with the interests of another party who claims title to the land. A person who occupies land openly and without interruption for 12 years may become the owner. Any other claimant to the land loses the right of action after that period under the Limitation Act 1980.

adverse witness Witness who is called by one party to an action, but who then gives evidence against that party. The party who called the adverse witness may cross-examine him or her. This is an exception to the rule of evidence, that a party may not cross-examine his own witness.

advertisement Publication in any form that is designed to persuade others to buy goods, or pay for services or do some particular act. Misleading advertisements for food and drugs are prohibited under the Food Act 1984. Advertisements on television must conform to standards laid down in the Independent Broadcasting Authority's Charter. The style, size and placing of billboards and advertisement hoardings are regulated by the Town and Country Planning Act 1971. The advertising industry also voluntarily maintains standards of fairness, decency and honesty through the Advertising Standards Authority.

An advertisement of goods for sale is an invitation to make an offer. It is not itself an offer.

advice centre Organization that provides opinions, advice and legal services to members of the public. Law centres are advice centres that provide free legal advice to citizens who live in the locality. They are generally located in places, such as deprived inner city areas, where there are few private solicitors, and consequently they deal largely with welfare and housing problems.

Citizens' Advice Bureaux offer advice to the general public both of a legal nature and of a practical nature. In addition, there are specialist centres such as Housing Advice Agencies.

advice on evidence Statement, prepared by **counsel** in a case after the preliminary pleadings, that sets out what witnesses and other evidence should be produced for the trial.

Advisory, Conciliation and Arbitration Service (ACAS) Body established by the Employment Protection Act 1975 to provide neutral advice, arbitration and conciliation services to employers and unions involved in collective bargaining or industrial disputes.

advocate Person pleading a case on behalf of another in court. Both **barristers** and **solicitors** may be advocates, depending upon whether

they have **rights of audience** before a particular court. Some
tribunals allow non-lawyer advocates, such as trade union officers,
who frequently appear before industrial tribunals. Any citizen can
appear as an advocate before an industrial, social security or
immigration tribunal.

Advocate General Judicial officer of the Court of Justice of the
European Communities. His function is to summarize the submissions
of parties to a case and express a preliminary view on the outcome
before the matter is considered by the full court. Each member state of
the EEC provides an Advocate General who must have qualifications
similar to those of a judge.

affidavit Written statement sworn under oath before a solicitor or
a **Commissioner for Oaths**. Affidavits may be used as evidence in
court proceedings in certain circumstances and may be required for
certain other official purposes.

affidavit of means Affidavit relating to a person's financial means,
most usually made in matrimonal proceedings. A person who has been
ordered to pay a debt or **damages**, but who is unable to do so, may
submit an affidavit of means to the court in support of an application
for time to pay.

affidavit of service An affidavit that certifies that a **writ** or court
order has been served on the person to whom it is addressed.

affiliate To join, adopt or enter into close relationship with another
person or body.

affiliation order Order by which a Magistrates' Court declares that a
particular man was the father of a child and is required to contribute
to the child's maintenance. It was abolished by the Family Law
Reform Act 1987. The modern equivalent is a family maintenance
order.

affiliation proceedings Proceedings taken in a Magistrates' Court by a
mother who is seeking an **affiliation order** against a man alleged to
be the father of her child.

affinity The relationship by marriage between one spouse and the blood relations of the other. There are some degrees of affinity within which marriage is considered to be void despite the fact that there is no direct blood relationship between the two parties. These are set out in the Marriage Act 1949 amended by the Marriage (Enabling) Act 1960 and the Marriage (Prohibited Degree of Relationship) Act 1986. *See also* **consanguinity**.

affirm Term with three applications.

First, to uphold a judgment. An appeal court will affirm a judgment if it agrees with the decision reached at the original trial.

Second, to declare an intention to proceed with a voidable contract. The effect of affirming a contract is that all rights, duties and obligations under it become binding upon both parties.

Third, to make a solemn and formal declaration to tell the truth instead of taking an oath.

affirmation Solemn and formal declaration to tell the truth. A witness or a juror in legal proceedings who objects to taking a religious oath may affirm instead (Oaths Act 1978). Similarly, a new member of the House of Commons or the House of Lords may affirm instead of taking the oath of allegiance.

affray Criminal offence committed when a person uses or threatens to use unlawful violence towards another and the conduct is such as would cause a person of reasonable firmness present at the scene to fear for his personal safety (Public Order Act 1986 s.3(1)). Typical examples of affray include street fights between rival gangs and fights in pubs or night-clubs.

agency Legal relationship that arises when one person is authorized to act as the representative of another. An agent may, for example, be authorized to make **contracts** on behalf of another person, who is called the **principal**.

agency by implication Legal relationship that arises between two parties by implication from the circumstances, but without express agreement.

agency by ratification Adoption by a party of a contract made by another person purporting to act on his behalf but without authority to do so.

agency of necessity Binding one party to a contract by another party, without the authority of the party bound, as a result of urgent necessity. The contract is binding only if it can be shown that the agent's actions were reasonably necessary in all the circumstances and that it was impossible for him to communicate with the principal before entering into the contract. A ship's captain, for example, may enter into a contract that binds the owners of the cargo in cases of accidents or emergency. Agency of necessity arises very rarely.

agent Person authorized to act as the representative of another, who is called the **principal**. The principal is bound by any act of the agent undertaken within the scope of his authority. A travelling salesman, for example, is the agent of his firm and has the authority to enter into binding contracts with purchasers on behalf of his firm.

agent provocateur Person who encourages another to commit a crime for the purpose of enabling the other to be prosecuted. A police officer who poses as the customer of a prostitute in order to prosecute for soliciting is an *agent provocateur*. A person charged with crime may not raise the defence that he was induced to act by an *agent provocateur*.

age of consent Age at which a person is legally capable of consenting to sexual intercourse or other sexual behaviour. Women may consent at 16. Intercourse with a girl under 16 is an offence under the Sexual Offences Act 1956 s.6; other sexual behaviour may be indecent assault under section 14. A woman committing any sexual act with a man under 16 also commits an indecent assault. For homosexual acts between men, the age of consent is 21 under the Sexual Offences Act 1967.

age of criminal responsibility *See* **criminal responsibility.**

age of majority Age at which a person attains full civil rights, such as the right to vote and legal capacity to act free of parental control. The age of majority is 18 (Family Law Reform Act 1969).

aggravated assault Category of offences created by statute that are considered to be more serious than **common assault** and therefore warrant more severe penalties. The offences include assault with intent to rob (Theft Act 1968 s.8), assault with intent to resist arrest (Offences against the Person Act 1861 s. 38) and assault on a police officer in the execution of his duty (Police Act 1964 s.51). *See also* **aggravation**.

aggravation Factor that increases the seriousness of an offence. For instance, the offence of rape would be aggravated if committed with a weapon.

Generally, aggravation leads to a higher sentence for the offence. In some cases, however, the aggravation changes the category of offence. For example, the offence of aggravated **burglary** is committed when a person commits burglary while in possession of a firearm, imitation firearm, weapon or explosive (Theft Act 1968 s.10).

agreement Consent or joining together of minds of two or more parties. Agreement is an important concept in the law of **contract**; if one party to a contract makes an offer which is then accepted by the other party an agreement has been formed and provides the basis of a contract. Not all agreements create contracts, however, since certain other legal requirements must also be met. *See also* **consideration**.

aiding and abetting Assisting or encouraging another in the committing of an offence. The aider or abettor may be charged as if he were the principal offender and is subject to the same penalties as the **principal** (Accessories and Abettors Act 1861 s.8).

alias Assumed name by which a person is known. It is short for *alias dictus*, meaning "otherwise called".

alibi Defence, raised by a person charged with a crime, that he or she was elsewhere than the scene of the crime and therefore could not have committed it. Alibi may be raised as a defence in court only if an **alibi notice** or warning has been given.

alibi notice/warning Warning by a court to a person charged with an offence about the procedure for the defence of alibi at his or her trial. Under the Criminal Justice Act 1967 s.7 (as amended by Criminal Justice Act 1987 schedule 2) an alibi notice must be sent to the prosecution seven clear days before the trial. A judge will refuse to admit evidence of the alibi unless such procedure has been followed.

alien Person not owing allegiance to the Crown. Under the British Nationality Act 1981 an alien is a person who is not a British citizen, a **Commonwealth citizen,** a British protected person, or a citizen of the Republic of Ireland.

alienation Term with two meanings.

First, in law, it is the transfer to another of the whole or part of an interest in property. A person alienates his or her house by selling the freehold.

Second, in more general usage, it is the estrangement of people either from themselves or from others.

alien enemy Any person who was born in or chooses to reside in a state that is at war with Great Britain, or who carries on business in enemy territory.

alimony Allowance paid by a husband to his wife by order of the court where a couple are separated or divorced. The word is no longer used. Either party may now apply to the court for **maintenance** for children, or periodical payments for the wife or ex-wife.

All England Law Reports Privately published general law reports that record judicial decisions in civil and criminal cases.

allegation Claim made by one party to an action which sets out the facts that he asserts to be true.

allegiance Loyalty owed to a **Sovereign** by a subject. Any person temporarily within the United Kingdom owes allegiance during the period of his or her stay. The offence of **treason** may be committed only by a person who owes allegiance to the Crown.

allotted day Day specified for a particular occurrence. For instance, a contract may provide an allotted day on which payment is due.

amalgamation In company law, the merger of two or more companies into one.

ambiguity Lack of clarity as to the meaning of words. When ambiguities arise in **statutes**, they must be resolved by the courts according to the principles of statutory interpretation. Ambiguity in a **contract** is resolved by seeking to discover the real intention of the parties to the contract.

ambulatory Something that has no legal effect until the happening of some future event. It may be revoked at any time before the event takes place. A **will**, for example, is ambulatory since it may be amended or revoked at any time during the life of the **testator** and does not become operative until the testator dies.

amendment Addition to something or a correction of an earlier error. An amendment to an **Act of Parliament** may be made by a later amending Act. When mistakes or omissions are made in **pleadings** in a civil case, they may be amended under various rules of the Supreme Court. In criminal cases, errors in **indictment** may be amended under the Indictments Act 1915.

amenity Placing, surroundings and circumstances of a plot of land which enhance its usefulness and the enjoyment of its occupier. A pleasant view, access to a highway and proximity to shops are all aspects of amenity.

amnesty Offer made by a person in authority not to prosecute a person for a particular type of criminal offence, or not to pursue a particular civil claim. An amnesty may be conditional on the doing of a certain act, and may be limited to a particular period. For instance, HM's collectors of taxes may agree not to claim back taxes from persons who will admit that they have avoided tax by working under an **alias**.

An amnesty is not legally binding on the authorities unless contained in a **statute**.

ancestor Person from whom another person is descended. In land law, an ancestor in title is a previous holder of a particular piece of land.

ancient lights Windows, skylights or holes through which natural light has entered any building without interruption for a period of at least 20 years. After this period the occupier of the building has a legal right to continue to receive the light (Prescription Act 1932, Right to

Light Act 1959). The owner of ancient lights may thus, for instance, get an **injunction** to prevent a neighbour from building a wall that would block the light.

ancient monument Building or area of land over which a preservation order is made. The Historic Buildings and Monuments Commission grants such an order if it deems the building or land to be of historic, architectural, traditional, artistic or archaeological interest (National Heritage Act 1983 s.33).

ancillary Additional and incidental to something else.

ancillary relief Matters relating to **maintenance** or other financial provisions given by the court to a former spouse in divorce proceedings.

animal The owner of an animal has certain legal responsibilities.

The owner of a dog that causes a road accident may be responsible if he was negligent in failing to control the dog. A person who owns a dangerous animal, as defined in the Dangerous Wild Animals Act 1976, must obtain a licence from the local authority and will be liable for any damage caused by his "pet", whether the result of his **negligence** or not. The owner of a dangerous dog that has attacked a member of the public may be prosecuted. Magistrates have the power to order that such dogs be destroyed (Dogs Act 1871).

annual general meeting (AGM) General meeting of all members of a **company**. It must be held at least once every calendar year and at least 21 days notice of the meeting must be given to all shareholders. The AGM will usually consider the company's accounts and balance sheets and the reports of the **company directors** and auditors. The election of new directors to replace those who are retiring also takes place at the AGM. *See also* **extraordinary general meeting (EGM)**.

annual return Document that must be filed with the Registrar of Companies annually, within 42 days of the **annual general meeting**, giving details of the company, including the registered office and registers of **share** and **debenture** holders. A copy of the auditor's report must accompany the annual return (Companies Act 1985 ss. 363–364).

annul To make void or of no effect. To annul a judgment is to deprive it of all legal effect.

annulment Declaration that something is void or of no effect. A court may annul a marriage if any of the conditions laid down in the Matrimonial Causes Act 1973 apply. The effect is quite different from obtaining a divorce, because the annulment declares that there was never any legally recognized marriage.

answer Reply made by a defendant in a **civil action** to a claim against him. In divorce proceedings, it is the response by one party to the divorce petition of the other.

antecedents Person's past history. Following conviction on a criminal charge, the court will inquire into the defendant's antecedents – that is, his or her **criminal record**. The criminal record is read out in court before sentence is delivered.

anticipation Dealing with or disposing of property before one has received it. For instance, it would be anticipation for a person who expected to receive a house under his father's will to agree to sell that house before his father died.

Anton Piller order Order issued by the High Court that requires the defendant in proceedings to permit a plaintiff to enter the defendant's premises in order to inspect, copy or remove any documents belonging to the plaintiff or relating to his property. It is used most often in cases alleging **infringement** of **copyright**. It is known as the Anton Piller order following the case of Anton Piller K.G. v Manufacturing Processes, Ltd. (1976) in which the order was first granted.

apology Defence to an action for **libel** that may be claimed by a newspaper or periodical. The defence is that the newspaper has published a full apology at the earliest opportunity (Libel Act 1843). The defence is available only if the newspaper can prove that the publication was neither malicious nor the result of gross negligence and if the newspaper pays money to the court to be paid to the plaintiff as compensation.

Apology is also a defence in cases of unintentional **defamation**.

appeal Request by a party to legal proceedings to have the case reconsidered by a more senior court.

In criminal cases in the Magistrates' Courts both the defence and the prosecution can appeal against the decision to the High Court. In the Crown Court appeals lie to the Court of Appeal, and the defence may appeal against either the conviction or the sentence; the **Attorney-General** may institute an appeal against a lenient sentence. In civil cases both the plaintiff and the defendant may appeal against any decision. All parties generally have only one right of appeal, although subsequent appeal to the House of Lords may be allowed if the case involves a point of law of general public importance.

appear Term with two applications.

First, to come before a court for a case. A defendant may be ordered to appear before a court.

Second, to come to court to represent a client. For example, a barrister or solicitor may say that he or she appears for the plaintiff.

appellant Person who institutes an **appeal** against a decision reached in a court of law.

appendix Document that is attached to another document. In appeals to a higher court, the appendix is attached to the notice of **appeal** and contains papers relating to the proceedings in the lower court.

appointed day Day on which an Act of Parliament is due to come into operation.

appointment, power of Powers given under a **settlement** or **trust** to authorize a particular person, called the donee, to dispose of the trust property. The disposal of the property is called the appointment. The power is described as general if the donee has a completely free choice to appoint to anybody; specific, if his choice is limited to a particular class of persons.

apportionment Proportionate division of benefits in relation to which two or more persons have legal rights. For instance, when rent is due to the owner of a house at a particular sum per year, and the house is sold part way through the year, the rent due will be apportioned between the old and the new owner according to the period of their ownership.

appraisement Valuation set on goods or property by suitably qualified persons. Goods to be disposed of under a will are frequently the subject of an appraisement.

appraiser Suitably qualified person who is selected to undertake an **appraisement**. Real property is usually valued by surveyors.

apprentice Person who enters into a contract with a craftsman or tradesman by which he provides his services to the craftsman in return for training. The contract must be in writing and will be binding on both parties even if the trainee is under 18, providing it can be shown to be for his overall benefit.

appropriation Setting aside something for a particular purpose. Thus, in the law of **sale of goods**, appropriation occurs when particular goods are set aside to be sold to a particular customer. In the law of theft, something is stolen by being appropriated dishonestly. Appropriation is defined as any assumption of the rights of the owner (Theft Act 1968 s.3).

approved school School to which children and young persons who had committed offences, or who were in need of protection, used to be sent by a court order. The modern equivalent is a **community home.**

arbitration Settlement of a dispute by an **arbitrator**. The parties to a contract, for example, may prefer to appoint an arbitrator to resolve any dispute arising under the contract as an alternative to court proceedings. The decision of an arbitrator is called an award and may be enforced by High Court order. Arbitration procedure is governed by the Arbitration Acts 1950, 1975 and 1979. Arbitration may also refer to a special procedure for resolving small claims in the **small claims court**.

arbitrator Independent person chosen either by the parties to a dispute or by the court, to resolve the dispute. The arbitrator is often a person with specialist knowledge relating to the dispute.

Archdiaconal Court Ecclesiastical court in a diocese, presided over an Archdeacon. It hears cases similar to those heard in the **Consistory Court**.

armed forces *See* **military law.**

armistice Agreement made between the governments of hostile states to suspend hostilities.

arraignment Procedure by which the **charges** on an **indictment** are put to an **accused** in the **Crown Court**. The accused is asked to plead guilty or not guilty.

arrears Money that a person is under a legal duty to pay but which remains unpaid after the date when payment was due.

arrest Physical restraint of a person.
    Arrest may be either lawful or unlawful. An arrest is lawful if it is for the purpose of bringing a person before a court to answer a criminal charge, and if there is a lawful justification for the arrest and the formalities required by law are observed. There is lawful justification in **arrestable offences** or in **arrest with a warrant**, or in an arrest to prevent a **breach of the peace**. The formalities of arrest require that a citizen should be told why he or she is being arrested.

arrestable offence Offence that allows the suspect to be arrested without a warrant. Arrestable offences are usually punishable by up to five years imprisonment. *See also* **arrest**; **arrest without a warrant**.

arrest with a warrant Arrest under a **warrant** issued by the Magistrates' Court in order to secure a person's attendance at court. Only a **constable** may arrest under a warrant, which he or she must have in possession at the time of arrest.

arrest without a warrant Arrest under the Police and Criminal Evidence Act 1984 ss.24–25 or for **breach of the peace.**
    Section 24 permits arrest if a constable reasonably suspects that a person is committing, has committed or is about to commit an **arrestable offence.**
    Section 25 permits arrest for minor offences observed by a constable when the offender refuses to identify himself.

arson Criminal offence of destroying or damaging property by fire, punishable by a maximum of life imprisonment (Criminal Damage Act 1971 s.1(3)).

articled clerk Apprentice **solicitor** – that is, a person serving under a written agreement, called "articles", with a practising solicitor. The role of the solicitor is to instruct the articled clerk in the practical skills and knowledge of the profession.

articles of association Document that deals with the internal management of a company. Articles of association are required by law in order to form a limited company. The document usually covers matters such as types, transfer and forfeiture of shares in the company, company meetings, appointment, powers and duties of directors and matters relating to company accounts.

articles of partnership *See* **partnership.**

artificial insemination Introduction of semen into a woman's uterus other than by sexual intercourse. Artificial insemination by a donor occurs when semen that does not belong to the husband of the woman is used. Under the Family Law Reform Act 1987 a child so conceived is, for all legal purposes, considered to be a child of the marriage unless the husband has not consented to artificial insemination by the donor.

artificial person Body or association of persons that is recognized as a legal entity that has rights and duties in the same way as an individual. A company, for example, has its own legal personality, which is separate from the members of the company, and it can sue and be sued in its own name.

assault Criminal offence under the common law and a form of **trespass** against the person in the law of **tort**, which causes that person to fear immediate physical violence. The threat must be capable of being carried out immediately; a threat by telephone, for example, is not assault. If the threat is carried out, the accused will be charged with an offence under the Offences Against the Person Act 1861 (*see* **actual bodily harm; grievous bodily harm**). The victim of an assault may sue under the law of **tort** in the civil courts and recover **damages**.

assay office Office that has legal authority to test and certify the quality of certain metals.

assembly *See* **public assembly.**

assessment Process of calculating something, or the conclusion reached by that process. Thus, the assessment of **damages** is conducted by a court. The assessment of taxes is conducted by a tax inspector and the taxpayer must pay the assessment.

assessor Lay expert who sits as a member of the High Court in order to assist the judge with aspects of a case requiring his expertise. For instance, marine surveyors are assessors who assist in cases dealing with collisions of ships.

assets Money or valuable property owned by a person or body.

assignment Transfer of a legal right. The assignor is the person who transfers the right; the assignee receives it. For instance, a father may assign the right to income from his investments to his son.

assisted person Person in a legal action who receives financial support from the State in the form of **legal aid**.

assize Court that dealt with criminal and civil matters, held in county towns and presided over by itinerant judges of King's Bench. Assize courts were abolished by the Courts Act 1971.

associate Officer of the court who is responsible for recording its verdicts and for keeping court records.

assurance Contract under which a person (the assured) pays a regular sum (usually to an assurance company) in return for a promise that he will receive a fixed sum on the happening of a particular event, such as retirement or the attainment of a specified age. *See also* **insurance**.

assured tenancy Tenancy of a residential premises, built or substantially converted after 1980, that is let by a landlord who is approved under the Housing Act 1980. Assured tenancies may be let at an open market rent, unlike other forms of tenancy for which the rent is controlled by law.

asylum Term with two applications.

First, a country or place of refuge. *See* **political asylum.**

Second, an institution for the detention and treatment of people suffering from a **mental disorder**. The modern equivalent is a mental hospital (Mental Health Act 1983).

attachment Term with two applications.

First, arrest for **contempt of court** by order of the court.

Second, the process by which a person's employer is directed to pay part of that person's earnings to the court in order to satisfy a judgment debt (Attachment of Earnings Act 1971).

attempt Criminal offence that is committed by doing an act, which goes beyond mere preparation for a crime, with intent to complete the crime (Criminal Attempts Act 1981).

attendance allowance Benefit paid by the Department of Health and Social Security to persons who are mentally or physically severely handicapped and need constant care (Social Security Act 1975).

attendance centre Centre where offenders aged between 10 and 21 may be required by a court to attend, as a punishment. Training and instruction will be provided by the centre and the offender must attend for a specified number of hours as determined by the court. The offender may be brought back to court and resentenced for the offence if he fails to attend.

attest To witness or affirm the truth of something. Witnesses are required, for example, to attest the signature of the **testator** of a will.

attestation Act of witnessing the signing of an official document. The witness will then sign the document to provide evidence that it was executed correctly. The Wills Act 1837 requires that the **testator's** signature be attested by two witnesses who are present at the time of signing.

attorney Person appointed by another and authorized to act as his or her representative. *See also* **powers of attorney.**

Attorney-General Senior legal advisor to the Crown. The Attorney-General advises government departments on legal matters, prosecutes in important criminal cases and represents the Crown in civil disputes. It is his duty to represent the public interest and he can institute legal proceedings on behalf of the public in circumstances in which individuals have no authority to commence an action.

audience, right of *See* **right of audience.**

audit Inspection of accounts, by an independent person, to determine whether they represent an accurate view of the financial state of an organization.

authority Person or body authorized to exercise legal powers in a particular field. Local education authorities, for example, are responsible for educational provision.

Authority may also refer to the legal power to do a particular act – for example, to act as an **agent** for another.

automatism Involuntary movement by a person who cannot control his actions or is unaware that he is doing them. A muscular spasm brought on by a fit is such a movement. A person who commits a criminal offence as a result of an involuntary movement – for example while sleepwalking – may raise the defence of automatism.

autopsy Examination of a corpse by a pathologist to determine cause of death. *See also* **coroner**; **post mortem.**

avoid To set aside or make void. For instance, if a person has been induced to enter a **contract** by the **fraud** of the other party, he or she has the option to escape liability under the contract by avoiding it.

avoidance Process by which something which would have had legal effect is avoided. *See also* **tax avoidance.**

award Decision made by an **arbitrator** in arbitration proceedings. The award is final and, if it is not carried out, the person benefiting under the award may apply to the High Court to have the order enforced. *See also* **arbitration.**

B

bail Release from custody of a person accused of crime before trial, or of a person convicted of a crime, pending appeal or sentence. Bail may be granted by the police under the Police and Criminal Evidence Act 1984 or by the court under the Bail Act 1976. Bail must be granted unless there is reason to believe that the accused would **abscond,** commit further offences while on bail, or interfere with the course of justice. Bail may also be refused for the protection of the accused.

A bail-bond is a written undertaking by the defendant or a **surety** that the defendant will appear for trial at the appointed time. Failure to do so renders the persons who have signed the bond liable to forfeit a sum of money specified in the bond.

bailiff Officer of a civil court who serves **writs** and **summonses** and may execute the judgment of the court in the case of **default**. If a party to **litigation** is ordered to pay damages by the court and fails to do so, the bailiff may execute judgment by seizing that person's property and selling it (normally by auction) in order to meet the debt.

bailiwick Territorial area over which a **bailiff** has jurisdiction.

bailment The temporary transfer of possession (but not ownership) by one person, the bailor, to another, the bailee, for some specific purpose.

ballot Process of reaching a decision by submitting various options to a vote. The voting is usually in secret using printed slips of paper. The Ballot Act 1872 introduced the system of secret voting for Parliamentary elections.

bank holidays Official public holidays on which banks are closed by law. Any bill falling due on a bank holiday may be paid on the following day.

bankrupt Legal status of a person who has been adjudicated bankrupt by the court because he is unable to pay his debts as they fall due.

The bankrupt's property passes to a trustee in **bankruptcy** and will be sold to pay the debts. The bankrupt is subject to a number of impediments; for example, any property he owns must be passed to the trustee; he must disclose that he is bankrupt before obtaining credit; he cannot be a local councillor, JP, MP or company director. These impediments cease when the bankrupt obtains a **discharge**.

bankruptcy Process prescribed by the Insolvency Act 1986 by which a person is adjudged bankrupt. When a debtor cannot pay his debts either the debtor himself or a creditor may present a bankruptcy petition to the County Court or High Court. The court makes a bankruptcy order and the debtor's property is vested in the **official receiver**. A meeting of all **creditors** is held, followed by a public examination of the debtor in court, at which a trustee may be appointed to administer the bankrupt's estate.

banns of marriage Proclamation of an intended marriage. The banns are read on three consecutive Sundays in the parish church of each party to the marriage, within three months of the wedding. The banns are read to allow anyone who knows of any reason why the marriage should not take place to lodge an objection. Normally a marriage is invalid by law if the banns are not published.

Bar Barristers' profession. To be called to the Bar is to be accepted as a qualified member of that profession. It is so described after the partition which divides the court room, beyond which only lawyers and parties to the action can go.

Bar Council General Council of the Bar, an autonomous body of barristers which operates within, but independent of, the Senate of the **Inns of Court**. Its function is to maintain the conduct, professional standards and etiquette of the Bar and to hear complaints made against its members by the public.

bare licensee Person who occupies or has rights in premises or land by permission of the owner, but who has no legal or equitable interest in the premises or the land. Under the Occupiers Liability Act 1984, the owner owes the bare licensee a **common duty of care**.

bare trustee Person who holds or manages property on **trust** for the sole benefit of a **beneficiary** of full age. The bare trustee has no interest in the property and no discretion as to dealing with it. He or she must simply convey it to the beneficiary when the beneficiary so directs.

barrister Lawyer who is a member of one of the four **Inns of Court** and has been called to the **Bar**. As part of their training barristers are required to undertake 12 months **pupillage** under the supervision of a qualified barrister. A barrister has exclusive rights of audience for trials in the higher courts. A barrister cannot sue for non-payment of his or her fees, and is immune from actions in **negligence** when presenting a case in court.

barter Exchange of goods or services for other goods or services without a **collateral** exchange of money.

basic award In a dispute that has gone to arbitration, an **award** made by an **industrial tribunal** to a person who has been unfairly dismissed. The tribunal may also make a compensatory award for any lost earnings.

bastard Illegitimate child who is both conceived and born out of wedlock. Prior to the Family Law Reform Act 1987 the law denied illegitimate children certain rights, including **inheritance** under the rules of **intestacy**. Since 1987 legitimate and illegitimate children are to be treated the same for all purposes.

battered child Child who has been subjected to physical assaults by a parent or other adult in charge of the child. *See also* **cruelty**; **care order**; **care proceedings**.

battered wife/woman Woman who has been regularly assaulted by her husband or male partner. The male may be prosecuted for **assault, actual bodily harm** or **grievous bodily harm**. A wife may seek a **non-molestation order** or an **injunction** to prevent further attack, which may be linked to proceedings for **divorce** or separation. Whether or not the parties are married, the woman may seek an injunction from the County Court under the Domestic Violence and Matrimonial Proceedings Act 1976.

battery Intentional use of unlawful force on another person without lawful reason or just cause. No physical harm is required; touching a person without authority (other than accidentally) is enough. Battery is both a criminal offence and the **tort** of **trespass** against the person, for which civil remedies, such as **damages** or an **injunction**, may be obtained.

belligerent In international law, a state engaged in a war with another state.

bench Judges or magistrates in a court of law.

Benchers Members of the governing bodies of the four **Inns of Court**, usually judges or senior members of the **Bar**. They have extensive powers, including full control over all property of the Inn and absolute discretion over the admission of students and the calling of lawyers to the Bar. Appeals against their decisions lie to the Lord Chancellor and the judges of the High Court sitting as a **domestic tribunal**.

bench warrant Order issued by a court for the immediate **arrest** of a person. It is used, for example, if a person fails to appear for trial, in breach of an order of **bail**.

benefice Ecclesiastical office in the Church of England that carries clerical duties in a particular parish and certain benefits such as an income and right to occupy a house. The chief benefices are rectories, parsonages, vicarages and curacies.

beneficial owner Owner of goods or land who is free to use them for his own benefit, as opposed to a **trustee**, who holds property in his or her own name but must deal with it for the benefit of another.

beneficiary Person for whose benefit property is held in trust, or person who is to benefit by receiving a gift under a will. A beneficiary under a will loses the right to the gift if he or she has acted as a witness to the will.

bequeath To dispose of personal property under a will.

bequest Gift of personal property in a will. The bequest is specific if a particular item of property is named, and residual if it refers to the **residue** of the **testator's** estate.

Berne convention International convention of 1886, the foundation of co-operation between countries in providing legal protection for artistic and literary **copyright**.

bestiality Committing **buggery** with an animal. It is a criminal offence under the Sexual Offences Act 1956 s.12.

best evidence Evidence from the best available source. In the law of evidence, a court will not admit evidence from a particular source if a better source is available. For example, oral testimony is preferred to all other evidence, unless the witness is dead or unavailable in a foreign country. Similarly, a copy of a document is unacceptable if the original is available.

betting Staking money on the result of an uncertain event over which the person who places the bet has no control. Taking bets is an offence under the Betting and Gaming Act 1963, but betting is lawful at licensed betting shops or with authorized bookmakers at racecourses. In most cases the recovery of debts arising from betting cannot be legally enforced.

beyond reasonable doubt Standard of proof which is required to establish a conviction in a criminal trial.

bicameralism Division of a legislature into two chambers. The Parliament of the United Kingdom is bicameral, with the unelected **House of Lords** as the upper House and the elected **House of Commons** as the lower. Another example is found in the United States, where the legislature is divided into the Senate and the House of Representatives, both elected.

bigamy Going through a ceremony of marriage while still married to someone else. The marriage may take place anywhere and need not be in England. Bigamy is a criminal offence under the Offences Against the Person Act 1861. It is a defence to show that the accused had reasonable grounds to believe that the first spouse was dead or that the first marriage was invalid or had been dissolved by divorce. A spouse who has been absent and unheard of for seven years is presumed dead and the partner may be allowed to gain a divorce and re-marry.

bill Draft Act which is introduced in Parliament and becomes law if it is passed by both Houses and receives the **Royal Assent**. Bills may be public or private. Public Bills alter the law throughout the country, whereas a private Bill confers special local powers, such as compulsory purchase powers to enable a local authority to develop a local area.

bill of costs Statement prepared by a **solicitor** for a client requiring payment for services rendered. The statement, to be valid, must be signed by the solicitor or a partner of the firm and it must be delivered to the client.

bill of exchange Document that contains a demand that the person to whom it is addressed should pay a specified sum of money to a particular person, or the bearer, at some future time. A cheque, for example, is a bill of exchange. If the person to whom it is addressed accepts it, by signing across the document, he becomes legally bound to pay the sum. Bills of exchange are negotiable instruments and are regulated by the Bills of Exchange Act 1882.

bill of health Document, issued by a port officer to the master of a ship, that describes the sanitary condition of the ship.

bill of indictment Written accusation of crime signed by an officer of the court. It contains a statement of the charge or charges against the accused; each charge must be listed as a separate count in the indictment. Until 1933 a grand jury had to consider whether there was sufficient evidence to bring the accused to trial and, if this was its opinion, it would endorse the indictment as a "true bill". The Administration of Justice Act 1933 abolished grand juries.

Bill of Rights Declaration delivered by the Lords and Commons and subsequently given statutory authority in 1688. The Act of 1688 provides the right to free speech in Parliament, freedom in Parliamentary elections and the right to petition the Crown. It also provides that suspension of laws without the assent of Parliament is illegal and that excessive fines ought not to be imposed on individual subjects.

bill of sale Deed that transfers ownership of personal property where the possession remains unchanged. The general rule in contracts for the sale of goods is that ownership of the goods does not pass until delivery of the goods. A bill of sale transfers ownership, and hence risk, before the actual delivery of the goods. Under the Bills of Sale Act 1878 the bill must be registered at the Central Office of the High Court within seven days of execution.

binding over Court order that requires a person to enter into a **recognizance** to be of good behaviour for a specified period of time. Under the Justices of the Peace Act 1361 and the Magistrates' Courts Act 1980 the court has wide powers to bind over; a person does not have to have committed a criminal offence to be eligible. The order is often used in domestic disputes or disputes between neighbours, when each party accuses the other of misbehaviour, and it is difficult for the court to ascertain the true facts.

binding precedent Court decision which another court must follow in a later case if the material facts of both cases are the same. Not all decisions create binding precedents; it depends upon the level of the court in which the decision is made. The general principle is that inferior courts must follow precedents set in superior courts, unless the inferior court can distinguish the earlier case on its facts.

birth certificate Certified copy of an entry in the register of births. It provides details of the time and place of birth, the name and sex of the child and the names of its parents. It is a legal requirement that registration should take place within 42 days of the birth.

blackball To veto something, or to exclude a person from membership of a club or society, in a **ballot** or **election**.

blackleg Person who acts against the declared wishes of a trade union, usually by continuing to work while his colleagues are on strike or by taking the job of a striking worker.

blackmail Making an unwarranted demand, with menaces, with the intent to bring gain to the blackmailer or loss to the person or persons blackmailed. It is defined in the Theft Act 1968 s.21 and carries a maximum penalty of 14 years imprisonment. The demand, which may be written or verbal, most commonly takes the form of a demand for property. The word "menaces" covers any threat of action detrimental to or unpleasant to the person addressed and will therefore include threats of violence as well as threats to make public confidential information.

Black Rod Officer of the House of Lords who is responsible for summoning members of the House of Commons to attend the opening or the proroguing of Parliament. He is called after the black wand, surmounted by a golden lion, which he carries as a symbol of his office.

blasphemy Criminal offence which involves causing hatred, contempt, insult or ridicule against the Christian religion. Blasphemy is now a very rare offence. The only prosecution since 1922 was brought in 1977 against the editor of *Gay News*, who was convicted of publishing a blasphemous poem about Christ.

blockade Use by a state of its own ships to block access to and from an enemy port in time of war. In international law a state mounting a blockade may confiscate ships that attempt to breach it, provided that the blockade is total and effective and the offending ship has notice of it.

blood test Chemical or other analysis of blood which renders evidence relevant to a proceeding.

A blood test may prove that a particular man is not the father of a child (but not that he is). An alleged father may be required to take a blood test in relation to a paternity suit under the Family Law Reform Act 1969. Blood tests may also be required in certain circumstances when drunken driving is suspected (for example, if the driver is unable to perform a breath test) under the Transport Act 1981.

Blood tests employing the DNA fingerprinting process have been used to identify offenders who have left a deposit of blood at the scene of the crime.

bodily harm Physical injury or pain including illness due to **nervous shock**. *See also* **actual bodily harm**; **grievous bodily harm**.

bond Contract made by deed in which one person binds himself or herself to pay some money to or perform some act for another person. The person who is bound to keep to the agreement is called the obligor; the person who benefits from it is called the obligee. Companies often issue bonds as security for money borrowed by them. *See also* **debenture**.

bookmaker Person who is in the business of taking bets. Betting is normally on sporting events, but it may be on anything, such as whether there will be snow on Christmas Day. A bookmaker must hold a bookmaker's permit (Betting, Gaming and Lotteries Act 1963).

bootlegging Production, distribution or sale of liquor in breach of the licensing laws. More recently, the term has been used to describe the recording or reproduction of artistic or musical works in breach of **copyright**.

booty of war Movable property seized in the name of one state from the forces of an enemy state in time of war.

borough Town, or area of a large town or city, that is an autonomous local government unit. Under the Local Government Act 1972 ss.245–246, the term is an honorary title that may be applied for by district councils.

Borough Court Ancient court that formerly exercised civil jurisdiction in a borough. Borough Courts were largely replaced by **County Courts** and the last few still operating were abolished in 1974. Borough Quarter Sessions were local criminal courts, which were abolished by the Courts Act 1971 and replaced by the **Crown Court**.

borstal Penal institution to which offenders aged between 15 and 20 were formerly sent. Until 1982 an indeterminate sentence in a borstal institution, lasting between six months and two years, could be imposed on any such offender. The aim of the sentence was to rehabilitate the offender, and detention was accompanied by training and instruction. Criticism of borstal training and, more especially, the indeterminate sentencing resulted in the abolition of borstal sentences in 1982. The modern equivalent is detention in a Young Offenders Institution under the Criminal Justice Act 1988.

Boundary Commission Body established to consider the boundaries of electoral constituencies and recommend changes according to shifts in population. Four Commissions exist, one each for England, Wales, Scotland and Northern Ireland.

bounty Money prize payable by the Government as a reward for performing a certain act. Bounty payments have been offered for the seizure of enemy ships in time of war, for the arrest of fugitive offenders and, more recently, for achieving export targets.

boycott Organized refusal to have any dealings with another person, body or organization.

brawling Making a disturbance or fighting in a public place. In law, brawling is the archaic offence of making a disturbance in a church. In modern times such behaviour could be charged as one of the offences under the Public Order Act 1986.

breach of contract Failure by one party to a contract to perform, or to perform as agreed, a duty required by the contract − for example, to deliver goods by an appointed time or to deliver goods of a certain standard. In such circumstances the other party is entitled to sue in the courts for breach of contract.

Breach of contract may also occur by express repudiation, when one party gives notice that he or she does not intend to perform the contract at a future date. Deliberate action by one party that makes performance of the contract impossible also amounts to breach of contract.

breach of privilege Breach of Parliamentary **privilege** as determined by the **Committee of Privileges**. It is also called contempt of Parliament.

breach of promise Act of **breach of contract** to marry. Action for damages in cases of breach of promise was abolished by the Law Reform (Miscellaneous Provisions) Act 1970 s.1(1). With the exception of the engagement ring, all gifts between engaged couples are returnable. The ring remains the property of the woman unless it was given on the condition that the marriage take place.

breach of the peace Conduct which causes citizens to fear violence.

Any citizen has a power of arrest for breach of the peace. The person arrested may be brought before a Magistrates' Court on an application that he or she be bound over (*see* **binding over**) to keep the peace. The statutory offence of breach of the peace has now been replaced by an offence of using threatening, insulting or abusive words or behaviour, or behaving in a disorderly fashion within the sight or hearing of persons who are likely to be caused harassment, alarm or distress thereby (Public Order Act 1986 s.5).

breach of trust Improper or negligent act or omission of a **trustee** while administering a **trust**. It may be a failure to carry out duties properly or an abuse of powers. The trustee is liable for any loss caused to the trust as a result of his or her act, and any profits accrued − for example by gambling with trust money − belong to the trust.

breaking and entering Forcing entry to a building or property for the purpose of **theft**.

breathalyser *See* **breath test.**

breath test Test administered by a constable requiring a person to provide a specimen of breath, using a device often called a breathalyser. The test is carried out if the constable has reasonable grounds to believe that the person has been driving or is in charge of a motor vehicle while having alcohol in his body. If the test is positive, a follow-up test is done at the police station. This test uses an Intoximeter machine to measure the level of alcohol in the person's breath. The motorist will be guilty of the offence of driving with excess alcohol if he has more than 35 micrograms of alcohol in 100 millilitres of breath (Road Traffic Act 1972 s.6 as amended by the Transport Act 1981 schedule 8). Failure or refusal to supply a breath sample is also an offence.

bribery and corruption Offering or giving money or other benefit to a person in order to influence him or her in the exercise of a duty; requesting or accepting such benefit by the person under the duty, coupled with a promise to favour the person who provides the benefit.

Bribery and corruption in commerce is an offence under the Prevention of Corruption Act 1916. In public affairs it is an offence under the Public Bodies (Corrupt Practices) Act 1889.

There are numerous other offences of bribery and corruption in various Acts.

bridleway Public right of way to pass on foot, horseback or bicycle.

brief Written instructions from a **solicitor** to a **barrister**, in anticipation of legal proceedings, in which the barrister is to represent the solicitor's client. The instructions normally include details of the facts of the case and an outline of the proposed legal argument. Documents that are to be used in the case, such as witness statements, are normally attached to the brief.

British Standards Institution Authority that develops and issues standards for production of consumer or industrial goods. Compliance with some standards is required by law. Many other standards are adopted voluntarily by manufacturers.

broadcasting Publication by means of radio or television transmission. Broadcasting is illegal unless it is licensed, but some exceptions are made − for example, for "citizens band" transmissions. The BBC broadcasts under a Royal Charter of 1926, commercial television and radio under the Independent Broadcasting Authority Act 1973.

brothel Premises used by two or more women for the purposes of habitual **prostitution**. It is an offence under the Sexual Offences Act 1956 to be knowingly concerned in the management of a brothel.

bucket shop Business that sells tickets for air travel at low prices in breach of provisions of international conventions which are binding on airlines by the terms of their licences.

buggery Intercourse by insertion of the penis into the anus of a man, woman or beast. It is an offence under the Sexual Offences Act 1956 s.12, except, by the Sexual Offences Act 1967, between consenting males aged over 21 in private.

building lease Lease of land granted by one party to another, the terms of which require the receiver to the lease to erect certain buildings on the land.

Building Regulations Regulations made by **statutory instrument** under the Public Health Acts, designed to protect public safety and health by maintaining standards of building design and construction. They are generally contained in the Building Regulations 1976, but separate regulations apply in London. The Regulations are enforced by local-authority building inspectors.

burden of proof Obligation of proving facts in order to succeed in a legal proceeding. The basic rule is that he who asserts must prove. In civil proceedings the burden of proof lies with the **plaintiff**. The standard of proof is "on the balance of probabilities". In criminal law the prosecution carries the burden of proof, because the defendant is presumed to be innocent until proven guilty. The standard of proof is that the case must be proved **beyond reasonable doubt**. In exceptional circumstances − for example, a defence of insanity − the burden of proof rests on the defendant. In such cases the standard of proof is "on the balance of probabilities".

burglary Criminal offence which is committed when a person enters a building as a trespasser with intent to commit an offence of theft, grievous bodily harm, rape or unlawful damage, or when a person, having entered a building as a trespasser, steals or attempts to steal anything in the building or inflicts or attempts to inflict grievous bodily harm on any person therein (Theft Act 1968 s.9). The maximum penalty is 14 years imprisonment.

burial Burial of a corpse. All corpses must be either buried or cremated and it is an offence to prevent this occurring − for example, by concealing the body. Before burial a disposal certificate from the Registrar of Deaths must be obtained. If there has been an inquest, the coroner's authority is required.

bye-laws Rules that regulate the administration of a particular geographical area. They have the force of law within the sphere of their legitimate operation and are a form of **delegated legislation**. A bye-law is made by a local authority under powers in an enabling Act. It may require Government approval and must be published to be valid.

bystander syndrome Tendency of a person who is present at, or a witness to, an event or crime not to actively participate in it, but merely to look on.

C

call The number of years a person has worked as a barrister. A barrister of 20 years call is a barrister called to the **Bar** 20 years ago.

call to the Bar Ceremony held by each **Inn of Court** to admit to the profession of barrister. A student who has been called to the **Bar** has the **right of audience** in all courts.

cancellation Invalidating a document, usually by drawing lines across it. To be effective it must be done by the author of the document or with his authority and with the intention of invalidating it.

canon law System of law which governs the Church. Enforced by the **ecclesiastical courts**.

capacity Legal ability to exercise rights and undertake duties. Most people have full legal capacity although in some circumstances capacity may be limited. In contract law, for example, persons under the age of 18 do not generally have the capacity to make a binding contract. In criminal law, children under the age of ten do not have the capacity to commit a criminal offence.

capital clause Clause in a company's **memorandum of association** that sets out the company's capital and the number and denomination of its shares.

capital gains tax Charge on capital gains accruing to a resident of the United Kingdom during a year of assessment ending on 5 April. Capital losses may be offset against gains in determining liability. There is a minimum gain below which tax is not charged.

capital offence Criminal offence that carries the death penalty on conviction. At one time most **felonies** were capital offences, but in the early 19th century imprisonment or deportation were substituted for the death penalty in most cases. Murder remained a capital offence until the Murder (Abolition of the Death Penalty) Act 1965. The only current capital offence is **treason**.

capital punishment Punishment of a crime by death. *See also* **capital offence**.

caption Part of a legal document that contains necessary formalities. For instance, the caption of an **indictment** must contain the signature of the officer of the court who prepared it.

care Degree of diligence which is legally required in specific circumstances. In the **tort** of **negligence** a plaintiff may recover compensation for loss or injury if he or she can establish that the defendant owed him a legal duty of care and has broken that duty by failing to satisfy the necessary standard of care. For example, car drivers owe a duty of care to pedestrians and may be liable in negligence if they fail to achieve the standard of a reasonable driver and cause injury.

care and control Responsibility of looking after and providing day-to-day care of a child. It is usual for children to be under the care and control of their parents.

care order Order which may be imposed by a Magistrates' Court to require a local authority to take a child into care. *See also* **care proceedings.**

care proceedings Proceedings in a **juvenile court** in which the welfare of a child is considered. Care proceedings arise: (i) when the parents are unable − from illness or homelessness, for example − to cope with looking after the child (ii) when the child is troublesome and is in need of **care and control**, usually when the child has committed a criminal offence, and (iii) when an emergency has arisen, such as child battering or sexual abuse. If a care order is issued the child is taken into the care of the local authority, which assumes the parents' rights and duties.

careless and inconsiderate driving Driving without due care and attention or without reasonable consideration for other persons using the road. It is an offence under the Road Traffic Act 1972 s.3.

Charges are often brought after a minor road accident, but an accident is not necessary for charges to be brought, because any error of judgment may amount to careless driving.

carnal knowledge Penetration of the sexual organ of the female by the penis of a man. Full sexual intercourse or ejaculation is not necessary. For the purposes of sexual offences, sexual intercourse is interpreted to mean carnal knowledge (Sexual Offences Act 1956 s.44).

cartel Term with two applications.

First, in international law, an agreement between states at war with each other to allow certain types of transaction – for example, postal or telephone services, or trade in particular commodities – to continue between them.

Second, an agreement between competitors in business to act together to the detriment of others trading in the same field. Certain cartels are illegal under the laws of the **European Community**.

case law Law which is created and developed through decisions reached in individual cases before the courts. Case law is built up from **precedents**, a precedent being a previous decision of a court which is binding on another court in similar circumstances. Case law and statute law are the two main sources of law. *See also* **binding precedent; precedent**.

case stated Statement of the relevant facts of a case, when the correct application of a point of law is in question, for the purpose of an **appeal** to a higher court. An appeal against a decision reached in a Magistrates' Court, for example, may be by way of case stated to the **Divisional Court**.

casting vote Deciding vote exercised by a chairperson or presiding officer when the votes cast on both sides are equal.

causal connection Connection which must be proved between a person's conduct and a particular consequence before the person may be held liable in law for the consequence. For instance, a person may be liable for **murder** only if there is a causal connection between what he or she did and the death of another. Similarly the **tort** of **negligence** depends upon proof of a causal connection.

cause Term with two applications.

First, a **civil action** or suit. The phrase "cause of action" refers to the set of facts that give the legal right to take a case to court.

Second, any act which brings about a particular consequence. Causation is a very important concept in **civil** and **criminal law**. A person will generally only be held responsible for acts or injuries which can be said to have been caused by his conduct.

cause list Published list of cases which are to be tried in the Supreme Court. A Weekly Cause List is published every Monday and gives details of cases which are expected to be heard during the course of that week. *See also* **daily cause list**.

cause of death Way in which a person's death is brought about. A doctor will examine a person on death and complete a medical certificate explaining the cause of death. If the cause of death is uncertain, or is violence, an accident or an industrial disease, the doctor will report the death to a coroner. The coroner will arrange a **post mortem** examination and may also decide to hold an **inquest.**

caution Term with two applications.

First, formal warning given to a person who has admitted an offence, as an alternative to prosecuting him. Cautions are administered by the police who follow guidelines issued by the Home Office. Cautions are particularly suitable for first offenders, trivial offences and **juvenile offenders**. For juvenile offenders, cautions are recorded and form part of the **criminal record.**

Second, warning not to deal with property without giving notice to the cautioner who claims some interest in it.

Central Criminal Court The **Crown Court** for London, which tries all serious crimes committed in Greater London. It is known as the Old Bailey and was established in 1834 by the Central Criminal Court Act.

central funds Funds controlled by the Treasury. They may be used to pay the court costs of either party in a criminal case, at the discretion of the trial judge. Central funds may also be used to pay the costs incurred in successful private prosecutions or the costs incurred by a defendant who is acquitted.

certificate Document issued by a court or other legal authority stating conclusively that a particular thing has been done.

certificate of incorporation Document provided by the Registrar of Companies to certify that a particular company has come into existence. It also confirms that the company has acquired limited liability. The Registrar issues the certificate if he is satisfied that the company has produced the documents required by the Companies Act 1985. *See also* **Articles of Association; Memorandum of Association.**

certificate of unruliness Finding by a **juvenile court** in relation to a child who has been brought before it by a social worker as being in need of care and control. A child found to be unruly may be placed in the care of the local authority.

certified copy Copy of a legal document which has been certified by an appropriate official as being a true copy. Before a person may be charged with an offence under a bye-law, a certified copy of the bye-law must be produced in court.

cesser To come to the termination of a right or interest. For instance, a term in a **mortgage** contract for "cesser on redemption" means that the mortgage comes to an end when it is redeemed by being paid off.

cession Voluntary transfer of territory by one state to another. It may occur as part of an agreement to end hostilities between states.

chain of representation Process by which a person named as **executor** in a will passes on this role to his executor if he dies before completing his duties. This happens only if he is the sole or last surviving executor.

challenge of jurors Process by which either the prosecution or defence in a criminal trial may object to a particular person serving on the jury. Previously, the defendant was permitted to challenge three jurors without giving any reasons. This right was abolished by the Criminal Justice Act 1988. The defendant may now challenge only if it is claimed that the person is disqualified from serving as a juror, or has an interest in the case. The prosecution may challenge any number of prospective jurors without giving reasons.

chambers Term with two applications.

First, rooms that barristers use collectively as their offices. The chambers are usually in one of the **Inns of Court** and each chambers has a clerk who represents the barristers when receiving **briefs** from solicitors.

Second, the private rooms of a judge in a court. Any legal work which does not have to be completed in open court takes place in a judge's chambers.

Chancery Division Branch of the High Court that deals with cases involving property law, succession and taxation, partnership and company law. The patents court also forms part of the Chancery Division.

change of name Adopting a different name. Providing there is no fraudulent intent, an adult may call himself by whatever surname he or she chooses. From a legal point of view there is no need to comply with any formalities and the name that a person is commonly known by will be the correct name. For practical reasons however, formal evidence of a change of name may be needed. This may be provided by means of a **statutory declaration** or a **deed poll.** The name of a legitimate child cannot be changed without the consent of the father.

character evidence Evidence relating to the character of one of the parties to legal proceedings. In **civil actions** character evidence is generally not allowed unless the character of either party is an issue in the case – for example, **defamation**.

In criminal cases the defendant may always call evidence of his good character. Evidence of his bad character is generally not allowed unless the defendant has claimed to be of previous good character or if he has attacked the character of a prosecution witness (Criminal Evidence Act 1898 s.1).

charge Term with three applications.

First, an accusation of a criminal offence.

Second, the statement made by a judge to a jury at the close of evidence in a criminal trial in which he or she explains the relevant law and the issues that the jury must consider when reaching its verdict.

Third, in property law, a creditor's right to repayment of a debt out of a specific fund or the proceeds of the sale of specific property. The property is said to have a charge on it and this provides the creditor with good security for the loan.

Charges Register Register kept by the Land Registry recording property which is subject to a **charge** or **encumbrance**.

charging order Order placed on a debtor's land or property by the High Court if an outstanding **debt** has not been paid. The **creditor** may apply to the court for such an order and the effect is that the property may be sold to compensate the creditor if the debt is not paid. The Charging Orders Act 1979 defines the type of property on which a charging order may be placed.

charity Body set up for a charitable purpose, as specified by the Charities Act 1960 and which is subject to control by the High Court. Charitable purposes fall under 4 headings: (i) relief of poverty; (ii) education; (iii) religion; (iv) other purposes beneficial to the community.

Charity Commissioners Body carrying out statutory responsibilities under the Charities Act 1960. A **charity** may register with the Commissioners, although this is not compulsory. However, if it does not it cannot receive the benefit which registration brings nor call itself a charity. The Commissioners advise and supervise charities. They have powers to remove charity trustees for dishonesty or incompetence.

charter Deed granted by the Crown in the form of **letters patent** which confers special powers and privileges on specific bodies. Referred to as a Royal Charter, it is now largely reserved for educational and professional organizations.

chattel Any property other than **freehold** land. Chattels may be subdivided into chattels real, which are interests in land, and chattels personal, which are movable objects and any intangible property which has a monetary value − for example, the goodwill of a business. *See also* **chose in action**; **chose in possession**.

cheat Offence in **common law** of obtaining property by **deception**. It was abolished by the Theft Act 1968, but the modern offence of obtaining property by deception (Theft Act 1968 s.15) is still sometimes referred to as cheat.

cheque Instrument of money payment, a **bill of exchange** drawn on a banker and payable on demand (Bills of Exchange Act 1882 s.73). A cheque is made payable to the payee and is signed by the drawer.

child Young person defined in different ways in different legal contexts. In criminal law, a child is a person under the age of 14. Under the Education Acts, a child is a person subject to compulsory schooling, generally under the age of 16. In family law, a person is a child and subject to parental authority until the age of 18. *See also* **child of the family**.

child abuse Subjecting children to physical or sexual abuse. The phrase is commonly used, but has no specific legal meaning. *See also* **cruelty; gross indecency; incest.**

child benefit Flat-rate cash benefit paid by the State to a person bringing up a child. It is payable until the child reaches the age of 16, or 19 if he or she is still receiving full-time education.

child destruction Criminal offence under the Infant Life (Preservation) Act 1929, committed when a person wilfully destroys the life of a child which is capable of being born alive, before it has an existence independent of its mother. *See also* **abortion**.

child labour Employment of children, regulated by the Children and Young Persons Acts 1933–63. It is illegal to employ a child below the age of 13. Older children may not be employed for more than two hours per day, nor before 7 am or after 7 pm or during school hours. Under the Employment of Children Act 1973 local education authorities are given powers to enforce the law.

child of the family Person who has been treated as a member of the family of another while a child. This concept was introduced into law by the Marriage (Prohibited Degrees of Relationship) Act 1986 s.1, by which a man or woman is permitted to marry the daughter or son of their previous spouse, but not if the daughter or son of the previous spouse has at any time lived with them as a child of the family.

Chiltern Hundreds Members of Parliament are prohibited from resigning unless they have accepted an office of profit from the crown. Since 1750 an MP has traditionally resigned by applying for one of two such offices, the Chiltern Hundreds or the Manor of Northstead.

chose Thing. *See* **chose in action**; **chose in possession**.

chose in action Thing which is recognized by law and which may be owned but which has no tangible existence. The right to a chose in action may be enforced in the courts. Examples include the **goodwill** of a business, **cheques, shares** and **debentures, copyright, trade marks** and **patents**. *See also* **chattels**; **chose in possession**.

chose in possession Personal property in the form of a tangible physical object. Because the property is tangible, in most cases ownership may be transferred from one person to another by simple delivery of the goods. *See also* **chattels**; **chose in action**.

circuit Number of courts which are grouped according to geographical area and to which judges are assigned to hear criminal and civil cases. Since the Courts Act 1971 the country has been divided into six circuits for the purposes of hearing cases in the High and Crown Courts. The six circuits are Midland and Oxford, North-Eastern, Northern, South-Eastern, Wales and Chester; and Western. Each circuit is staffed by two High Court judges and a number of **circuit judges**.

circuit judge Judge who is appointed to a **circuit** to hear cases in the County and Crown Courts. Circuit judges are appointed on the recommendation of the **Lord Chancellor**, from the ranks of senior **barristers** or **solicitors**.

circumstantial evidence Any fact from the existence of which a judge or jury may infer the existence of a fact at issue. For example, evidence from a witness that he or she saw the accused carrying a blood-stained knife near the scene of an alleged stabbing is circumstantial evidence; it may be inferred from this fact that the accused inflicted the wound.

51

citation Term with two applications.

First, a reference to a case or statute which supports a principle used in legal argument, usually in a court of law. For example, a barrister may cite an earlier case in which a point of law was first established, in order to support his argument.

Second, the calling of a person to give evidence in a court of law.

citizen's arrest Apprehension by a citizen of a person whom he or she has reasonable grounds to believe is committing or has committed a criminal offence. The person who is detained must be brought before a police officer or a magistrate as soon as possible. Powers of arrest are governed by the Police and Criminal Evidence Act 1984.

citizenship Relationship between an individual and a state. The individual owes allegiance to the state and enjoys its protection and right of abode in it.

city Urban area which has been granted the title of city by **charter** or **Act of Parliament** or which has acquired the right to be called a city by being the seat of an ancient bishopric.

civil action Proceedings in court to enforce or protect private rights. This will generally cover all court proceedings other than criminal matters.

civil law Term with two applications.

First, in England and Wales law that regulates rights and duties as between citizens. The most important branches of civil law are contract law, the law of tort and family law.

Second, a system of law that has its foundations in ancient **Roman Law**.

civil liberties Rights and liberties of the individual which are protected by law. The term is particularly used in relation to liberties related to democracy, such as freedom of association and expression, and rights related to organs of the State, such as the **right of silence** and right to **natural justice**. No single statute defines the extent of civil liberty. *See also* **Bill of Rights**; **Human Rights**.

claim of right Defence to a criminal charge based on a claim by the defendant that he had a specific right to perform the act which is alleged to be a crime. For example, if a person charged with the theft of a coat from a cinema raises the defence that it was his own coat, he is making a claim of right. If he is believed, it would amount to a complete defence.

clean break Once-and-for-all monetary settlement between husband and wife in a divorce, after which neither party has any claim against the other. Courts may order clean-break settlements if both parties are working or capable of doing so and there are no children of the marriage.

clean hands Principle of the law of equity that a plaintiff will not be granted a remedy unless he or she comes to court with "clean hands" – that is, he or she is not tainted by unfair or fraudulent conduct.

clerk of the court Officer of the court who has administrative responsibilities for running the court and seeing that particular formalities are observed.

Clerk of the House of Commons Chief adviser to the **Speaker** of the House of Commons on privileges and procedure.

Clerk of the Parliaments Officer of the **House of Lords** in charge of the Parliament Office, which provides administrative and support services to the Lords.

clerk to the justices Clerk who is responsible for the administration of the Magistrates' Court to which he is appointed. His main function is to assist magistrates on questions of procedure and law, although he must take no part in making decisions. Clerks are appointed from barristers and solicitors of at least five years standing.

client Person who seeks the advice of a professional man or woman. In the legal profession, a client is a person who employs a solicitor or a barrister for advice or assistance. A solicitor who **briefs** a **barrister** is called a professional client.

clog on the equity Clause in a **mortgage** contract which, if enforced, would make the mortgage irredeemable or very difficult to redeem. For example, it would be a clog on the equity if a mortgage deed provided that if one periodic payment were a week late, then the principal sum to be repaid would double. The courts refuse to enforce such clauses.

closed-shop agreement Agreement between employers and employees that the employers will only employ workers who belong to or agree to join a particular trade union. The Employment Act 1982 controls closed-shop agreements which are more correctly known as "union-membership agreements".

close season Periods during the year when it is illegal to hunt fish or game. Various statutes determine these periods, which vary according to the fish or game in question. The hunting seasons for game, for example, are controlled by the Game Act 1831.

closing order Term with two applications.

First, an order made by a local authority to close any building or part of a building which is considered to be unfit for human habitation (Housing Act 1985 ss.276–279).

Second, an order made by a local authority to determine the closing hours of shops (Shops Act 1950).

closure Procedure used to terminate a debate in Parliament. Any member of the House may propose that "the question be now put" and if this is accepted by the **Speaker** and the motion receives at least 100 votes, then the question that is being debated must be put to a vote of the House even if other members wish to speak.

club Voluntary organization formed for any lawful purpose other than to make a profit. It may be a social club, for example, or a sports club or a political club. The law recognizes two main kinds of club: (i) a members' club, to which members contribute to a common fund for the benefit of the club and of which all members own the assets jointly; (ii) a proprietary club, which is owned by a proprietor to whom the members pay a subscription in return for certain benefits.

code Body or collection of laws which may form an entire system of law or may simply relate to one branch of the law.

code of practice Collection of principles guiding conduct in particular circumstances, but not principles of strict law. For example, codes of practice issued under the Police and Criminal Evidence Act 1984 regulate the conduct of the police in relation to the treatment of suspects in custody, interrogation, identity parades and access by arrested persons to legal advice. Copies of the code must be available to be read by any arrested person kept in custody.

codicil Document produced by a **testator** which alters, explains or adds to a **will** which he has previously executed. For it to be valid, the formalities required when making a will must be complied with (Wills Act 1837).

coercion Claim by a wife that she committed a crime under **duress** from her husband. Coercion, if proved, is a good defence to a criminal charge other than treason or murder. The **presumption** that any crime committed by a wife in the presence of her husband was committed under coercion was abolished by the Criminal Justice Act 1925.

cognizance Knowledge which a judge is presumed to possess, such as the jurisdiction of the courts and the structure of Parliament. If a judge takes cognizance of a fact there is no need to produce evidence to prove that fact.

cohabitation Living together as husband and wife whether legally married or not. When a man and woman marry, they take on a duty to cohabit, which includes the implied acceptance of sexual intercourse with each other. A couple who cohabit outside marriage may incur duties and responsibilities towards each other which the courts may recognize.

collateral Term with two applications.

First, something – for example, a transaction – which is linked to but independent of some other thing – for example, another transaction. If, for instance, a man buys a motorcycle on credit, his father may enter into a collateral guarantee with the vendor by which he promises to pay the money due if his son defaults on payment.

Second, security that is additional to the main security for a debt.

collective bargaining Procedure used by employers and groups of employees to negotiate wages and conditions of employment. Employees are usually represented by a **trade union**, which negotiates on behalf of the members to obtain improved conditions of employment, most commonly pay increases. The trade union may use a threat of **strike** action in an attempt to enforce its demands.

collusion Agreement between two or more parties to act in a way which is intended to deceive a court or to be prejudicial to a third party. Collusion in divorce proceedings, for example, occurs when a couple deceives a court into believing that one partner has lawful grounds for divorce. Since the Divorce Reform Act 1969 (as amended) collusion is no longer a bar to obtaining a divorce.

comity of nations Practice whereby the courts of one nation recognize and give effect to the decisions of the courts of another nation as a matter of mutual respect.

commerce All dealings concerning the purchase, sale or exchange of goods and services.

Commercial Court Specialized court of the **Queen's Bench Division** of the High Court, which deals with disputes involving commercial markets and the traders, shippers, bankers etc. who operate in them. The court is staffed by High Court judges who are nominated by the **Lord Chancellor** to be commercial judges.

commercial law Body of law regulating trade and commerce. It encompasses contract law, the law of **sale of goods**, the law of **consumer credit** and **consumer protection**, the law of **agency,** company law, partnership law, banking law and shipping law.

commission Term with two applications.

First, the conferment of duties and responsibilities. Thus, a commissioner is somebody on whom particular duties and responsibilities have been conferred. The individual or body on whom the duties and responsibilities are conferred may also be described as a commission. For example, a law commission is a group of lawyers and other legal experts appointed by Parliament to recommend reforms in the law.

Second, a fee due to an agent who completes a transaction on behalf of another. It may be a fixed fee or a percentage of the value of the transaction.

Commission for Racial Equality Body established under the Race Relations Act 1976 and having the following duties: (i) to work towards the elimination of discrimination, (ii) to promote equality of opportunity and good relations between persons of different racial groups and (iii) to keep under review the working of the Act and where appropriate to propose amendments.

The Commission may bring proceedings before the **County Court** in respect of unlawful acts, such as discriminatory advertising, or an employer having a policy of not calling candidates for job interviews on racial grounds. *See also* **racial discrimination**.

commission of the peace Body of persons appointed by the Crown to act as **justices of the peace** in a specified geographical area. Since the Local Government Act 1974, a separate commission of the peace is issued for each county.

Commissioner for local administration Person appointed to investigate alleged maladministration by local councils, the police and the water authorities (Local Government Act 1974). Often referred to as the local government **ombudsman,** he or she does not deal with complaints about the merits of a decision, only with matters such as unnecessary delay, neglect, bias, etc. The commissioner produces a public report after investigating a complaint and may recommend remedial action.

commissioner for oaths Person appointed by the **Lord Chancellor** to administer oaths. A commissioner for oaths is usually a **solicitor**, who automatically acquires the right on admission to the profession (Solicitors Act 1974 s.81). A person would go to a commissioner for oaths, for example, to swear an **affidavit** for use in a law suit.

committal Legal process by which a person who is being dealt with by one court is sent to be dealt with by another court or to prison or some other penal institution.

committal for sentence Procedure by which **justices of the peace** in a **Magistrates' Court** send a person who has been convicted of a crime to the **Crown Court** for sentence. This occurs when the magistrates are of the opinion that, in view of the seriousness of the offence, their powers of sentencing are inadequate.

committal for trial Procedure whereby a **Magistrates' Court** considers the case against a person accused of a serious crime, in order to determine whether there is sufficient evidence to send the case to the **Crown Court** for trial. The magistrates are called examining justices and the procedure is called committal proceedings.

Committee of Privileges *See* **Privilege.**

common Area of land over which local inhabitants have certain rights, such as the rights to collect firewood or apples, graze cattle or simply enjoy private recreation. Commons are protected in law from development and may be registered under the Commons Registration Act 1965.

common assault Attack on a person, or **assault**, which does not cause **actual bodily harm**. The offence may be tried only in a **Magistrates' Court** and is punishable by up to six months imprisonment (Criminal Justice Act 1988 s.39).

common duty of care Standard of care which must be observed by all owners and occupiers of premises to ensure that visitors to their premises are reasonably safe. This duty is established under the Occupiers Liability Acts 1957 and 1984.

common jury In criminal law, a **jury** composed of ordinary members of the public as opposed to specialists. *See also* **special jury**.

common law Law made by judges when deciding cases. In theory it consists of rules that already exist through **precedents** or custom and which therefore simply require pronouncement by the judge. Common law and **statute** law are the two major sources of law. Much of the law of contract, for example, is based on the common law.

common law marriage In the law of evidence, the **presumption** that a man and woman who have been living openly as man and wife are lawfully married. In law they are taken to be married unless the contrary is proved. The presumption is particularly important in the law of **succession**, by which the spouse of a person who has died will normally inherit in the absence of a will.

Common Serjeant Senior permanent judge of the **Central Criminal Court**.

Commonwealth citizen Person who falls within one of a number of citizenship categories created by the British Nationality Act 1981. These categories are British citizen, British Dependent Territories citizen, British Overseas citizen, British subject, or a citizen of one of the independent Commonwealth countries.

Commonwealth of Nations Association of autonomous communities which were at one time colonies, protectorates or dominions of Britain. It was given legal status by the Statute of Westminster 1931. Originally, each member recognized the Sovereign of the United Kingdom as its own head of state, represented in each country by a **Governer-General**. Since 1949, the membership of republics has been permitted.

commorientes Deaths of two persons which occur either simultaneously or so closely together that it is impossible to determine which of the two died first. In cases where one would benefit under the will of the other, the Law of Property Act 1925 s.184 provides that the older is presumed to have died first. Thus, if a husband aged 40 and wife aged 39 both die in a car accident, it will be presumed that the husband died first. If he has left property to his wife, that property will notionally pass to the wife, and then be distributed as part of her estate.

community charge Tax levied by local government authorities, chargeable annually on adults living in each authority's area. Popularly called a "poll tax".

community homes Homes provided by local authorities for children in their care, established under the Children and Young Persons Act 1969.

Community law Law of the European Economic Community, created by the EEC Treaty and the institutions of the Community. Since the UK's entry into the EEC, following the European Communities Act 1972, some community law, which is said to have direct effect, automatically becomes part of the law of England. Other community law in the form of directives takes effect in England only after the rule has been accepted by an **Act of Parliament**.

community service order Sentence which may be imposed by the court on any offender over the age of 16. The sentence requires the offender to carry out between 40 and 240 hours of work in the community over a period of 12 months. Examples of suitable work include gardening for old people and helping in institutions for handicapped people. The sentence is an alternative to prison and may be imposed only if the offender is willing to carry out the work. Breach of the order will result in his or her being re-sentenced for the original offence.

commutation of sentence Substitution of a less severe sentence for another. A **death penalty**, for example, was often commuted to **life imprisonment**.

company Body of persons combined together for the purpose of trade or business, constituted by law and enjoying special privileges. Companies are regulated by the Companies Act 1985. Those which have Ltd. or plc (public limited company) after their name have limited liability. This means that individual members of the company (described as shareholders) will not be liable to pay the company's debts in the event of **insolvency**.

company director Person responsible for managing the affairs of a **company**. Every company must have at least one director and a public company must have at least two. The appointment and powers of the directors are determined by the articles of association of the company. It is not necessary for a director to be a shareholder of the company, but in practice most directors are.

company secretary Person nominated by a company to carry out certain legal duties on its behalf. The secretary is responsible for calling meetings and filing yearly accounts with the **Registrar of Companies**, and he or she is the person to whom writs must be addressed if the company is sued.

compellable witness Person who may be required to attend court to give evidence in legal proceedings and may be punished for contempt of court for refusing to do so. Generally, all witnesses are compellable. Exceptions are the Sovereign, foreign diplomats and the spouse of the accused in a criminal trial. *See also* **competent witness; subpoena**.

compensation Sum of money paid to a person who has suffered loss or injury at the hands of another – for example, a payment of money to compensate for the **compulsory purchase** of land. A compensation order may also be made by a court to order a convicted criminal to pay a sum of money to the victim of the crime (Powers of the Criminal Courts Act 1973). *See also* **damages; restitution**.

competent witness Person who is qualified to give evidence under oath in legal proceedings. Witnesses may be incompetent if they are suffering from a mental disorder, drunkenness or the influence of drugs. Children are generally incompetent, unless the court is satisfied that they are capable of understanding the duty of telling the truth.

competition *See* **unfair competition**.

complaint Term with two meanings.

First, the method of commencing civil proceedings in a Magistrates' Court in order to obtain a court order. The making of a complaint is followed by the issue of a **summons**.

Second, the procedure by which one person, usually a police officer, applies to a Magistrates' Court for an order against another person to be bound over to keep the peace or to be of good behaviour. *See also* **binding over**.

completion Final performance of a contract for the sale of land or property. This takes place when the vendor conveys the property with good title and free possession to the purchaser, who in return hands over the purchase price. *See also* **conveyance**.

composition Agreement between the creditors of an insolvent person or company by which each agrees to accept a lesser sum than is due (normally *pro rata*). The purpose is to ensure that all creditors are treated equally and that no creditor is paid in full to the disadvantage of the others. Compositions are binding and may be approved by the court under the Insolvency Act 1986.

compounding a felony Criminal offence of agreeing not to prosecute a **felony** in return for some benefit such as payment of money or return of the stolen goods. The offence disappeared in 1967 when felonies were abolished. The Criminal Law Act 1967, s.5 created the new offence of compounding an **arrestable offence**.

compromise Agreement to settle a dispute between individuals out of court. Both parties usually make certain concessions to reach the agreement.

compulsory purchase Purchase of land from the owner without his consent. Many public authorities, such as the Civil Aviation Authority, local authorities, British Rail and the Ministry of Transport, have the power to acquire land in this manner in order to carry out their specific functions. Land may be compulsorily purchased by the Ministry of Transport — for example, in order to develop new motorways. A compulsory purchase order must be authorized by a Minister of the Crown. *See also* **compensation**.

concealment of birth Criminal offence which is committed by any person who attempts to conceal the birth of a child and dispose of the body (Offences Against the Person Act 1861 s.60). The offence is committed whether the child died before, at, or after birth.

conciliation Process of bringing together persons or organizations in dispute with each other in order to try to reach a settlement. Industrial disputes are often referred to the **Advisory, Conciliation and Arbitration Service**. In divorce proceedings, **probation** officers or court welfare officers offer a conciliation service to explore the possibility of reconciliation between husband and wife or, failing that, to reach agreement on issues relating to **custody** of children and **access** to them.

concurrent sentences Two or more sentences for different offences which are served by the convicted person at the same time. A person who is convicted of two separate thefts may be sentenced to two years imprisonment for each, to run concurrently, so that the offender will spend only 2 years in prison. *See also* **consecutive sentence**.

concurrent writ Copy of an original **writ** which has the same legal force as the original. Concurrent writs are issued when it is thought that the person to be served with the writ might be in one of a number of different places.

condemnation Decision of a court that a vessel has been lawfully captured. The effect of the decision is that ownership of the vessel is transferred to the captor. In England such issues are decided in the **Admiralty Court**.

condition Term in a contract, the non-fulfilment of which is a **breach of contract**. For instance, in building contracts it may be a condition that the work be completed by a specified date. Failure to complete by that date would be a breach of contract.

conditional discharge Sentence imposed on a person who has been convicted of a criminal offence. The person is discharged from the court without punishment on the condition that he or she does not commit any other offence for a period of up to three years. An offender who does commit another offence may be brought back before the court and given an alternative sentence for the original offence.

conditions of sale Terms on which a contract of sale will be made. At auctions, standard conditions of sale are normally advertised in the catalogue or prominently displayed. In sales of land, standard conditions of sale set out in the Property Act 1925 s.46 apply unless the parties to the sale agree on different conditions.

condone To pardon or forgive an offence. In matrimonial law the courts used to accept condonation as a defence to proceedings for **divorce**, if it could be shown that the injured party had full knowledge of the facts. It was dependent upon the spouse not repeating the offence. Condonement is no longer a bar to divorce.

conduct money Money paid to a witness who is required to appear at trial to give evidence, which must be sufficient to pay necessary expenses which are incurred in order to attend the trial. *See also* **subpoena**.

conference Term with two applications.

First, a meeting which takes place between a **barrister** and **solicitor**, either with or without the client, in order to confer on some relevant matter.

Second, a deputation of members by which either House of Parliament communicates important matters to the other.

confession Statement made by a person suspected of crime to a person in authority, usually a police officer, which admits some part in the crime. Generally, confessions are admissible in evidence against the suspect. However, if a confession was induced by threats or inducements or oppression likely to render it unreliable, the trial court must exclude the confession under the Police and Criminal Evidence Act 1984 s.76.

confession and avoidance Legal **plea** whereby one person admits the accusation with which he or she is charged but raises a new matter in order to avoid liability for the act. The new matter in effect justifies the behaviour. For example, an assault may be admitted but justified on the basis of **self-defence**.

confidential communication Written or verbal communication which is confidential in the sense that it cannot be disclosed in subsequent legal proceedings. Communications taking place between a **solicitor** or **barrister** and a **client** are the most common form of confidential communications.

confiscation Seizure of private property by the State as a punishment. Persons found in possession of illegal goods, such as drugs or house-breaking implements, may have them confiscated under powers in the Criminal Justice Act 1988.

conflict of interest Circumstance in which a person in a position of duty or trust finds that the action required by that position is contrary to some other personal interest. Under legal ethics and the professional practice rules of the **Bar** and the **Law Society**, a lawyer should not act for a client in a case in which a conflict of interest arises.

A judge or magistrate must decline to hear a case in which he or she has an interest. If a judge or magistrate does try such a case, this will be a breach of **natural justice**. For example, if a judge is asked to preside in a case in which a company is being sued and the judge is a shareholder in the company, he or she must decline to hear the case.

Members of Parliament must declare any commercial interests, which are recorded in the Register of Members' Interests. If a member speaks in the House on a matter in which he or she has a commercial interest, this must be declared at the beginning of the speech.

conjugal rights Marital rights of **cohabitation**. Until 1971, if one partner left the matrimonial home, the other could apply to a court for the **restitution** of conjugal rights. If successful, the court would order the deserting spouse to return to cohabitation. Conjugal rights were abolished by the Matrimonial Proceedings and Property Act 1970 s.20.

connivance Giving tacit assent or encouragement to another to commit a wrongful act. In matrimonial law, for example, encouraging a spouse to commit **adultery** denied the petitioner the right to a divorce if the adultery took place. This rule was abolished by the Divorce Reform Act 1969.

consanguinity Relationship by blood. Marriage between people who are close blood relatives is prohibited by the Marriage Act 1949. The prohibited blood relationships are listed in schedule 1 of that Act. *See also* **affinity**; **incest**.

consecutive sentences Two or more sentences imposed by a court on a person convicted of criminal offences, which are to be served one after the other. *See also* **concurrent sentences**.

consent Voluntary and informed grant of permission that something should be done or not done.

Offences like **rape** and **indecent assault** are committed only when there is lack of consent. Surgical operations committed without consent may be both civil **trespass** against the person and criminal **assault**. A marriage ceremony to which one of the parties does not consent is void. Consent may be negated by threats (for example, if a person agrees through fear) and by fraud (for example, if a person agreed to an operation after being told it was to save his own life, when in fact the real purpose was to remove a kidney to transplant to another person).

conservation Preserving and protecting natural things such as trees, animals, flowers, meadows and rivers. Various Acts of Parliament create specific offences for behaviour which interferes with the conservation of certain natural species. The Badgers Act 1973, for example, creates a number of offences in order to protect badgers.

conservation area Area designated by a local planning authority to be of historic or architectural interest and therefore to be preserved (Town and Country Planning Act 1971 s.277).

consideration Promise to do or give something of value which, if given in return for a similar promise by another party, may create a legally binding **contract**. For example, in a contract for the sale of a car the consideration is the promise to hand over the car in return for a promise to pay the purchase price.

consignment Quantity of goods which are sent from one place to another. The consignor is the person who sends the goods. The consignee is the person who is to receive them.

Consistory Court Court held in a cathedral and called by the bishop of a diocese to try matters of ecclesiastical law.

consolidation Process by which a number of similar things are combined together or dealt with together.
   For instance, consolidation of actions occurs when a court orders that, for convenience, a number of similar proceedings, such as claims for damages arising out of a coach crash, be dealt with together. Consolidation of mortgages occurs if a mortgagor has taken out two separate mortgages with a single mortgagee, and the mortgagee decides to combine them in a single mortgage.

Consolidation Acts Acts of Parliament that make no substantial change in the law but merely bring together a number of scattered statutory provisions dealing with the same subject. For example, the Sexual Offences Act 1956 gathered together a large number of sexual offences which had previously been found in a variety of Acts.

consortium Term with two applications.
   First, the right of each spouse to the love, affection, comfort and companionship of and sexual intercourse with the other.
   Second, two or more organizations working together for a common purpose.

conspiracy Term with two applications.

First, in criminal law, an agreement by two or more persons to pursue a course of conduct which would amount to a criminal offence if carried out according to their intentions (Criminal Law Act 1977). Thus, conspirators may be liable simply for plotting an offence without doing anything to put the plan into effect. Conspiracy to **defraud**, conspiracy to outrage public decency and conspiracy to corrupt public morals are also offences.

Second, an agreement between two or more persons to injure another person's trade. For this **tort** of conspiracy the injured party may obtain **damages** or an **injunction**.

constable Officer under a duty to keep the peace, prevent crime, investigate crime and apprehend offenders. In law all police officers are constables whatever their rank. Constables are given special powers. For instance, only a constable may arrest someone whom he believes is about to commit an **arrestable offence**, or execute a **search warrant**. Constables must act under the orders of the Chief Constable of the police force to which they are attached. It is an offence under the Police Act 1964 s.51 to obstruct or assault a constable in the course of his duty.

constabulary Alternative name for police force. A number of police forces operate in different parts of the country. Most forces are partly controlled by a Police Authority, except the Metropolitan Police Force in London which is directed by the Home Secretary. There are a number of specialized constabularies such as the British Railways Police and London Transport Police. Police officers are known as **constables** and the head of each force is the chief constable.

constituency Geographical area whose adult citizens elect a **Member of Parliament**. Hence it also refers to the voters within that area, individually referred to as constituents.

constitution Rules which define an institution and regulate its internal operation. Thus, the constitution of a club is the set of rules by which all members agree to abide and which therefore amounts to a contract between all of the members.

The constitution of a country prescribes how authority is to be exercised in the State and how this authority should be passed on.

Constitutions may be written in a single document, as is the constitution of the United States, or found in a collection of **statutes**, **common law** rules and conventions, as in the United Kingdom. *See* **constitutional law**

constitutional law Body of laws that define and regulate the institutions of a state, the relationships between such institutions, and the relationship between individual citizens and the state.

The constitutional law of the United Kingdom regulates **succession** to the throne, the powers of the **Sovereign** and the Royal Prerogative, the composition of **Parliament**, elections, the formation of governments, the appointment of **judges**, the powers of the police, the relationship between central and local government, citizenship and **immigration**, and **civil liberties**.

construction Interpreting a law or document and resolving ambiguities within it with reference to its context. Thus, the construction to be placed on a **contract** is the meaning which should be ascribed to it in all the circumstances. *See also* **statutory interpretation**.

constructive dismissal *See* **unfair dismissal.**

constructive malice Formerly, in the law of **murder**, an intent to commit a violent **felony** or to use violence to resist lawful **arrest**, which was considered as equivalent to an intention to kill, making the criminal guilty of murder, if death resulted from his use of violence. Constructive malice was abolished by the Homicide Act 1957 s.1.

constructive notice Presumption that something has been brought to the notice of a particular person. The law will normally hold that a person has constructive notice of something when reasonable steps were taken to bring it to his notice and he or she had ample opportunity to take notice of it. Under the Law of Property Act 1925 s.177, for example, a purchaser of a house who has had an opportunity to inspect the title deeds before sale is held to have constructive notice of any defect in the title to the land which is passed to him.

constructive trust Any **trust** which is deemed by the court to exist even though it was not the intention of the parties to create a trust. Typically, the principle is invoked to prevent one party from being unjustly enriched at the expense of another. For instance, two persons may live together in a house owned by one of them, and the person not the owner spends money to improve the house and increases its value. If the owner later evicts the other person, it may be held that he holds the house on a constructive trust and that that part of its value which may be attributed to the improvements made by the evicted person should be held for the benefit of the evicted person.

consumer credit Provision of finance to a private individual for the purpose of buying specific goods or paying for specific services, whether by **hire-purchase**, loan or other means. Consumer-credit agreements are regulated by the Consumer Credit Act 1974 which regulates the practices of creditors, and the terms of consumer-credit contracts. In particular, the Act allows for cooling-off periods to allow people to avoid credit agreements made by high-pressure sales techniques.

consumer protection Legal measures to protect the consumer in relation to purchasing goods or services.

The Consumer Protection Act 1987 provides remedies against the manufacturers of unsafe goods: they are held absolutely liable for certain defects of goods that cause injury. The Sale of Goods Act 1979 builds in clauses in contracts for **sale of goods** to ensure that the goods are of merchantable quality. The Unfair Contract Terms Act 1977 strikes down certain types of contractual terms that attempt to restrict the consumer's rights. The Fair Trading Act 1973 regulates standards of trading in general. *See also* **fair trading**; **unfair contract terms**.

Consumer Protection Advisory Committee Body that investigates trade practices which may mislead or adversely affect the economic interests of consumers. The Director General of Fair Trading refers such questions to the Committee with recommendations for improvements and the Committee must report to the Secretary of State confirming or amending the Director's proposals. The Secretary of State may then make **regulations** giving effect to the proposals.

consummation of marriage Act of **sexual intercourse** between a husband and wife after the marriage ceremony, required by law to validate the marriage. If one spouse is unable or unwilling to consummate the marriage, the other may be entitled to have the marriage annulled. *See also* **annul**; **annulment**.

contemnor Person guilty of **contempt of court** or **contempt of Parliament**.

contempt of court Act which tends to interfere with the course of justice in legal proceedings (for example threat to a witness, attempt to bribe the judge) or to physically interfere with court proceedings (for example, throwing a brick at the judge, setting off a smoke bomb in court) or to ridicule the court or judges (for example, a newspaper article that suggests incompetence or corruption) or to prejudge a case (for example, an article that suggests that a defendant committed the offence) or to prejudice a jury against the accused in a criminal trial (for example, an article that suggests that a person accused of murder is a brothel keeper).

The Contempt of Court Act 1981 declares that a published article can be in contempt only if published within certain fixed time limits relating to the case.

Contempt may be dealt with by the court in question and may be punished with imprisonment.

contempt of Parliament Breach of the **privileges** of Parliament, for example, by abducting an MP, telling lies on the floor of either House or publishing misleading reports of Parliamentary proceedings.

In the House of Commons the **Speaker** may refer alleged contempts to the **Committee of Privileges**, which investigates the matter. A decision on whether to punish a **contemnor** is made by a resolution of the whole House. Punishment may be admonition, suspension (in the case of an MP) or imprisonment.

Contingencies Fund Fund that can be used as a source of finance for the armed services and other arms of government in anticipation of the voting of funds by Parliament. Formerly the Civil Contingencies Fund, the present arrangements were established by the Contingencies Fund Act 1970, 1974.

contraband Goods that have been smuggled into a country. *See* **smuggling**.

contract Agreement entered into by two or more parties who intend to create legal relations between themselves and who each give **consideration** in return for a promise by the other. The contract so formed is binding. If a party breaks his promise he is in **breach of contract** and may be required to pay **damages**. Contracts which are illegal or against public policy (for example, contracts relating to prostitution or gambling) will not be enforced by the courts. *See also* **sale of goods**; **unfair contract terms**.

contractor Term with two applications.

First, a person who enters into a **contract**.

Second, a person who enters into a contract to provide a service for another, but who does not become an employee of that person. He or she remains independent and keeps control of the manner in which the work is carried out.

contribution order Order made under the Civil Liability (Contribution) Act 1978, by which the court orders a person who is partly responsible for loss or damage to make a contribution to the party who has satisfied a claim for damages by the person who suffered the loss or damage.

contributory negligence Failure by a person to take the degree of care for his or her own safety to be expected of a reasonable person in the circumstances. If a person is injured or suffers loss partly as a result of somebody else's **negligence** and partly through his or her own contributory negligence, the **damages** which the other party must pay will be reduced according to the extent to which each was responsible (Law Reform (Contributory Negligence) Act 1945).

control group Group (of people) matched as closely as possible with respect to all relevant variables with an experimental group. The experimental group is submitted to the single independent variable of which the effects are being examined. The use of a control group allows the researcher to be sure that the differences between the two groups are caused only by the effects of the single variable.

conversion Term with two applications.

First, the deliberate taking of another's property or use of another's property for one's own benefit. At **common law** it was a **tort** and also the basis of **theft** until the Theft Act 1968. Under the Torts (Interference with Goods) Act 1977, conversion is extended to include negligent loss of another's property by someone having temporary custody of it.

Second, in equity, the notional change of land into money or money into land.

conveyance Term with two applications.

First, the transaction of documents by which ownership of land is passed from one person to another, recorded in a document called a deed, which is usually registered at the Land Registry.

Second, a vehicle. The Theft Act 1968 s.12 makes it an offence to take a conveyance without the consent of the owner. The offence is designed to deal with "joy-riding", taking a vehicle for a short period before dumping it.

conviction Finding by a court that a person is guilty of a **criminal** offence. *See also* **sentence**.

copyhold Ownership of land granted by a Lord of the Manor under the feudal system to men who occupied the land in return for services to the Lord. The tenant was given a copy of the entry in the manor records relating to his land. This form of land ownership was abolished by the Law of Property Act 1922 and existing copyholds were converted into **freeholds**.

copyright Exclusive right of the creator of literary, artistic or musical works to control the use of them and to exploit them commercially. Copyright normally lasts until 50 years after the creator's death. Copyright may be sold. Thus an author may sell his copyright in a novel to a publisher. In some cases the creator retains copyright and allows his work to be published in return for a fee (called a royalty) for each copy sold. Breach of copyright, by selling pirate or bootleg copies of a book or record, for example, may be a crime and the copyright holder may seek an **injunction** to prevent further breaches of copyright and may also make a claim for any profits made by the offender (Copyright Act 1985).

co-respondent Person who is called to answer a legal claim jointly with another. When **adultery** is alleged in **divorce** proceedings, the person named as having committed adultery with one of the spouses is called the co-respondent.

coroner Public officer, legally or medically qualified, who enquires into deaths where violence, suicide or unnatural causes are suspected. The coroner may order a **post mortem** and will hold an **inquest** to determine the cause of death.

corporal punishment Punishment for criminal offence by infliction of physical pain. Not available in the United Kingdom.

corporation Institution or body other than a natural person that has a **legal personality**.

A corporation aggregate consists of an number of persons – for example, a local authority or a **company**.

A corporation sole is an office which has a legal personality separate from the person who occupies it at any given time. The monarchy and a bishopric are examples of corporations sole.

corroboration Evidence which supports some other evidence in a material way, but is from an independent source. In criminal trials the judge is required to warn the jury of the danger of convicting on the strength of uncorroborated evidence in cases of rape or sexual assault and when the primary evidence is that of an alleged **accomplice** of the accused.

corrupt practices *See* **bribery and corruption**.

costs in civil proceedings Expenses involved in taking a civil case to court. Each party is primarily liable for his or her own costs, but at the end of a case the court may order the losing party to pay the winner's costs. No order for costs may be made in relation to cases dealt with under **arbitration**, the procedure for disposing of small claims in the County Court. *See also* **legal aid**; **taxation of costs**.

costs in criminal proceedings Expenses involved in prosecuting and defending a criminal charge. Primarily, each side is responsible for its own costs, although many defendants receive legal aid. The court has power to order that the costs of an acquitted defendant be paid out of **central funds** or by the prosecution (normally the **Crown**

Prosecution Service). A convicted defendant may be required to make some contribution towards the prosecution costs. If a **private prosecution** is successful, the court may order that the cost be met out of central funds.

counsel Name for a **barrister**. Leading counsel is a **Queen's Counsel**. All other barristers are known as junior counsel whatever their age.

count Part of an **indictment** which specifies the charge against the accused. An indictment may contain a number of counts.

counterclaim Claim which is brought by the **defendant** in civil proceedings against the **plaintiff**, which will be tried at the same time.

counterculture Set of sub-cultural values contradictory to the accepted norms of the host culture, with particular reference to the family, work and politics. For example, the use of drugs, sexual liberation and freedom of self-expression were characteristic of the counterculture of the 1960s.

counterfeit Something manufactured to resemble a currency coin or note so that it may be accepted as genuine. Offences of making, possessing and using counterfeit notes and coins are found in the Forgery and Counterfeiting Act 1981.

counterpart Document, signed by a person who takes a tenancy under a **lease**, which is in identical terms to the lease itself. The **lessor** signs a document called the lease. The lease agreement is complete and binding when the lessor exchanges the lease for the counterpart with the lessee.

county Largest unit of local government in England and Wales. There are 52 counties. The seven large conurbations are not counties; six were metropolitan counties until these counties were abolished under the Local Government Act 1985.

County Courts Local courts, staffed by professional judges, which deal with civil proceedings in which the claim is for less than £5,000. Minor cases are dealt with by the **small claims court**, which is part of the County Court.

court Term with two applications.

First, a place in which legal disputes may be authoritatively determined.

Second, the judge, judges or magistrates who have authority to determine legal disputes.

court-martial Court, consisting of army, navy or air force officers, which tries charges of crime or breach of **military law** against service personnel. Appeal is to the Courts-Martial Appeal Court, which consists of the judges who sit in the **Court of Appeal** (Criminal Division).

Court of Appeal Court which hears appeals from judgments in the **High Court of Justice**, **County Court** and **Crown Court**. The Court is divided into the Civil Division which is chaired by the **Master of the Rolls**, and the Criminal Division, which is chaired by the **Lord Chief Justice**. Normally, three judges hear each appeal. Further appeal may be allowed to the **House of Lords**.

Court of Chivalry Court held before the Earl Marshal of England which hears disputes relating to heraldry, typically whether a person is entitled to a particular coat of arms.

court of first instance Court in which the initial determination of a case takes place.

court of last resort Court which is competent to hear the final appeal in a case. In the United Kingdom the Judicial Committee of the House of Lords is generally the court of last resort, but final appeal in cases which involve an issue of EC law is to the **European Court of Justice**.

Court of Protection Court, headed by a **Master of the Supreme Court**, which administers the property of persons suffering from mental disorder (Mental Health Act 1983).

court of summary jurisdiction Court with power to hear a criminal case without any form of preliminary hearing. Magistrates' Courts exercise summary jurisdiction over offences that by law may only be tried summarily and also over offences that are triable either summarily or on **indictment**, when the accused chooses summary trial.

covenant Term with two applications.

First, a promise to do something, usually contained in a **deed** (for example, to pay an annual sum to a **charity**).

Second, a term in a contract which specifies what one party is obliged to do for the benefit of the other. Such covenants may be implied by law. For instance certain **leases** of land may incorporate implied covenants to keep the property in good repair.

credit Amount, or the time allowed for payment, of a loan or other debt. *See also* **consumer credit**.

creditor Person to whom a debt is owed.

cremation Disposing of a corpse by burning in a crematorium (regulated by the Cremation Acts 1902 and 1952). It has been legally recognized in England since 1884. *See also* **coroner; death certificate**.

crime Conduct or omission, which is subject to punishment after adjudication and conviction by a court. Crimes may be based on common law or created by statute.

criminal Person convicted of crime.

criminal appeal Appeal against the decision of a criminal court. Either the prosecution or defence may appeal against the decision of a **Magistrates' Court** on the ground that the court applied the law wrongly. Appeal is by way of **case stated** to the **Divisional Court** of the High Court, which may either confirm the previous decision, quash the conviction or send the case back to be reheard with a direction as to the relevant law.

Only the defendant may appeal against a jury verdict in the **Crown Court**. Appeal is to the **Court of Appeal** (Criminal Division) which may affirm the verdict or quash it or in exceptional cases order a retrial. The defendant may appeal against his or her sentence from either court. Under the Criminal Justice Act 1988, there is a new power for the prosecution to appeal against what it regards as a lenient sentence in the Crown Court.

criminal bankruptcy order Procedure for declaring **bankrupt** a
person who has been convicted of a crime, which has resulted in loss
exceeding £15,000 to known persons. The assets are administered by a
trustee in bankruptcy and realized for the benefit of the persons who
suffered loss as a result of the crime (Powers of the Criminal Courts
Act 1973 ss.39–41).

criminal damage Offence of intentionally or recklessly causing the
destruction of or damage to property belonging to another without
lawful excuse (Criminal Damage Act 1971). Lawful excuse includes the
destruction of property to prevent greater damage to other property. It
is lawful, for example, to pull down a wooden shed to prevent a fire
spreading to a house.

criminal injuries compensation Scheme, administered by the
Criminal Injuries Compensation Board, for compensating the victims
of violent crime when the offender either cannot be found or does not
have the means to pay compensation himself or herself, regulated by
the Criminal Justice Act 1988.

criminal intent To describe whatever culpable state of mind is
required for a particular crime. Thus, it may include, for example,
intention and **malice aforethought**.

criminal law Body of laws that define **crime** and are concerned with
criminal responsibility and **proof** in criminal trials.

criminal libel Publication of a statement which tends to expose a
person to hatred, ridicule or contempt and which is likely to provoke a
breach of the peace or is of a serious nature and done deliberately.
It is punishable by imprisonment for one year under the Libel Act
1843 s.5. *See also* **libel**.

criminal record Record of a person's criminal convictions and
punishments, stored on the Police National Computer. A person's
record is produced after conviction when the court is considering the
appropriate **sentence**. *See also* **rehabilitation of offenders**.

criminal responsibility Condition of a person who has capacity to
commit crime, who has committed the conduct specified in the

definition of a crime with the necessary **criminal intent** and cannot rely upon any **defence** to a criminal charge.

Mentally disordered persons who cannot understand the nature and quality of their acts and children under ten cannot be criminally responsible. Children between 10 and 14 can be criminally responsible only if they understand the difference between right and wrong.

criminology Study of criminal behaviour, the causes of crime, criminals and measures to punish or deal with persons convicted of crime. Criminology draws upon a number of sciences and social sciences, including psychiatry, physiology, sociology and statistics. A branch of the subject known as the "new criminology" is concerned with the political processes by which certain types of human behaviour are labelled as criminal.

cross-examination Questioning in court by **counsel** on behalf of one party to the proceedings of a witness who was called by the other party and who has already given evidence. The purpose of cross-examination may be to discredit the witness generally or expose flaws in his or her story. Leading questions are allowed in cross-examination.

Crown The Sovereign. In the criminal courts, all proceedings brought by the police are brought in the name of the Crown.

Crown Court Court, situated in a major town or city, in which are held criminal trials on **indictment** before judge and jury. The Crown Court was set up by the Courts Act 1971 to replace **Quarter Sessions** and **Assizes**. Crown Courts are staffed by Crown Court judges and **recorders** and also by High Court judges, who visit the more important courts periodically to try the most serious cases.

Crown privilege Principle of evidence that the court will not insist on the production of documentary evidence if its production would be contrary to national security or the public interest.

Crown proceedings Action for **damages** brought against the **Crown** under the special procedure laid down in the Crown Proceedings Act 1947. A special procedure for suing the Crown in **contract** and **torts** was required because of an old rule that the Sovereign could not be sued in his or her own courts.

Crown Prosecution Service Body of lawyers established under the Prosecution of Offences Act 1985, responsible for prosecuting criminal cases on behalf of the Crown. It is headed by the **Director of Public Prosecutions** and is independent of the police.

cruelty Ill treatment, **assault**, abandonment or neglect in a manner likely to cause unnecessary suffering. Such conduct committed against a child in a person's charge is an offence under the Children and Young Persons Act 1933 s.1.

Cruelty to a spouse may be a ground of divorce, because it constitutes unreasonable behaviour giving rise to irretrievable breakdown of the marriage, under the Matrimonial Causes Act 1973.

There are various offences of cruelty to animals under the Protection of Animals Act 1911 and the Cruelty to Animals Act 1876.

cumulative sentence Sentence passed on a convicted person which begins at the end of a sentence already being served by that person.

custody Term with two applications.

First, physical or legal possession of something or somebody, usually a child. *See also* **custody of children**.

Second, detention of a person under legal powers or by order of a court.

custody for life *See* **life imprisonment**.

custody of children Legal responsibility or authority for the care of children. Normally the natural parents have custody over a child. Disputes over custody are settled by the courts in the interests of the child. If the parents are not married the courts act under the Guardianship of Minors Act 1971. Issues of custody which arise in the course of divorce are dealt with under the Matrimonial Causes Act 1973. *See also* **care order**.

custody officer Police officer, normally of sergeant rank, who exercises responsibilities under the Police and Criminal Evidence Act 1984 in relation to prisoners in custody in a police station. The officer must see that the prisoner is fed and rested and allowed access to a solicitor. He must ensure that there are good grounds for detention and that the time limit for detention is not exceeded.

custom Term with two applications.

First, a practice which has been followed continuously for as long as anybody can remember in a particular locality and which is considered to be binding in law. Hence it is a source of law.

Second, in **international law**, the established practice of states and therefore evidence of law.

customs Popular name for Her Majesty's **Customs and Excise**.

Customs and Excise Customs are duties payable on goods exported from and imported into the United Kingdom. Excise duties are payable on goods produced and consumed in the United Kingdom. The collection of the duties is administered by Commissioners of Customs and Excise.

D

daily cause list List of cases to be heard in the **High Court of Justice** on a particular day. It is posted in the High Court and copies are available to lawyers and parties to actions.

damages Monetary compensation which one party to a **civil action** is ordered to pay to another party by the court. Damages may be awarded for loss resulting from **tort** or for **breach of contract**. Nominal damages of a small sum are awarded when a breach of a legal right has occurred, but the court does not find that the plaintiff has suffered real loss.

dangerous driving Driving a motor vehicle in a manner which is likely to cause injury to the driver or any other road users, or damage to property.

Dangerous driving may amount to an offence of **careless and inconsiderate driving,** or **reckless driving**. If damage or injury is caused, the driver may be sued for **damages** for **negligence**.

dangerous drugs See **drugs, controlled.**

dangerous premises Premises which are not sufficiently safe to provide reasonable protection for lawful visitors to them. Under the Occupiers Liability Act 1957 the occupier of premises is under a duty to ensure that they are safe.

Even trespassers are given some protection against dangerous premises: if an occupier has reasonable grounds to believe that trespassers may enter his premises he must protect them against known dangers (Occupiers Liability Act 1984 s.1). *See also* **common duty of care**.

data protection Safeguarding the privacy of the individual by regulating the storage and use of information about him or her on computer. Under the Data Protection Act a Data Protection Registrar is appointed by the Government to supervise a register of data users. No individual or organization may hold data about individuals without obtaining a licence from the Registrar. The Act also provides that individuals should have a right to access to information held about them.

days of grace Period after the day on which the performance of a legal obligation is strictly due that is allowed for its performance. In some areas of commerce the practice of allowing three days of grace has become so well established that it is now recognized by the courts in determining the obligations of the parties.

Day Training Centre Institution run by the **probation** service to provide training for offenders who are socially inadequate in some respect. Attendance at such a centre may be a condition of a probation order (Powers of the Criminal Courts Act 1973 s.4).

death certificate Certificate stating the cause of death. It must be completed by a doctor who had been treating a patient during the 14 days prior to death. The certificate must be given to the Registrar of Deaths before the corpse is buried or cremated. A certificate will not be issued if the cause of death is suspicious or unknown. *See also* **cause of death; coroner; inquest; post mortem.**

death duty Formerly, taxes payable in respect of a person's property on his death. The modern equivalent is the **inheritance tax**.

death penalty Order by a court that a person convicted of a crime should be executed. Before 1957 the death penalty was the mandatory sentence for **murder**. Between 1957 and 1965 murder was divided into two categories: capital murder, for which the penalty was death, and non-capital murder, for which the penalty was **life imprisonment**. The death penalty for murder was abolished by the Murder (Abolition of the Death Penalty) Act 1965. The death penalty may still be imposed for high treason.

debenture Type of charge or **mortgage** given by a limited company in return for a loan of money to the company. The debenture acknowledges the debt and specifies the terms of the repayment and the rate of interest payable.

debt Sum of money which a person (the debtor) is under a legal obligation to pay to another (the creditor) by a specified date. If the debtor does not pay, the creditor may sue for the recovery of the debt, but will succeed only if the debt is acknowledged by the debtor or proved to the satisfaction of the court.

deceit Untrue statement made by a person who either knows it is false or does not care whether it is true or false. If the statement is intended to be acted upon, a person who has relied on it to his detriment may sue the maker of the statement for **damages** under the **tort** of deceit.

deception False representation, made recklessly or deliberately, in words or action, of a matter of fact. Deception itself is not a crime, but there are a number of deception offences. These include: obtaining property by deception (Theft Act 1968 s.15); obtaining a pecuniary advantage by deception (Theft Act 1968 s.16); obtaining a service by deception (Theft Act 1978 s.1); evasion of liability by deception (Theft Act 1978 s.2).

declaration Term with two applications.
First, a **statutory declaration**.
Second, a **declaratory judgment**.

declaratory judgment Pronouncement by a court of the legal position in relation to stated facts. A person may seek a declaration in order to determine whether a proposed course of conduct is lawful or not.

decree Court order by which the legal position or status of a person or thing is altered.

decree absolute Court order by which a married couple are finally **divorced** or their marriage is **annulled**.

decree nisi Court order that suspends the relationship of marriage. It must be granted six weeks before a **decree absolute**. If any person can show good reason why the divorce should not take place, the decree absolute will not be granted.

deed Written document containing details of an agreement which is legally binding because it has been signed, sealed and delivered. Certain types of transaction are required by law to be completed by deed – for example, a **conveyance** of property.

deed of covenant *See* **covenant**

deed poll Any **deed** which is made by and declares the intention of one party only. It is most commonly used as a formal method of changing one's name.

deemed Assumed to be. For example, a word used in a **statute** may be deemed to have a particular meaning, which indicates that it is used in a sense which is different from normal usage.

defamation Publication of untrue statements which have a tendency to lower a person in the estimation of right-thinking members of society or to cause people to shun that person. Defamation is sub-divided into **libel** (publication in permanent form − for example, the written word) and **slander** (transitory publication − for example, the spoken word). Defamation is a **tort** and the wronged party can sue the defamer for **damages** or an **injunction**. *See also* **fair comment; justification**.

default Failure to fulfil a legal obligation.

default notice Notice given by the **creditor** in a consumer credit agreement to a **debtor** who has failed to pay the required instalments. It informs the debtor of the **breach of contract** and of the remedy required. Under the Consumer Credit Act 1974 the creditor cannot repossess the goods until a default notice has been issued in the form prescribed by the Act.

default summons Procedure for starting a **civil action** in the **County Court** to recover a **debt**.

defective goods Goods of which it can be shown that "the safety of the product is not such as persons generally are entitled to expect" (Consumer Protection Act 1987 s.3). In deciding this question the court will consider the manner in which the product is marketed, the use of any warnings on the product, and the purpose for which the product might reasonably be used. If a defective product causes injury to a person who uses it, that person may claim compensation from the producer, importer or supplier of the product under the Consumer Protection Act. *See also* **sale of goods**.

defector Person who leaves his or her country of origin, without gaining the permission that is necessary under the law of that country, and who intends not to return.

defence Term with two applications.

First, plea which if successfully raised in court is a full answer to the case brought against a defendant. For example, in a **civil action** for **damages** that arise from an allegation of negligent driving it would be a defence to argue that the driving was not negligent. In a criminal trial for **assault** it is a defence for the defendant to argue that he or she acted in **self-defence**.

Second, the document (pleading) in which the defendant to an action sets out his or her defence to the plaintiff's claim.

defendant Person against whom a legal action is brought. In a criminal case, a defendant is a person charged with a criminal offence. In a **civil action** for **damages,** the defendant is the person who is alleged to have caused loss to the **plaintiff**.

deferred sentence Sentence that is postponed so that the court may assess the defendant's conduct after conviction (Powers of the Criminal Courts Act 1973 s.1, as amended by Criminal Justice Act 1982 s.63).

defraud Dishonestly to deprive a person of something that belongs to that person or to which he or she is entitled. Under the Criminal Law Act 1977 s.5(2), **conspiracy** to defraud is a criminal offence. In some other instances fraud may amount to a crime of **deception**.

delegated legislation Law in written form, made by a person or body who has been authorized by Parliament to make law relating to certain matters. For example, Acts of Parliament define the general principles of social security law and delegate the power to determine the details of particular benefits to the Minister of Social Security. Delegated power to legislate is also conferred on bodies such as local authorities and universities. It may be given effect in the form of **bye-laws, Orders in Council, regulations** and **statutory instruments**.

delinquency The breaking of laws and conventions. Juvenile delinquency refers to offences commonly committed by people under 20, and is often explained in relation to peer group pressure and deprivation.

demise To grant a **lease** of land to another.

demise of the Crown Transfer of the royal kingdom from one monarch to his successor on death or **abdication**.

demonstration Public meeting and rally to protest or show support for a particular cause. Regulated by the law of **public assembly**.

demurrer In civil law, the claim by one party to legal proceedings that the other party's claim, even if proved, was not adequate in law to win the case. It was abolished in 1883.

denunciation In international law, assertion by a state that it will no longer be bound by a **treaty** or convention. Generally, a state cannot escape its obligations in this way unless the denunciation is accepted by the other parties to the treaty or convention.

department of state *See* **government department.**

dependent domicile Circumstance in which a person's **domicile** depends upon the domicile of another person. A child below the **age of majority** has the same domicile as the parent or guardian who has custody of the child. Formerly, a wife automatically took the domicile of the husband on marriage, but this rule was abolished by the Domicile and Matrimonial Proceedings Act 1973.

deponent Person who gives evidence by **affidavit** or **deposition**.

deportation Removal of a person from a country by law. In the United Kingdom any person who is an illegal immigrant, or who has been granted permission to stay in the country but whose presence is no longer desirable, may be deported. Appeal against a deportation order is made to the Immigration Appeals Tribunal.

deposit of title deeds Depositing of a deed showing ownership of land with a money-lender, usually a bank, as security for a loan. In law the person with whom the deeds are deposited gains a right over the land in the form of an equitable mortgage. If the loan is not repaid, the person who has the deeds may sell them or the property in order to satisfy the debt.

deposition Written evidence or verbal evidence which has been recorded on paper, given under oath. Generally, in a court of law such evidence is unacceptable since the witnesses must attend in person and be available for cross-examination. However, it may be accepted in some circumstances, such as if the witness is unavailable. Under the Magistrates' Courts Act 1980 s.105, for example, a deposition of a witness who is close to death is acceptable.

depravity State of moral corruption. Under the Obscene Publications Act 1959, a book, magazine, picture or film is obscene if it has a tendency to deprave and corrupt people who are likely to read or see it. If a person is charged with an **obscenity** offence the question whether publication has a tendency to deprave, according to the ordinary standards of society, is decided by the magistrates or a jury.

deprivation Punishment by which an ecclesiastical court divests a cleric of his **benefice**.

derogate To destroy, restrict or limit a legal right. In property law, a person cannot "derogate from his own grant". This means that a person who agrees to convey property to another cannot then do anything which reduces the value of the property before the **conveyance** takes place.

descent Transfer of property on death by inheritance rather than by will. Until 1926 strict rules of inheritance gave priority to males, the eldest son being the first to benefit. The Administration of Estates Act 1925 abolished the rules of descent and male and female children, whatever the order of birth, now have equal claim to the **estate**. *See also* **intestacy**.

desertion Voluntary abandoning by one spouse of the other, so that they no longer live together. Desertion for two years or more may give the deserted party the right to a **divorce**, if it is evidence that the marriage has irretrievably broken down.

design right Property right to protection against the copying of an original design which is not registerable under the Registered Designs Acts 1949–61. Design is defined under the Copyright, Designers and Patents Act 1988 s.213(2) as "the design of any aspect of the shape or configuration (whether internal or external) of the whole or part of an article.

detention centre Former penal institution to which boys between the ages of 14 and 21 could be sent for a period of between 21 days and four months. This penalty could be imposed only if the young offender had committed an offence for which an adult could have been imprisoned. Since the Criminal Justice Act 1988 such offenders are sent to a Young Offender Institution.

determine Term with two meanings.
First, to reach a conclusion, decide an issue or appeal.
Second, to bring something, for example a **contract**, to an end.

deterrence Something which discourages a particular act. One of the main aims of the criminal justice system is deterrence. In theory this works in two ways: the offender is deterred from committing further crimes by receiving punishment and other members of the public are deterred from criminal activity by the knowledge that offenders are punished.

detinue Formerly, an action in the law of **tort**, brought by a person who claimed that another person had unlawfully detained his or her goods. If the action was successful, the claimant was entitled to recovery of the property or compensation for the loss. Detinue was abolished by the Torts (Interference with Goods) Act 1977 and the tort of **conversion** was extended to cover such cases. *See also* **trespass; trover**.

development Altering the existing use of buildings or land. Under the Town and Country Planning Act 1971 "any material change in the use of buildings or other land" requires planning permission before it can be carried out.

devilling Practice whereby a **barrister** obtains assistance, usually research or paperwork, from another barrister in the handling of a case. The barrister who was instructed by the **solicitor** remains responsible for the case and must pay the assisting barrister (the "devil") for help received.

devise Gift of **real property** (land and buildings) under a will. The devise may be general – for example, all a person's land – or specific – for example a house – or residual, all of the remainder of a person's land which has not been given to other people.

devolution Term with two applications.

First, the transfer of property from one person to another by the process of law – for example, to relatives of a person who has died intestate. *See also* **intestacy.**

Second, in a political sense, the delegation of power from central government to local or regional authorities.

dilapidations Any repairs which a tenant must complete on the termination of a tenancy in order to hand the property over in good repair.

diminished responsibility Defence to a charge of **murder** which, if successful, reduces the crime to **manslaughter.** It was introduced by the Homicide Act 1957 s.2 and is defined as an abnormality of mind which substantially impairs a defendant's mental responsibility. The abnormality may be due to retarded development of the mind, disease or injury.

diplomatic asylum Grant of refuge in an embassy, consulate or high commission to a person who fears persecution on political grounds by the state in which he finds himself. Under international law embassies, consulates and high commissions are treated as part of the territory of the state to which they relate. Thus, the person given diplomatic asylum is immune from the authorities and law of the state in which the diplomatic premises are situated.

diplomatic immunity Rule of international law that diplomatic representatives are not subject to the law of the state in which they are posted. However, a state may **waive** the immunity and allow a diplomat to be tried for a crime or sued for civil wrong. Diplomats are also exempt from taxation and rates. The rule is given effect in the United Kingdom by the Diplomatic Privileges Act 1964.

diplomatic privilege Privilege of **diplomatic immunity.**

direction to jury Statement made by a judge to a jury after the evidence has been presented in a trial and before the jury retires to consider its verdict. The direction will include a summary of the evidence, a statement of the relevant law and an explanation of the functions of the jury. If the direction is misleading and the defendant is convicted he may appeal against the conviction.

Director of Public Prosecutions Official, appointed by the Home Secretary and under the supervision of the Attorney-General, whose function it is to institute, undertake or carry out criminal proceedings on behalf of the Crown. Under the Prosecution of Offences Act 1985, he or she is the head of the **Crown Prosecution Service** and is responsible for the development and implementation of policy in relation to prosecutions.

disability Lack of power in law to do something. A person of unsound mind, for example, is disabled from entering into contracts.

disaffection Disloyalty towards, or loss of allegiance to, authority.

disappearance Absence of a person in circumstances from which death may be presumed for legal purposes such as **succession** or remarriage of the spouse. A person who has been absent without being heard of and without apparent explanation for seven years is presumed dead unless proved to be alive. If somebody has been absent for a shorter period, a court may deduce death after hearing relevant evidence.

disbar To expel a **barrister** from an **Inn of Court,** either as a form of punishment for professional misconduct or at the request of a barrister who wishes to join another profession – for example, to become a **solicitor**. A barrister who has been disbarred may no longer practise in the profession.

discharge To release from legal obligation. The word is used in many contexts. A **contract** is discharged, for example, when both parties are released from performing any further obligations under the contract. A jury is discharged if it is unable to reach a verdict. A person who has been declared **bankrupt** is discharged when the court orders that he should no longer be under the disabilities of bankruptcy. In criminal law a court may grant an **absolute discharge** or a **conditional discharge** to a person convicted of a crime.

disciplinary action Action taken by an employer against an employee who misbehaves, disobeys or fails to perform his or her job properly. The **Advisory, Conciliation and Arbitration Service** has published a code of practice on disciplinary rules and procedures which an employer should follow when taking disciplinary action, and an employer who fails to comply with it may have difficulty in justifying his or her action if an employee sues for **wrongful dismissal** or **unfair dismissal**. The procedure requires the employer to provide formal verbal and written warnings before dismissing an employee and to give the employee the opportunity to explain his or her side of the story.

disclaimer Statement by which a person announces that he or she will not accept legal responsibility. For instance, banks who give financial advice may disclaim any legal responsibility for any loss which a customer may suffer in following the advice. A court will normally uphold a disclaimer provided that sufficient notice of it is given to the other party. A disclaimer which forms part of a contract is called an **exemption clause**.

disclosure Act of revealing information which is not obvious. In contract law the parties are generally not required to provide information which is not requested, unless the contract is one of utmost good faith. *See also* **discovery of documents**.

discontinuance Voluntary termination of civil proceedings by a **plaintiff**. In proceedings commenced by a **writ of summons**, the plaintiff may discontinue the action, so long as he or she gives the **defendant** written notice within 14 days of receiving a defence to the claim.
   The **Crown Prosecution Service** may serve notice of discontinuance on a defendant in criminal proceedings, usually when a review of the evidence discloses that it is insufficient for the case to proceed.

discovery of documents Process by which a court orders one party to a **civil action** to hand over documentary evidence relating to the case. The general rule of law is that each party to an action must disclose all documentary evidence before trial whether it assists or impedes that party's case. Failure to do so entitles the other party to apply to the court for an order of discovery.

discretionary trust Arrangement whereby property is placed in **trust** for certain **beneficiaries** and the trustees have absolute discretion in the administration of the trust.

discrimination Unfair treatment of people of a particular sex, race or marital status due to prejudice. Any form of discrimination, particularly in relation to employment, is illegal and is controlled by the Race Relations Act 1976 and Sex Discrimination Acts 1975, 1986.

It is a defence against a charge of discrimination in employment to show that being of a particular race, sex or marital status is a genuine occupational qualification − for example, a male prison officer for a male prison.

dishonesty Motive for cheating or deceiving another by a particular act. Dishonesty is an essential requirement of the offences of **theft** and **deception** (Theft Acts 1968 and 1978). The question of dishonesty is a factual matter for the jury or Magistrates' Court to determine after hearing the evidence. For a conviction of theft they must be satisfied that, by the standards of ordinary decent people, the defendant acted dishonestly and must have realized this to be so.

dismissal Termination of an employee's contract of service by the employer or failure to renew a fixed-term contract of employment when the term ends. Constructive dismissal arises when an employee is forced to leave a job by the unfair conduct of the employer. *See also* **unfair dismissal**; **wrongful dismissal**.

disorderly conduct Uncontrolled or undisciplined behaviour that breaches normal standards of conduct and is either harassing or offensive to those who may witness it or contains the threat of violence. It is an offence to be found drunk and disorderly in a public place. Disorderly behaviour which is likely to cause harassment, alarm or distress is an offence under the Public Order Act 1986 s.5.

disorderly house Premises to which members of the public are invited and in which conduct that is considered an outrage to public decency takes place. Such premises include **brothels** and premises used for strip-tease, or indecent exhibitions. It is an offence to keep a disorderly house under the Disorderly Houses Act 1751.

disposition Term with two applications.

First, the transfer of ownership in property from one person to another.

Second, the characteristics of a person accused of a criminal offence which may be determined by evidence of previous behaviour or convictions.

dispute Conflict over a legal claim or right. Civil **litigation** arises when two or more parties are in dispute.

disqualification from driving Deprivation of the right to drive a motor vehicle. A driver may be disqualified in two ways: (i) by accumulating 12 **penalty points** for driving offences in three years (the court will disqualify such an offender for at least six months); (ii) by committing a driving offence which the court considers to be so serious that an immediate disqualification is justified (the offence of drunken driving carries immediate disqualification for a minimum of 12 months and causing death by reckless driving carries automatic disqualification for a minimum of two years).

A driver may be disqualified for other offences at the discretion of the court. A person who has not yet passed his or her driving test may also be deprived of the right to hold a licence.

disqualification from jury Deprivation of the right to serve on a **jury**. Those who are disqualified include members of the **judiciary**, **barristers**, **solicitors**, police and prison officers, members of the clergy and any person suffering from a mental disorder (Juries Act 1974).

Any person who has served a prison sentence of more than five years is also disqualified. Under the Juries (Disqualification) Act 1984 other convicted criminals are disqualified for ten years if they have received a prison sentence, **suspended sentence** or **community service order**, and five years if they have been put on **probation**.

dissolution of marriage Termination of marriage by **decree** of **divorce**.

dissolution of Parliament Ending of a Parliament, followed by a general election. The Prime Minister has the right to request a dissolution, which is performed by the monarch, and to fix the date of the subsequent election.

distrain To seize goods by means of **distress**.

distress To seize personal property of another in order to obtain performance of a legal duty or repayment of a debt. A landlord, for example, may take property of the tenant and hold the property until he has received payment of outstanding rent. Payment of rates and taxes may also be enforced by distress.

distress notice Notice given by a person who has seized property by means of **distress** to the person from whom the property was seized to inform him of what has been done and what action he can take to get his property back.

distress warrant Written notice issued by a court to a **bailiff** which authorizes the bailiff to **distrain** the personal property of a debtor who has failed to pay rent, or to pay a fine.

distribution Sharing the property of a person who has died without making a valid will among the next of kin. *See also* **intestacy**.

district registry Local office, usually situated in County Court offices, which issues **writs of summons** for cases in the High Court, and deals with matters relating to cases up until the time of trial. Such offices are staffed by district registrars appointed by the **Lord Chancellor**.

disturbance Interference with a right relating to land. For instance, a **right of way** may be disturbed by placing a fence across the route. The person whose right has been interfered with may seek an **injunction** to prevent the disturbance.

disturbance payment Payment which must be made under various Acts of Parliament to occupiers of houses or land who are forced to leave under legal powers to compensate for the expense and inconvenience of moving. For instance, if a house is subject to **compulsory purchase** for a road widening scheme, the owner will be paid the value of the house plus an extra sum as a disturbance payment.

dividend Term with two applications.
First, money received by shareholders in a company, paid out of

company profits. The amount received will depend upon the extent and type of the shareholder's investment.

Second, money received by a **bankrupt's creditors** after payment of expenses and **debts**, which have priority.

Divisional Courts Court consisting of at least two judges drawn from each of the three divisions of the **High Court of Justice**, which are generally responsible for hearing **appeals** from inferior courts.

The Divisional Court of the Family Division hears matrimonial appeals from **Magistrates' Courts**. The Divisional Court of the Chancery Division hears appeals in **bankruptcy** cases. The Divisional Court of Queen's Bench hears appeals on points of law from Magistrates' Courts and **Crown Courts**.

divorce Termination of marriage by **decree**, issued by a court. Under the Divorce Reform Act 1969 the only ground for divorce is that the marriage has irretrievably broken down. Under the Matrimonial Causes Act 1973 this may be proved by showing that one spouse has committed **adultery** or shown **unreasonable behaviour** or deserted the other for a period of at least two years.

A marriage will also be considered to have irretrievably broken down if the couple have lived apart for two years and both want a divorce. If one spouse does not want a divorce, and none of the above factors exist, then the couple must live apart for five years before the other spouse will be granted a divorce.

The couple must have been married for at least 12 months before either party can apply for divorce. Most divorces are by agreement and are dealt with in the County Court. If the divorce is defended it will be heard in the **Family Division** of the High Court. *See also* **annulment; decree absolute; decree nisi; desertion**.

divorce registry Section of the Registry of the **Family Division** of the **High Court of Justice**. It deals with pre-trial proceedings in **divorce** actions.

dock Place in a court room where the defendant is placed during the course of a criminal trial.

dock brief Practice in which an accused person in the **dock** chooses a barrister to represent him or her simply by requesting a barrister present in court to do so. The barrister is duty bound to take the case for a fixed fee. The practice is now virtually obsolete because of the availability of **legal aid**.

document of title Document that provides proof of possession and control of goods and entitles the person with the document to deal with the goods as if the owner. A delivery order, for example, issued by the owner of goods to the keeper of the warehouse where the goods are being stored, authorizes the keeper to deliver the goods to a particular person.

domestic court Magistrates' Court that sits to hear domestic proceedings as defined by the Magistrates' Courts Act 1980. Such proceedings include **maintenance** issues and questions relating to the **custody** of children. There must be at least three **magistrates** on the **bench,** including one male and one female.

domestic proceedings Domestic disputes which are heard in a Magistrates' Court. These include applications for separation and **maintenance** orders from spouses who are not initially seeking divorce, and questions that concern **custody** and **adoption** of children.

domestic tribunal Body which deals with disputes that arise from the internal regulation of an organization such as a social club, sports club, professional body or trade unions. Some specific domestic tribunals have been created by statute − for example, the Solicitors' Disciplinary Tribunal, created by the Solicitors Act 1974.

domicile Country in which a person intends to make his or her permanent home. The law of the country of a person's domicile is the appropriate law to determine that person's status; whether or not he or she is legitimate or old enough to marry, for example. The law of the domicile also governs **succession** to that person's property on death.

A person's domicile of origin is acquired at birth and is usually the same as that of the parents. A person who has reached the **age of majority** may acquire a domicile of choice by going to a country and deciding to make it his or her permanent home. *See also* **dependent domicile**.

dower Formerly. the right of a wife to a portion of her husband's land for her life after his death. It was abolished by the Law of Property Act 1925.

draft Term with two applications.

First, a preliminary version of a legal document.

Second, a legally enforceable order for the payment of money by one person to another – for example, a cheque.

drink and driving Criminal offence of driving with excess alcohol in the blood or driving while unfit through drink which, if proved, carries automatic **disqualification from driving** for a minimum period of 12 months. *See also* **breath test**.

There is also an offence of being drunk in charge of a vehicle under the Road Traffic Act 1972 s.5(2). It is committed where a drunk person is in control of, although not driving, a vehicle in a public place. Similar offences exist for driving or being in charge of a vehicle while unfit through drugs.

driving licence Certificate issued by the Department of Transport to authorize a person to drive a motor vehicle on public roads. Any person over 17 (except those with bad eyesight and certain medical conditions) may apply for a licence. Initially a yearly provisional licence is issued. After passing a driving test a person may receive a full licence, which is valid until the age of 70. After that, licences are issued at three-year intervals. *See also* **disqualification from driving**.

drugs, controlled Drugs, which are listed in a schedule to the Misuse of Drugs Act 1971, that are subject to legal controls. The Act specifies a number of offences relating to controlled drugs, including manufacture, possession, supply and importation. Controlled drugs are placed in classes A, B, or C according to the danger entailed, class C being the least dangerous. Higher sentences are available in relation to the more dangerous drugs.

drunk and disorderly Offence committed by a person who is drunk in a public place and behaves in a manner that might lead to a **breach of the peace** or that might present a danger to himself or others. It is frequently dealt with by **arrest** and detention until the offender is sober, when he or she is given a police caution and released.

97

due process Normal course of legal proceedings through the court system, conducted according to the principles of **natural justice**. All citizens are entitled to due process of law.

duplicity Situation in which two unrelated offences have been included in one **charge** or in one **count** on an **indictment**. Generally the indictment should charge one offence only. Duplicity is an error, which may be dealt with by amendment of the charge or indictment before trial or by the court quashing the indictment so that it may not be proceeded with.

duress Term with two applications.

First, a **defence** to a criminal charge. The defence is that the accused person committed the crime under threat of death or serious bodily harm from another. If duress is established, the accused will be acquitted. Duress is a defence to all crimes except **murder** and **treason**.

Second, a defence which may be raised in proceedings to enforce a **contract**. The defendant claims that he or she entered into the contract under threat or pressure from the other party.

duty of care Relationship between two persons in which one person has a responsibility to protect the interests of the other or to avoid injuring the other or his property. If a failure to fulfil a duty of care leads to loss, damage or injury, there may be a basis for an action for **damages** for **negligence**.

duty solicitor scheme Voluntary arrangement by which a number of **solicitors** in private practice agree to provide regular legal advice and representation to any person needing it at a Magistrates' Court or police station. The solicitors, if not paid by the client, will normally receive a fee from the **legal aid** fund for each client advised or represented.

dying declaration Oral statement made by a person immediately before death in the knowledge that death is imminent. Normally, statements made outside court are not admitted as evidence. An exception is made for a dying declaration because it is thought that no person would wish to die with a lie on his or her lips.

E

E & O E "Errors and omissions excepted", a conventional abbreviation which, when written on legal and business documents, indicates that the maker of the document does not accept any legal liability for minor accidental errors or omissions.

easement Right attached to ownership of a particular piece of land, by which the owner has rights in relation to a neighbouring piece of land which he does not own. The owner of land may enjoy a right of way across his neighbour's property, for example. Other examples include the right to receive natural light across neighbouring land and the right to receive water flowing across that land.

An easement which confers a right on the owner of particular land may be contrasted with a general **right of way**, which confers rights on the public at large.

ecclesiastical court Court that adjudicates on the law of the Church of England. *See also* **Consistory Court**.

economic duress Extreme commercial pressure exerted by one party on another to induce him or her to enter into a contract. The party induced into the contract may be entitled to escape from the agreement.

EEC *See* **European Community (EC)**

election Term with two applications.

First, method of choosing representative members of Parliament or local government under the Representation of the People Acts 1983 and 1985. Elections to Parliament are held on a date chosen by the Prime Minister (so long as the sovereign grants a dissolution) within five years of the last election. Elections to the European Parliament are on a fixed, five-year schedule. Elections to county councils are held in May every four years, district elections in May in the intervening years.

Second, procedure whereby a person accused of a crime chooses −

elects – whether to be tried before a **Magistrates' Court** or by jury before the **Crown Court**.

embezzlement Formerly, criminal offence committed by a clerk or servant who stole property from an employer or intercepted property for personal use before it came into the possession of the employer. The offence was abolished as an independent crime in 1968 and incorporated into the crime of **theft** (Theft Act 1968).

emergency powers Power of the **Crown** to issue a declaration of a state of emergency under the Emergency Powers Acts 1920 and 1964. A state of emergency may be declared for one month at a time. Under it the Government is given wide-ranging powers to make laws without going through normal Parliamentary procedures.

emigration Leaving a country for the purpose of taking up permanent residence in another country. Under the law of the United Kingdom there are no controls on emigration. *See also* **immigration**.

empanel To form a **jury** by random selection from citizens called for jury service. *See also* **challenge of jurors**.

employer and employee Master and servant. The master enters into a contract of service with the servant and agrees to remunerate the servant for carrying out the work in a competent and loyal manner. A person who is under a contract for services, such as a builder who is contracted to build an extension, is not an employee, but an independent contractor. *See also* **vicarious liability**.

employment appeal tribunal Tribunal that deals with appeals from decisions of an **industrial tribunal** in matters such as **redundancy**, **equal pay** and **sex discrimination**. It is composed of judges nominated by the Lord Chancellor and lay members with special knowledge or experience of industrial relations, who represent employers and workers.

enabling legislation Act of Parliament that confers powers on Parliament itself or some other person or body to make **legislation**.

enclosure Process by which **common** land is enclosed for private use, the land ceasing to be common. It is regulated by the Commons Acts of 1876 and 1879.

encroachment Taking possession of part of a piece of land unlawfully. For instance, it is an encroachment for one landowner to move his boundary fence on to his neighbour's land. The owner can recover his land by action for possession in the civil courts or by simply seizing it back.

encumbrance Right relating to land or goods which belongs to someone other than the owner of the land or goods. For example, if the owner of land takes out a **mortgage** with a bank, the bank gains a right to take and sell the property if the mortgage repayments are not made. The mortgage is therefore an encumbrance on the land. An encumbrance remains when the land to which it relates is sold.

endorsement Term with three applications.

First, a signature on a legal document which operates to transfer legal rights from one person to another. For instance, if a cheque is payable to Brown, he may renounce his right to it by endorsing it with his signature on the back. The cheque then becomes payable to whoever possesses it.

Second, a statement printed on a **driving licence** by order of a court after a conviction for a driving offence.

Third, a statement in legal document, such as a **writ**.

endowment Term with two applications.

First, property over which a widow formerly had a right of **dower**.

Second, an arrangement by which a person or institution receives a certain income indefinitely. For instance, a person might endow a college by promising by **deed** that the rent from a certain estate should be paid to the college.

enforcement of judgment Measures taken under authority of a court to give effect to a judgment. For instance, if a **defendant** who has lost a civil case and been ordered to pay **damages** to the **plaintiff** does not pay as required, the plaintiff can ask the court to enforce the judgment by ordering the **bailiff** to seize the defendant's goods so that they may be sold to pay the damages. *See also* **distrain**; **distress**; **distress notice**; **distress warrant**.

enfranchise To give a person the right to vote.

engross To make a copy of a legal document for signing.

entail Type of ownership of land under which, on the death of the owner, the land must pass to his first lineal descendant.

entering judgment Formally recording the **judgment** in a civil case. The term is particularly used when one party to a civil case does not appear in court to contest it. The party who does appear wins by **default** and this is described as entering judgment on his behalf.

enticement Formerly, the **tort** of persuading a wife to leave her husband or *vice* versa. It was abolished by the Law Reform (Miscellaneous Provisions) Act 1970.

entrapment Causing or encouraging another person to commit a crime for the purpose of apprehending and convicting him. In some countries a person who has been entrapped into committing a crime by a person in authority, such as a police officer, has a **defence** to a criminal charge. This defence is not accepted in English law. *See also* **agent provocateur**.

equal opportunities Absence of discrimination on grounds other than one's abilities to perform a special function. Equal opportunities employers take on employees without discrimination, particularly on the grounds of physical disability, race, gender and other culturally and racially determined characteristics.

Equal Opportunities Commission Body established under the Sex Discrimination Act 1975 with broad responsibility for promoting sexual equality. Its activities include undertaking research, supporting persons who take cases before the courts and seeking to influence law reform.

equal pay Equal pay for "like work", regardless of the employee's sex, required by the Employment Protection Act 1970. An employee, usually a woman, who feels that she has cause for complaint may apply to an industrial tribunal for a hearing, but the employer may avoid liability by showing justification for the differences in pay.

equitable assignment Transfer of an intangible property right, or **chose in action**, for which the strict legal formalities have not been observed, but which is enforced in **equity** against any person who has notice of the transfer.

equitable easement Easement that is recognized and enforced under the principles of **equity**. *See also* **easement**.

equitable interest Right, in relation to land, that is enforceable by the principles of **equity**. For instance, a **mortgage** may confer on the mortgagee an equitable interest in the relevant property, or a person may get an equitable interest in a house by contributing to the purchase price, even though that person is not one of the legal owners.

equity System of rules and principles for determining disputes. It developed alongside the rules of the **common law** and was applied originally by the Court of Chancery. The principles of equity are largely based on notions of fairness and they frequently provide a remedy in cases in which the strict formalities of common law have not been observed. The rules of equity and common law were fused in a single system of **civil law** when the Court of Chancery was amalgamated with the common law courts by the Judicature Act 1873.

equity, maxims of Set of broad principles on which the rules of equity are based. Among the most important maxims are the following: (i) "He who comes to equity must come with clean hands." Equity will not provide a remedy on the basis of fairness to a person who has himself behaved unfairly. (ii) "Equity looks to the intent not the form." A minor defect in formalities will not prevent equity from providing a remedy. (iii) "Equity acts *in personam*." Equity is primarily concerned to enforce personal obligations and ensure that persons act fairly, not to deal with rights in relation to things. (iv) "Equity will not allow a wrong to be without a remedy." (v) "He who seeks equity must do equity." A person may seek an equitable remedy only if he or she is prepared to observe equitable obligations.

equity of redemption Right of a person who has mortgaged his house or land to pay off the total **debt** incurred under the mortgage and receive full ownership of the property.

escape Offence under **common law**, to escape from lawful custody. Under the Prison Act 1952 s.39 it is also an offence to help another person to escape.

escrow Document by which obligations will be created if a certain condition is fulfilled. For instance, a person might lodge an escrow with his solicitor to provide that if his or her daughter gets a degree he or she will pay her £5,000.

established church Official church of the state, legally recognized as such. The Church of England is established. It is represented in the House of Lords by the two archbishops and 24 bishops. The Church of Scotland is also established. The Sovereign must be a member of both churches.

estate Term with three applications.
First, area of land held by one person.
Second, the total property owned by a person.
Third, the duration of a person's right to land. Thus, a five-year **lease** is an estate of five years. *See also* **entail; freehold**.

estate duty Formerly, tax payable on the total value of a person's property at death. Abolished by the Finance Act 1975 and replaced by **capital transfer tax**.

estate tail Holding in land which is subject to an **entail.**

estoppel Rule of law that in certain circumstances a person may not deny a fact which he has previously asserted or which has been decided upon by a court in a case to which he was a party. For example, a person who makes a statement in a **deed** is not allowed to deny that statement in later legal proceedings.

ethnography Observation and descriptive study of the distribution, activities and social interactions of particular social or cultural groups.

European Commission of Human Rights Body established under the **European Convention on Human Rights,** consisting of representatives of the states who signed that convention. Its purpose is to enforce the convention, to hear complaints against member states and to determine whether a breach of the convention has occurred. Cases may be referred to the **European Court of Human Rights**.

European Community (EC) European Community of states, created by the Treaty of Rome 1959. The aims include the creation of a single market free from tariff barriers, the standardization of regulations governing the production and distribution of goods, and the use of a common currency. *See also* **Community law**.

European Convention on Human Rights Convention inspired by the League of Nations, drafted in 1950, signed by 19 states. It sets out a list of human rights and freedoms, including rights to freedom of religion, fair trial, freedom of political association and expression. Each signatory state agrees to protect the rights in its own territory. The Convention is enforced by the **European Commission of Human Rights**.

European Court of Human Rights Court that hears and adjudicates on allegations of breaches of the **European Convention on Human Rights**.

European Court of Justice Court consisting of one judge from each of the member states of the **European Community**, which adjudicates on matters of **Community law**.

European Parliament Assembly of the **European Community** consisting of directly elected representatives from each member state.

euthanasia Death caused deliberately in the interests of the person who is killed. Euthanasia is not a legal concept and deliberate killing will normally be **murder**, even when done at the request of the victim. However, pressure groups have campaigned to make euthanasia lawful in certain circumstances – for example, in relation to severely disabled children who have a short life-expectancy and are in constant pain, or to old people who are suffering from terminal illness and have asked to be assisted to die.

eviction Ejection of a person from land or premises. Tenants of rented premises are protected by law from arbitrary eviction.

evidence Things said in, or produced before, a court of law for the purpose of establishing facts. There are strict rules, largely related to relevance and credibility, that govern what may be admitted as evidence. *See also* **hearsay evidence; testimony.**

examination Process by which evidence is taken from a **witness** under oath in court by means of questioning. *See also* **cross-examination.**

examination-in-chief Questioning of a witness under oath in legal proceedings by the counsel that is representing the party who called the witness. *See also* **cross-examination.**

examination, public *See* **public examination.**

exception Term with two applications.
   First, objection taken to something, particularly in civil proceedings.
   Second, in conveyancing, a clause in a deed or lease or conveyance in which the lessor or guarantor makes an exception of some part of what he or she is leasing or conveying.

exchange of contracts In relation to agreements to sell land, the handing over by each party to the other of a signed copy of the agreement, which thereby becomes a binding **contract.**

executory contract Legally binding agreement to perform certain acts in the future. *See also* **contract.**

excise *See* **Customs and Excise.**

exclusion order Order made under the Prevention of Terrorism (Temporary Provisions) Act 1989 by which the Home Secretary may ban a person whom he believes has been involved in terrorism from entering the country.

execution Enforcement of a court order. For instance, in civil proceedings in which the court has ordered the **defendant** to pay **damages** to the **plaintiff,** execution of judgment would occur if the court ordered a **bailiff** to seize goods from the defendant so that they might be sold to pay the debt.
   The term may be used to refer to the carrying out of the **death penalty.**

executor Person appointed under a **will** to distribute the property of a dead person according to the terms of the will.

executory interest Right to land which is to come into effect at some specified time in the future or on the occurrence of a specified event. For instance, a father could create a **trust** under which the trustees are directed to convey a house to his son in the event of the son's marriage. Prior to marriage, the son has an executory interest in the house.

exemplary damages Sum of money which a court, in civil proceedings, orders the defendant to pay to the plaintiff in excess of the actual loss suffered, when the defendant has behaved maliciously or has sought to make a profit from his wrong. For instance, a newspaper which has boosted its circulation by publishing a libel about a pop star might be required to pay exemplary damages.

exempt agreement Agreement for the provision of credit which is exempt from regulation under the Consumer Credit Act 1974. *See also* **consumer credit; regulated agreement**.

exemption clause Part of a **contract** which seeks to limit, restrict or modify the liability of one of the parties which might otherwise arise under the contract. For instance, dry cleaners may insert a clause in their standard contract which exempts liability for loss or damage. Exemption clauses in contracts made by businesses with consumers may be disregarded by the courts if they are unreasonable under the Unfair Contract Terms Act 1977.

exhibit Object or document presented in court as evidence – for example, a blood-stained handkerchief in a murder trial.

exoneration Process by which a person is freed from an accusation of guilt or other wrongdoing. A person charged with a criminal offence is exonerated by a **verdict** of not guilty. A person sued in a **civil action** is exonerated if he or she is not made liable to pay **damages**.

expectant heir Person who hopes to inherit under the will of another, or who will receive property on the death of another.

expert witness Person who has particular expertise and is permitted to give **evidence** at a hearing on issues of fact. This is an exception to the rule that a court will hear evidence of what a person has observed, but not of his opinion. Surgeons, engineers and fingerprint specialists are common expert witnesses. Generally the expert gives evidence orally, but under the Criminal Justice Act 1988 permission may be granted for expert reports in writing to be produced in court.

explosive Article manufactured for the purpose of producing a practical effect by explosion. Examples include gunpowder, dynamite, fireworks and ammunition. The Explosive Substances Act 1883 regulates the manufacture, possession and use of explosives.

express Description of information that is explicitly stated, either by word of mouth or in writing, as opposed to information which is not stated, but may be inferred.

express malice Intention to kill another person. A killing with express malice is **murder**. *See also* **malice aforethought**.

express term Contractual term which is specifically stated by one party to a contract and agreed upon by the other. It may be made verbally or in writing.

expropriation Compulsory deprivation of a person's right to property.

extended sentence Term of imprisonment which exceeds the normal maximum for the crime committed. Under the Powers of the Criminal Courts Act 1973 the courts have the power to impose an extended sentence on offenders who persistently offend, often repeating the same offence.

extinguishment Termination of a right or duty. For instance, an **easement** of **right of way** is extinguished if the owner of the right buys the land over which the right exists. Similarly, the right to sue for a **debt** is extinguished as soon as the debt is paid.

extort To induce another person to confer a benefit by means of threats or intimidation. It may amount to the crime of blackmail.

extradition Process by which one state hands over to another a person who has taken refuge in the first state and is wanted for a criminal offence in the second. Extradition proceedings are governed by various Extradition Acts from 1870 to 1935 and by the Criminal Justice Act 1988. The United Kingdom will extradite people only to states with which an extradition treaty has been agreed.

extrajudicial Outside the ordinary course of legal proceedings. **Distress**, for example, is an extrajudicial remedy. An extrajudicial statement made by a judge is one not made in the course of a judgment and therefore not an authoritative statement of the law.

extraordinary general meeting (EGM) Meeting of all members of an organization (usually a limited company), called specially to deal with a particular matter and not part of the annual schedule of meetings. In company law, every limited company must hold an **annual general meeting** of all shareholders and an EGM whenever the holders of ten per cent of the **share** capital request one.

extraterritorial Outside the limits of a country's legal jurisdiction. However, diplomats who enjoy **diplomatic immunity** are considered to be extraterritorial in international law.

F

fact Information relevant to the decision in proceedings before a court. In cases in which a **jury** is involved it is normally its duty to determine the true facts of the case. The judge is concerned with issues of law. *See also* **finding**.

factory Premises in which people are employed in manual labour, defined or identified under the Factories Act 1961. The definition covers a wide range of premises, including those involved in manufacturing, repairing, cleaning, demolition and the slaughter of animals.

faculty Term with two applications.

First, special permission granted under ecclesiastical law to do something that is not permitted under the **common law**. An example is permission to marry without having the **banns of marriage** read.

Second, a group of scholars, such as a university department or the Faculty of Advocates, which is the professional body of lawyers qualified to present cases in the higher courts of Scotland.

fair comment Defence to an action for **defamation** on the ground that the statement was a fair comment on a matter of public interest. The defence is available only if the comment is made honestly and without malice (Defamation Act 1952).

fair rent Amount of rent which a **rent officer** considers to be fair having regard to the age, character and location of the property which is being let. The landlord, tenant or **local authority** can apply to the rent officer for an assessment of a fair rent and the rent officer will inspect the premises and hold an informal hearing at which both sides can put forward their views.

The fair rent is registered and will apply to the property indefinitely, even if there is a change of landlord or tenant, until a new registration is requested. The figure cannot be reviewed for a period of two years.

fair trading Commercial fairness in relation to goods supplied to consumers. The Fair Trading Act 1973 introduced the notion of fair trading and set up an office of fair trading to review commercial activities in order to protect the consumer from unfair practices. The office is run by the Director General of Fair Trading.

false accounting Offence under the Theft Act 1968 s.17, committed by dishonestly falsifying, destroying, concealing or defacing an account with an intent to gain for oneself or cause loss to another.

false arrest Unlawful detention of a person by somebody who claims to be exercising a lawful power of arrest. The arrest may be unlawful either because there were insufficient grounds for arrest or because the necessary formalities of arrest were not complied with. It may also amount to **false imprisonment**.

false imprisonment Crime at **common law** and also one form of the **tort** of **trespass** against the person, committed when one person intentionally restrains the freedom and liberty of another. It is not necessary for the person to be restrained in a prison; restraint in a room, building, car, or any such place is false imprisonment so long as the restraint is total. Wrongful arrest by a police officer or citizen also gives the victim the right to sue for **damages** for false imprisonment.

false pretences False statement of fact made in order to obtain money or goods. It was formerly an offence under the Larceny Act 1916, but it has now been replaced by the offence of obtaining property by deception (Theft Act 1968 s.15).

false representation *See* **misrepresentation**.

falsification of accounts *See* **false accounting**.

family Social unit which includes husband, wife and children living together. In some contexts, a family includes all blood relations.

Family Division Branch of the **High Court of Justice** that deals with family matters such as disputed divorce cases, the distribution of property on divorce and the custody and adoption of children.

family provision Financial provision which a court can order to be paid out of the **estate** of a deceased person to persons who were financially dependent upon the deceased and who have not been adequately provided for in the deceased person's will. Under the Inheritance (Provision for Family and Dependents) Act 1975 applications are permitted from the spouse or any former spouse who has not remarried, children, including adopted or foster children, and any other person who was financially dependent on the deceased at the time of death.

fatal accidents Accidents that cause a person's death. Close relatives of any person killed by the **negligence** of another are entitled to claim **damages** against the negligent person under the Fatal Accidents Act 1976. A spouse, parent, grandparent, child, grandchild, nephew, niece or cousin can sue.

federal state Country in which executive and legislative power is shared between a central, national government and smaller, provincial governments.

fee Term with two applications.
First, agreed payment for services rendered.
Second, form of land ownership in which the land may be inherited, as opposed to land of which ownership is limited to the life of the present holder.

fee simple Form of land tenure which equates to absolute ownership. It is more commonly called **freehold**. The fee simple is of indefinite duration and may be sold or passed to an heir on the owner's death.

feeble-minded Person of severely subnormal intelligence under the Mental Health Acts 1959 and 1983.

felony Formerly, one of a category of serious criminal offences, including **murder, rape**, and **robbery**. The offence incurred forfeiture of the offender's land and goods to the Crown. Forfeiture was abolished in 1870, but the offences were still known as felonies. All other offences were known as **misdemeanours**. The distinction was abolished by the Criminal Law Act 1967 s.1(1).

feminism Doctrine that promotes equality between women and men, starting from the premise that women face discrimination.

fiction, legal Untrue statement that, formerly, was routinely taken to be true for the purpose of certain legal proceedings. Fictions were commonly used by judges as a means of overcoming undesirable obstacles in the law. In modern times, law reform has made the use of fictions unnecessary.

fiduciary Involving trust between two or more persons. Thus, a fiduciary relationship arises when one person puts his trust in another and the other is under a legal duty to act in the first person's best interests. Examples include relationships between **trustee** and **beneficiary** and between **solicitor** and **client**. The person under the duty may be described as a fiduciary.

final judgment Decision of a court which finally disposes of a case after trial.

financial provision order Court order imposed on one party to require him or her to make financial provision for another. Examples are an order for **family provision** under the Inheritance (Provision for Family and Dependents) Act 1975 and an order for **maintenance** of a spouse or child.

financial services Services provided to clients that involve banking, lending, investment and insurance. The providers of such services and persons who give commercial advice in relation to them are regulated by the Financial Services Act 1986.

finding Conclusion on an issue of fact in a court, tribunal or inquiry. In a civil case, when there is a dispute about the evidence, the judge must reach a finding of facts and then apply the law to those facts. In a criminal case before a judge and jury, the judge directs the jury on the law and the jury must then pronounce a **verdict**. The verdict involves a finding of fact, although this is not announced separately.

fine Punishment for a criminal offence whereby the offender is required to pay a sum of money to the Crown. The amount is decided by the court after considering the nature and gravity of the offence and the offender's financial means. Most statutory crimes carry a maximum fine.

An offender who fails to pay a fine may be imprisoned for **default**.

fingerprint Print of the tips of fingers and thumbs taken by the police as a means of identification. Under the Police and Criminal Evidence Act 1984 ss. 27 and 61, police may take fingerprints following conviction for a criminal offence. A senior police officer may authorize fingerprints to be taken from a suspect, but records of these fingerprints must be destroyed if the suspect is acquitted or not prosecuted.

firearm Lethal barrelled weapon of any description from which a shot, bullet or other missile can be discharged (Firearms Act 1968). Various offences relate to the unauthorized manufacture, sale, possession and use of firearms and also to certain uses of imitation firearms.

firearms certificate Certificate required for the purchase, acquisition or possession of any **firearm** under the Firearms Act 1968. Applications for a certificate are made to the chief police officer in the area where the applicant lives. Certificates must be renewed every three years.

firm Common name for a **partnership**.

first impression Case which comes before a court where the point of law involved has not previously been decided and therefore the court must decide the point for the first time.

fish royal Whale, porpoise or sturgeon thrown ashore or caught near the coast, considered to be the property of the Crown. This privilege was maintained in the Wild Creatures and Forest Laws Act 1971 s.1.

fit for habitation Requirement that rented accommodation should be good enough to live in. The local authority may be requested to inspect property and determine whether it is fit for human habitation. Under the Housing Act 1957 it must consider the following factors: state of repair, stability, damp, natural lighting, ventilation, water supply, drainage, lavatories, and cooking facilities.

If the property is considered to be unfit, but repairable at reasonable expense, the local authority will serve a notice on the owner that requires the work to be carried out within 21 days. If the property cannot be repaired at reasonable expense the local authority may make a demolition order for the property to be pulled down.

If the landlord is the local authority, the tenant may seek remedies in the Magistrates' Court.

fitness for purpose Requirement that goods sold by a retailer must be reasonably fit for the purpose for which they are intended. If the purchaser makes known to the vendor that the goods are required for a particular purpose and relies on the vendor's judgment, the purchaser is entitled to a refund, under the Sale of Goods Act 1979 s.14(3), if the goods prove to be unsuitable.

fitness to plead Mental state of the accused. If the accused is suffering from a severe mental abnormality, which would make it impossible to conduct a meaningful trial, the Home Secretary has the power to commit the accused to a mental institution (Mental Health Act 1959 ss.72, 73).

A person who is unable to understand the charges or to appreciate the difference between a plea of guilty and one of not guilty is considered to be unfit to plead. If the question is raised at the start of the trial a special jury will be called to decide the issue.

fixed charge Mortgage over specific property. Thus, a **mortgage** on land is a fixed charge because the lender has a claim over the land if the mortgage repayments are not made.

fixed costs Set amount of lawyer's costs recoverable in proceedings.

fixed penalty Fixed fine for certain motoring offences which the offender can pay within 21 days of the offence. The effect of paying a fixed penalty is that no offence or conviction is recorded.

fixed penalty notice Written notice which may be attached to a stationary vehicle and which notifies the driver that an offence with a **fixed penalty** has been committed.

fixed-term tenancy Lease of land or property for a limited period. Neither landlord nor tenant may end the agreement unilaterally before the period is up.

fixture Object which has become fixed to land and in law becomes part of the land. Thus, a house is a fixture because it has foundations in the land. Things attached to a building, such as shop signs or curtain rails, are also fixtures. Articles which simply rest on the ground are not fixtures. A purchaser of land may claim as part of the purchase all objects which were fixtures at the time of the contract of sale.

floor of the court Part of the court room between the judge and the first row of **counsel**.

flotsam Goods which have fallen from a ship and are found floating. If not claimed by the owner, they belong to the **Crown**. *See also* **jetsam**.

folio Unit of measure of legal documents for the purpose of calculating certain court charges. Generally a folio is 72 words.

footpath Route along which the public has a **right of way**, but only by foot. The landowner may not obstruct the path and must maintain gates and styles through fences and hedges. *See also* **bridleways**.

forbearance to sue Not proceeding in or commencing a **civil action**. When a dispute is settled without going to court, the party making the claim will agree to accept a certain sum in return for forbearing to sue. This agreement is a binding **contract** and the courts refuse to hear a case if such an agreement has been made.

foreclosure Court proceeding by which a mortgagor loses his or her right to the mortgaged property because of a failure to make payments as required by the **mortgage** agreement. The property will be sold by order of the court. The mortgagee is entitled to the portion of the money raised by the sale that is needed to pay off the mortgage debt and any interest owing. The mortgagor receives what is left.

foreign enlistment Offence under the Foreign Enlistment Act 1870 for a British subject to enlist in the armed forces of a foreign state which is at war either with the United Kingdom or with any other state with which the United Kingdom is not at war.

foreign judgment Decisions of a court other than the courts of England and Wales. Generally, a foreign judgment is not enforceable.

Nor does it set a **binding precedent**. However, in many cases the effect of a foreign judgment will be recognized by an English court. For instance, a foreign judgment of divorce may be recognized in an English court as affecting the status of the parties. Also, foreign judgments may be enforced if a reciprocal arrangement has been made between the two countries. Thus, the decisions of Northern Irish and Scottish courts are enforceable in England and Wales, as are judgments given in other countries of the **European Community**.

Although a foreign judgment does not create a binding precedent and is not a source of law in England and Wales, it may be **persuasive precedent**. This is especially true of judgments of the higher courts in Commonwealth countries.

foreign jurisdiction Territory over which any law other than the law of England and Wales applies. Thus, Scotland is a foreign jurisdiction because it has its own system of law.

foreign law Law of any country other than England and Wales. A case in an English court may involve a question of foreign law — for instance, whether a person has been lawfully married in another country. In such cases a foreign lawyer or academic may appear in court as an **expert witness** to give evidence. If no expert is available, the court will assume that the foreign law is the same as English law.

foreman Person elected by a **jury** to act as spokesman in giving its **verdict**.

forensic medicine Aspects of medical science that are commonly relied upon by courts to determine the facts of cases. Branches of forensic medicine include pathology (the study of causes of injury or death) and psychiatry (the study of mental disorder). Evidence of these matters is given by an **expert witness**.

forensic science Application of scientific methods to provide evidence relating to the facts of a case. The Home Office has forensic science laboratories which assist the police in criminal cases. Common areas of forensic science are ballistics, explosives and fingerprints.

foreshore Part of the shoreline that is covered when the tide is in, but exposed when the tide is out. The foreshore is owned by the Crown, which has the right to take anything found on it. *See also* **fish royal**.

forfeiture Compulsory taking of something from a person by law without compensation. Formerly, a person who was convicted of treason or felony forfeited all his property, but this was abolished by the Forfeiture Act 1870. However, forfeiture is still used in **criminal law** as a quasi-punishment. For instance, obscene material kept for publication may be forfeited under the Obscene Publications Act 1959 s.3. Also tools or vehicles used for crime may be forfeited under the Criminal Justice Act 1988.

Forfeiture may operate in **civil law** as a remedy. In company law, for example, a person who holds shares that must be paid for in two instalments will forfeit them if the second instalment is not paid.

forgery Making a false document with the intent that another should accept it as genuine and act in reliance upon it. It is an offence under the Forgery and Counterfeiting Act 1981. The document is false if it appears to be something which it is not; for example, a cheque which is signed in a name other than the name of the signer. The offence also applies to information stored on video tape or computer discs.

forthwith Immediately.

fostering Circumstance in which a person other than a parent or close relative of a child has been entrusted with care of the child. Fostering arrangements normally relate to children under the care of a local authority. The foster-parent has parental duties, but not parental rights (*see* **parental rights and duties).**

franchise Term with two applications.

First, the legal right to vote, for example in Parliamentary or local elections.

Second, the right to trade under the name of another. Some chains of restaurants, for example, are franchises. Each restaurant is owned by an individual who has purchased the right to trade under the name of the chain.

fraud Act of deceiving another, intending either to benefit oneself or cause loss to another. Fraud may amount to an offence of **deception** or **conspiracy** to **defraud**. In civil law, if a **contract** is induced by fraud, the victim of the fraud will not be bound by the contract. Fraud may also amount to the **tort** of **deceit**.

fraud on a power Circumstance in which a person who has been given a legal power to act for a particular purpose exercises the power for his own benefit or for some unauthorized purpose. For instance, if a solicitor has been given a **power of attorney** to sell a client's house at the best available price, it would be a fraud on the power if the solicitor sold the house to his brother for half its true value.

fraudulent conversion Formerly, dishonest taking of another's property. Under the Theft Act 1968 the theft is now committed by **appropriation** of another's property.

fraudulent conveyance Sale of a house or land to one person in order to avoid fulfilling a contractual obligation to sell it to another or to avoid the property being taken by creditors. A court will declare the fraudulent conveyance void.

fraudulent misrepresentation *See* **misrepresentation**.

fraudulent preference Transfer of property or money by a debtor to particular **creditors** shortly before or at a time of **insolvency**, to the detriment of other creditors who have a right to repayment. The court may declare that such a transfer is **void**.

freedom of information Access to official information, the opposite of official secrecy. At present, though it is an aspiration of some individuals and groups, it is not part of the law of the United Kingdom. *See also* **Crown privilege**; **data protection**.

freehold Absolute ownership of land. The freehold owner is entitled to immediate possession of the land and may pass ownership to another by sale of the property or by inheritance on death.

free pardon Exercise of the royal prerogative by which a person who has been convicted of a criminal offence is released from any punishment linked to the offence. A free pardon is in effect granted by the **Home Secretary** and may be used when it is thought that the conviction was a **miscarriage of justice**.

friendly suit Court action brought without hostility in order to determine a legal point or obtain the permission of the court to act in a particular way.

frolic of his own Phrase used to describe an employee's actions which amount to a **tort**, committed while at work but not while doing the job the employee is employed to do.

For instance, a group of workers who, with their employer's permission, are visiting a tea-room during working hours some distance from work may be considered to be on a frolic of their own. If so, the employer will not be liable for injuries sustained during the "frolic". Employers are not generally liable for the **tortious acts** of their employees unless committed while carrying out their job. *See also* **vicarious liability**.

frustration Method of discharging a **contract** when an event occurs, beyond the control of either party, which makes the contract impossible or illegal to perform, or radically different from what was intended. For instance, a contract in which a group is to perform at a concert hall is frustrated if the hall is accidentally burnt down before the performance is due to take place.

If a contract is frustrated both parties are excused from further performance of the agreement, although any money paid in advance must be repaid. *See also* **discharge**.

fugitive offender Person accused of an offence in a Commonwealth country or Dependent Territory of the United Kingdom who is apprehended in another Commonwealth or Dependent country. Under the Fugitive Offenders Act 1967 the offender may be returned for trial to the country in which the offence was committed. *See also* **extradition**.

full age Age of majority. It has been 18 since 1970, following the Family Law Reform Act 1969 s.1.

fundamental breach Breach of a contractual term which has fundamental consequences. At one time the law would not allow a party to a **contract** to exclude liability for any fundamental breach of contract. However, since the Unfair Contract Terms Act 1977 and the **House of Lords** decision in Photo Production Ltd. v Securicor

Transport Ltd. (1980) it is now a question of interpretation whether an **exemption clause** covers the breach in question.

funeral Ceremony followed by burial or cremation of a dead person. Burial or cremation cannot take place until a certificate is obtained from the Registrar of Deaths or, if an **inquest** has been held, until the **coroner** authorizes it.

future estate Estate which will come into a person's possession at some future time.

future lease Tenancy of land which is to begin at a specified future date.

future property Property which will come into a person's ownership at some future time.

G

gage Something given by one party to another as security against the performance of an act. A modern example is a **mortgage,** by which the landowner borrows money and gives the lender a right to claim the land if repayment is not made.

gambling *See* **gaming.**

game Wild animals hunted for food or sport. Game includes hares, rabbits, grouse, pheasants etc. The hunting of game is subject to legislation, which lays down the limits of **close seasons**. Landowners may hunt game on their own land or sell the right to do so.

gaming Playing a game, usually of chance, for stakes. Various **statutes** govern commercial gaming, which may take place only on licensed, registered premises. Players must be 18 or over. Premises which are used regularly for the purposes of gaming by large numbers of people are called gaming houses and are controlled by the Gaming Act 1968.

garnishee order Court order whereby any money which is owed by a third party to a **defendant** found liable in a **civil action** is paid directly to the **plaintiff** in the action. For instance, a garnishee order issued to a bank would require the bank to pay money out of the defendant's account to the plaintiff, providing the defendant was in credit. Such an order may be requested in circumstances if the defendant has failed to pay compensation to the plaintiff, despite being found liable to do so in an earlier court hearing.

garrotting Term with two applications.

First, the former criminal offence of choking a person in order to rob him or her. Punishment was by imprisonment and flogging under the Garrotters Act 1863.

Second, in certain countries, executing convicted criminals by choking.

gazumping Vendor's act of withdrawing from an agreed sale of land "subject to contract" in order to enter into another agreement with a new buyer at a higher price. The original purchaser has no remedy since agreements to sell land are not legally binding until the **exchange of contracts**.

gender The sum of socially and culturally determined differences between male and female. By contrast, differences of sex are genetically determined.

General Commissioners of Income Tax Persons appointed by the **Lord Chancellor** to hear appeals against tax assessments made by Tax Inspectors.

general damages Damages assumed to follow naturally from the wrongful act complained of in a court of law. For instance, in an action for **negligence** against a driver who had injured a pedestrian, the injury, pain and suffering are general damages which follow naturally from the incident. The **plaintiff** is automatically entitled to compensation for such damage. Other damage which may have followed from the incident, but is not a natural consequence of it, must be proved in the court before the plaintiff is entitled to compensation. *See* **special damages**.

general lien General right to retain property of a person against whom a claim remains to be settled until a full settlement is achieved. Although a **lien** exists in many cases, a general lien applies only to specific professions such as solicitors, bankers and stockbrokers.

General Medical Council Professional body created by **statute** which registers and controls doctors and has the ultimate power to remove a doctor from the medical register for unprofessional conduct.

general sessions Former court of two or more **justices of the peace**. It was known as the court of **quarter sessions** when held at specific times during the year. It was abolished by the Courts Act 1971.

general words Words added to a **conveyance** of property to denote that the conveyance includes all rights and **easements** in the property. Since the Law of Property Act 1925 general words are implied in all conveyances even if not included.

genetic engineering Specific manipulation of the genetic make-up of a living organism designed to create or emphasize desired traits or characteristics, or to eliminate unwanted ones. Research on the possibilities of genetic engineering is strictly limited by law and under regular review in many countries. *See also* **unborn child**.

genocide Criminal offence under **international law** of intentionally attempting to extinguish a race or ethnic group by killing or inflicting conditions on the group which are intended to destroy it. It can be committed during peace or war and was declared to be an offence by the United Nations Convention in 1948 following the Nazi treatment of Jews during World War II.

gentleman's agreement Agreement, not enforceable in a court of law, that relies upon the honour of the parties to the agreement to keep it.

gift Voluntary transfer of property from one person to another without payment of any sort. The gift may be made on death by a will or by transfer of the title in the property during life. Ownership passes when there has been a physical transfer of the property coupled with an intent to pass ownership. A promise of a gift is not enforceable in a court of law unless the promise is made by **deed**, since English law does not recognize agreements without **consideration**.

glebe Land which is attached to a particular **benefice** for the use of the cleric holding the office.

golden rule Rule of **statutory interpretation** which states that a statute is not to be interpreted literally if the effect would be absurd or repugnant.

For instance, in the case of Re Sigsworth (1935) the court had to interpret the Administration of Estates Act 1925, which states that the property of a person who dies without making a will should be divided among the children. Mrs. Sigsworth was murdered by her son. Therefore, if the court interpreted the statute literally, her son would have inherited her estate. The court decided that such a result would be absurd and repugnant. It therefore applied the golden rule and held that, by implication under the Act, any child who had murdered a parent could not benefit from the parent's death.

good behaviour Order of a **Magistrates' Court** to a person appearing before the court to be of good behaviour for a specified period of time. *See also* **binding over**.

good faith Anything done honestly and therefore considered to have been done in good faith.

good offices Act of a third party in mediating between two parties in dispute with each other.

goods All **personal property** except money (Sale of Goods Act 1979).

goodwill Custom and reputation which a successful business has established. This is a valuable asset and a businessman is entitled to sell it along with the physical property and premises of the business.

Governor-General Official representative of the Crown in a Commonwealth country or British colony.

grand jury Jury which existed to determine whether a charge should be heard against an accused person. It was abolished by the Criminal Justice Act 1948. *See also* **Bill of Indictment**.

grant Term with two applications.
First, the transfer of ownership in property when actual delivery of the property is not possible. For instance, a **conveyance** is a grant that transfers ownership of a piece of land. Similarly, a **patent** right, which is not a physically identifiable piece of property, is transferred by grant.
Second, the allocation of rights or money to particular persons, usually for specific purposes.

grant caeterorum Authority to administer a residue of a deceased person's **estate**, after part of the estate has been administered or executed by someone else.

grant durante dementia Authority granted by a court to a person to administer the **estate** of a deceased person, when the **executor** named in the will is mentally unfit to do so.

grant durante minore aetate Authority granted by a court to a person to administer the **estate** of a deceased person, when the **executor** named in the will is still a minor and cannot perform the duties of an executor until reaching the **age of majority**.

grant of probate Certificate issued by the Probate Registry. It confirms that a particular person is to act as the **executor** of a **will** on the death of the **testator**. The effect of such a grant is that the assets and liabilities of the person who has died are vested in the executor as from the moment of death.

Gray's Inn One of the four **Inns of Court** in London.

Great Britain Islands comprising England, Scotland, and Wales. The name is often used incorrectly as a synonym for the United Kingdom, which includes Northern Ireland.

Great Seal Seal used to indicate the Sovereign's approval on important State documents such as **letters patent.**

green card Common name for the International Motor Insurance card. It is an **insurance** scheme that covers vehicles brought into this country and driven by visitors and vehicles registered in the United Kingdom and taken overseas.

green form Common name for the scheme introduced by the Legal Advice and Assistance Act 1974. Under the scheme any person with a disposable income which falls within certain financial limits may visit any solicitor in the scheme and receive free advice and assistance to specified value. The current value is £50 but this may be raised by the **Lord Chancellor** as necessary.

The work is pre-court work which includes drafting documents, writing letters and giving advice. Under the Legal Aid Act 1979 the scheme may be used to fund representation in court by duty solicitors.

The name comes from the green form on which the application is made. *See also* **legal aid.**

green paper Government publication containing policy proposals for discussion, particularly by Parliament.

grievous bodily harm (GBH) Severe bodily harm. There are two offences of GBH under the Offences Against the Person Act 1861.

First, wounding or inflicting GBH on any person with or without a weapon. Second, the more serious offence of wounding or inflicting GBH with the intent to do so or in order to resist arrest.

Causing death by an act which was intended to inflict grievous bodily harm is **murder**. *See also* **actual bodily harm**.

gross indecency Unlawful activity that involves contact with the genitalia, including masturbation and oral sex. It is a criminal offence for a man to commit an act of gross indecency with another man if the other is under 21, or to commit an act of gross indecency with another man other than in private, even if both partners are over 21 (Sexual Offences Act 1956 s.13).

It is also a criminal offence for a person of either sex to commit an act of gross indecency with or towards a child under 14 (Indecency with Children Act 1960).

guarantee Promise to answer for any **debt, default** or civil responsibility of another person. It is legally binding only if it is made in writing.

guarantee payment Payment which an employer is obliged to pay to an employee who has been laid off because of an occurrence such as fire, bad weather, recession etc. (Employment Protection (Consolidation) Act 1978 s.12). An employee cannot receive more than 20 days' guarantee pay in a year and only full-time staff with at least a month's service are eligible.

guarantor Person who promises to answer for another's **debt, default** or civil responsibility.

guardian Person who has the responsibility of protecting and managing the affairs of another person, such as a child who has not reached the **age of majority**, who does not have full capacity to do so. Normally parents have full responsibility for their children. However, if the parents are dead or unable to perform the role, a guardian may be appointed either by a **will**, a court or a **deed**, and the guardian has full parental rights.

guardian ad litem Person who brings proceedings, in a civil action, on behalf of another person who is unable to do so, such as a child.

guillotine Procedure in the **House of Commons** that limits the time for consideration of a bill, to ensure its enactment by a set date.

guilty Term with two applications.

First, the decision of a **jury** which has heard the **evidence** in a criminal **trial** and has decided that the **accused** has committed the alleged offence.

Second, the **plea** of an accused person who admits the alleged offence when asked to plead at the start of the trial.

H

Hague Conventions Series of international agreements, signed in 1907 by most of the major powers, which regulate the conduct of war, especially in relation to shipping.

halfway house Accommodation for those unable to live wholly independently in the community, including people who have been discharged from an institution but are not yet able to live without support.

hallmarking Process by which the quality of items made from gold, silver or platinum is tested by an assay office and signified by impressing a stamp on the metal. The stamp creates a mark on the metal called a hallmark. Hallmarking is regulated by the Hallmarking Act 1973.

handling stolen goods Offence committed by keeping, moving, selling or disposing of stolen goods (or arranging to do any of those things), knowing or believing them to be stolen (Theft Act 1968 s.22). It is also known as receiving stolen goods.

Hansard Official verbatim report of the proceedings of both Houses of Parliament and of standing committees. It is generally published on the day after the sitting reported.

harassment Causing irritation, distress or fear to another by persistent persuasion, threats or abuse or by physically interfering with that person or his property.

By the Public Order Act 1986 s.5 it is an offence to use threatening, abusive or insulting words or behaviour, to exhibit disorderly behaviour, or to display anything which is abusive or insulting and likely to cause harassment.

By the Protection from Eviction Act 1977 s.1 it is an offence to harass an occupier of rented premises for the purpose of making him or her leave those premises.

By the Administration of Justice Act 1970 s.4 it is an offence to harass a debtor or his family in order to force payment of the debt.

Sexual harassment is not a technical legal term, but persistent offensive comments or physical interference with an employee by an employer may be adjudged constructive **unfair dismissal**.

harbouring Giving shelter, money, food or other assistance to an escaped prisoner or a person seeking to avoid arrest. By the Criminal Law Act 1967 s.4 it is an offence to assist a person who has committed an **arrestable offence** to escape apprehension or conviction. *See also* **escape**.

hard labour Sentence of imprisonment "with hard labour". The punishment was abolished by the Criminal Justice Act 1948 and any reference to hard labour in a statute is now to be understood as a reference simply to imprisonment.

health and safety Duty of an employer to protect the health and safety of his employees in their workplace under the Health and Safety Act 1974. The Act contains detailed rules about guarding moving machinery, providing protective clothing, and other such matters.

The Act also created the Health and Safety Commission, which produces regulations and codes of practice to assist in the promotion and maintenance of health and safety.

hearing Trial of a case at which both sides present their case and the court reaches a decision.

hearing in camera Court proceeding to which the general public is denied access. **Juvenile courts** are held in camera because it is thought not to be in the interests of a child to be publicly known as a criminal. Other proceedings may be held in camera – for example, if they involve issues of national security or sensitive personal issues such as impotence.

hearsay evidence Statement by one person about what another person is reported to have said or written. Generally hearsay evidence is not admissable in legal proceedings. However there are many exceptions – for example, **confessions** to the police, business records, and statements made by people unavailable to the court.

heir Person who succeeds to a deceased person's property under the law of **succession**. An heir apparent is someone who would become the heir if a particular person died.

An heir presumptive is someone who would be the heir if a particular person died immediately, but whose claim might be displaced. A wife is the heir presumptive of her husband, but can be displaced by divorce.

heirloom Item of personal property, such as a valuable clock or piece of jewellery, which by the custom of a family passes to the heir along with the house and does not form part of the general estate which is used to pay off debts etc.

hereditament Land and buildings which pass, on the death of an intestate owner, to that person's **heir** under the law of **succession**. *See also* **intestacy**.

Her Majesty's Stationery Office (HMSO) Printers to the Government. In court, the contents of an Act of Parliament must be proved by reference to the copy of the Act as published by HMSO.

heterosexuality The condition of being sexually attracted to the opposite sex.

High Commissioner Senior diplomatic representative (equivalent to an ambassador) of one Commonwealth country to another.

High Court of Justice Court which tries and hears appeals in **civil** cases. It is organized in three divisions: the **Chancery Division**, the **Queen's Bench Division**, and the **Family Division**. The High Court primarily sits in the Royal Courts of Justice in London. However, High Court judges may travel on **circuit** and hear civil cases in the more important **Crown Court** centres.

high seas Area of sea, outside the **territorial waters** of all states, which is subject to the branch of **international law** known as the law of the sea.

highway Road along which members of the public have a legal right to travel. Local authorities are under a duty to maintain highways and may be liable for any injury resulting from the failure to do so. *See also* **obstruction of the highway**.

Highway Code Code of guidance in relation to driving on, or use of, public roads which the Minister for Transport is required to issue under the Road Traffic Act 1972. A breach of the code is not an offence, but it may be evidence of **negligence** or of **reckless driving** or **careless and inconsiderate driving**.

hijacking Offence, under the Hijacking Act 1971, of seizing control of an aircraft while in flight by threat or force.

hire-purchase agreement Contract by which one person hires goods to another, with a promise that if the other makes a certain number of periodic payments, the ownership of the goods will be transferred to him or her. Such agreements are regulated by the Consumer Credit Act 1974. *See also* **consumer credit**.

historic buildings Buildings designated as being of historical interest under the National Heritage Act 1983. They are subject to a number of controls relating to alterations, demolition and use. The controls are enforced by the Historic Buildings and Monuments Commission. Special grants may be available for preservation and upkeep.

holder in due course Person who takes possession of a cheque or **bill of exchange** which appears to be perfectly valid, having given something of value, such as goods or services, for it.

holding out Pretending to be in a particular position of authority or an **agent** of some other person when this is not in fact true. For instance, a person may hold himself to be a partner in a particular **firm** when this is not the case. The person who is holding out will be held to be personally liable to any third parties who suffer as a result of his actions.

holding over Name given to the act of a **tenant** in remaining on the land when the **lease** which entitles the tenant to possession of the land has expired. In doing so the tenant has become a trespasser unless the landlord consents, in which case a **tenancy at will** is created, save for certain statutory exceptions, such as the regulation of business tenancies in the Landlord and Tenant Act 1954.

Home Office Government department responsible in England and Wales for internal affairs, including the administration of justice, law enforcement, the criminal law and the treatment of offenders, matters of public order and safety, immigration and nationality, and community relations.

Home Secretary Senior minister at the **Home Office.**

homeless person Person who has no accommodation in England, Scotland or Wales. A person is considered to be homeless if the accommodation is insufficient for that person and his or her family unit.

The Housing (Homeless Persons) Act 1977 imposes a legal obligation on **local authorities** to rehouse people who are considered to have a priority need. This includes people with dependent children under 16, people with a vulnerable member of the family such as a disabled person, people with a pregnant member of the household or people who have become homeless because of an emergency such as a fire. The obligation to rehouse may be avoided if it can be shown that a person made him or herself intentionally homeless.

homicide Killing of one human being by another. Some types of homicide are not illegal — for instance, killing while fighting a war, accidental killings, execution of a convicted criminal by the State.

The law recognizes five types of unlawful homicide: **murder, manslaughter, infanticide,** causing death by **reckless driving** and assisting **suicide.**

homosexual conduct Sexual behaviour with a member of the same sex. Lesbianism is not a criminal offence, but certain types of homosexual conduct between men are illegal. *See also* **buggery; gross indecency.**

hospital order Order made by a **Magistrates' Court** or a **Crown Court** under mental health legislation, that a person convicted of a criminal offence be detained in a particular hospital and receive treatment for an indefinite period of time. Release is acquired by

133

application to a Mental Health Review Tribunal, which reviews the situation. In more serious cases, the Crown Court may also make a restriction order, thus giving the Secretary of State increased powers and responsibility in detaining a defendant.

hostile witness Witness who, called to court by one person to support that person's case, gives evidence contrary to the interests of that party. Generally, a party to proceedings cannot cross-examine his own witnesses, but this may be allowed of a hostile witness.

House of Commons Elected lower chamber of Parliament, with members representing every part of the United Kingdom. The Commons has a dominant role in legislation and in accountability of the Government. Almost all senior ministers are members of the Commons. The proceedings of the Commons are presided over by the **Speaker**.

House of Lords Upper chamber of Parliament, with members who are hereditary peers, life peers (including Lords of Appeal), archbishops and bishops. The House of Lords can only suggest amendments to, or delay, legislation proposed by the Commons. The **Lord Chancellor** presides over the Lords.

    The House of Lords is the final **Court of Appeal** for legal cases in Great Britain and Northern Ireland, except for criminal cases in Scotland. The Court of Appeal consists of the Lord Chancellor and the Lords of Appeal.

housing association Group of people that receives Government approval to construct new homes or convert old buildings into modern developments and receives grants from the Housing Corporation to cover the capital and building costs. The houses are then let at **fair rents**.

housing benefit Financial payment made to a person to assist or cover the cost of payment for living accommodation. The benefit is governed by the Social Security Act 1986 and claimants must show that their income does not exceed a specified amount.

human error Ascription of the cause of an accident, frequently used by inspectors and inquiries in relation to air and rail crashes and other disasters.

human rights Minimum rights which most countries agree should be guaranteed to every individual. Among the more important human rights are freedom of movement, freedom of association, freedom of religious belief and worship, freedom of expression, freedom from arrest without due cause and fair trial. In 1946 the United Nations General Assembly adopted a Universal Declaration of Human Rights, which influenced later international conventions such as the Covenant on Civil and Political Rights and the Covenant on Economic and Social Rights, both 1966. The great majority of European states, including the United Kingdom, are signatories to the European Convention on Human Rights.

hung jury Jury which is unable to reach a verdict. *See also* **jury**.

husband and wife Relationship created between a man and a woman who have gone through a legally recognized ceremony of marriage. At one time a married woman was considered to be legally incapable of forming **contracts** or of owning or dealing with any property without her husband's consent.

I

identification Process of establishing the identity of a person charged with an offence. At trial, evidence may be given that a witness to the offence subsequently identified the defendant as the offender.

The police operate three procedures to allow an opportunity for identification: (i) an identity parade, in which the accused stands in a row of persons of similar general description and the witness is asked to point out the offender; (ii) identification in a crowd (typically the accused travels down an escalator in a crowd and the witness is asked to pick him out); and (iii) confrontation, in which the accused and witness are brought face to face. The police must first try to arrange a parade. If that is impractical, they must offer identification in a crowd. They must make it clear to a suspect that, if he refuses both these procedures, he or she will be confronted.

illegal Unlawful, contrary to law.

illegitimacy Legal status of a person born while his natural parents were not married. An illegitimate person suffered a number of disadvantages, including not being an **heir** if his or her father died without making a will. Illegitimacy as a legal concept was abolished by the Family Law Reform Act 1987.

illicit Unlawful.

immemorial existence Existence beyond the living memory of the oldest inhabitants of an area, used as a test to determine whether a local **custom** is a source of law. Strictly, custom is law only if it has been observed uninterrupted since 1189. However, if a custom has existed as long as anyone can remember, the courts will presume that it has existed since 1189, unless the contrary is proved.

immigration Entering a country to live there. It is regulated by the Immigration Act 1971. A person may be refused entry at the point of arrival by an immigration officer employed by the Home Office. A person who is refused leave to enter may appeal to the Immigration Appeals Tribunal. *See also* **emigration**.

immorality Failure to conform to the moral standards of society. Immoral behaviour does not necessarily contravene the law. Immoral behaviour by a child may be a ground for a **juvenile court** order that the child be taken into the care of the local authority.

Courts will not enforce an immoral **contract**, such as one relating to **prostitution**.

immovable property Land, buildings, and **fixtures** attached to land.

immunity Freedom from responsibility or liability. The police may grant immunity from prosecution to a criminal in return for information. This procedure has been approved by the courts as a proper exercise of discretion in investigating and prosecuting offences. *See also* **diplomatic immunity**.

impeachment Term with two applications.

First, the procedure by which a person, having been charged by the House of Commons, may be tried for a crime before the House of Lords. It was last used in 1805 against Lord Melville.

Second, term used of a **lease** of land granted to a tenant "without impeachment for waste". It permits the tenant to cut down trees and plants and make normal use of other natural resources on the land.

impertinence Argument in the **pleadings** in a civil case that is not relevant to the question before the court. Impertinent pleadings may be struck out by the court. *See also* **striking out pleadings**.

implead To take proceedings against a person.

implication That which is inferred from the circumstances, but of which there is no direct evidence.

implied malice Acting with intention to cause **grievous bodily harm**, which is sufficient criminal intent for a **murder** charge if a person is killed as a result. *See also* **malice aforethought**.

implied term Term of a **contract**, stated neither orally nor in writing, but implied. For example, when goods are sold for a specified purpose, there is an implied term in the contract of sale of **fitness for purpose**. Or a term may be implied if it is thought that both parties to a contract would have agreed to the term if they had thought about the matter.

implied trust Any **trust** arising from the presumed, but unexpressed, intention of the parties. The category includes a **constructive trust** and a **resulting trust**.

import To carry goods from one country into another.

import duty Tax imposed under the Customs and Excise Management Act 1979 on goods which are **imported** into the United Kingdom. *See also* **Customs and Excise**.

importune To offer services to a person or to request something from them. Under the Sexual Offences Act 1956 s.32 it is an offence for a man to importune persistently for an immoral purpose in a public place. In this context the immoral purpose may be homosexual practices or **prostitution**, when the importuner is an agent for the prostitute. *See also* **soliciting**.

impossibility Circumstances in which a particular act cannot be performed or a particular consequence cannot be achieved.

In contract law, it is generally no defence to a claim for **breach of contract** that performance of the contract was impossible, unless the whole basis of the contract is destroyed, in which case the contract becomes void under the doctrine of **frustration**.

In **criminal law**, a person may be liable for **attempt** or **conspiracy** to commit a crime even though that crime is impossible. For instance, if a man imports a suitcase full of dried leaves, wrongly believing them to be a controlled drug, he may be liable for attempting to import a controlled drug, even though that offence was impossible.

impotence Inability of a man to have sexual intercourse. In family law impotence may be relevant in proving that a marriage has not been consummated.

impound To take goods belonging to another and keep them in a secure place under some authority of law. Thus, cattle which stray on to neighbouring land and cause damage may be impounded as security for payment of compensation for the damage. Cars parked illegally may be impounded by the police until a fee is paid. Drugs and obscene books may be impounded by officers of **Customs and Excise**, pending court proceedings for **forfeiture** and destruction.

impressment Historically, the arrest of a man for forcible service in the armed forces.

imprisonment Sentence of a court, following the **conviction** of a person for a criminal offence, that the convict should spend a certain time in prison. For offences created by Act of Parliament the maximum term of imprisonment is set by the Act. For **common law** offences the maximum is **life imprisonment**. *See also* **parole**.

imprisonment for debt Power of civil courts to commit to prison a debtor who had not paid a **debt** when it was due. By the Debtors Act 1869 this power was limited to a maximum period of six weeks and only for those debtors who had the means to pay, but refused to obey a court order to pay. The power of the **County Court** to imprison has since been further limited, by the Administration of Justice Act 1970, to debtors who fail to pay **maintenance** orders or public debts relating to rates and taxes.

improvement notice Term with two applications.

First, a notice issued by factory inspectors under the Health and Safety at Work Act 1974, that requires a factory owner to remedy an unsafe state of affairs. Failure to comply with the notice may lead to prosecution.

Second, a notice issued to a private landlord by a local authority, requiring him to improve the standard of basic amenities in a dwelling house. *See also* **health and safety**.

inalienable Incapable of being transferred from one person to another. Some forms of ownership of land, such as **entail**, are inalienable.

incest Sexual intercourse committed by a man with his daughter, granddaughter, sister, or mother, or by a woman over 16 with her father, grandfather, son, or brother. It is an offence under the Sexual Offences Act 1956 ss.10–11.

inchoate offence Offence which is committed even though a person fails to achieve his ultimate criminal objective. There are three inchoate offences, **attempt** to commit crime, **conspiracy** and **incitement**.

incident Related to or dependent upon something.

incitement Criminal offence committed by persuading others to commit crime. The offence of incitement is complete even if the persuasion is ineffective.

Formerly, there was a special offence under the Race Relations Act 1976 of incitement to racial hatred. This is now replaced, under the Public Order Act 1986 ss. 17–18, by the offence of using threatening or abusive words or written material which is likely to stir up racial hatred or is intended to do so.

incitement to disaffection Attempt to persuade a member of the armed forces to **mutiny**, to leave the forces or not to do his duty. It is an offence under the Incitement to Disaffection Act 1934.

income tax Tax on a person's income, levied under the Income and Corporation Taxes Act 1988. The tax is subject to personal allowances of income which is not taxed. The tax is levied at a rate of so many pence in the pound.

incorporation Process by which an organization has a legal personality conferred upon it. *See* **corporation.**

incriminate To give evidence which tends to prove that a particular person was responsible for a crime.

incumbent Person holding an office or position at a particular point in time, used particularly of offices in the Church. For instance, the vicar of a parish is the incumbent of the office of vicar.

indecency Action, speech or display that contravenes accepted standards of decency. It is an offence to commit **conspiracy** to outrage public decency. The offence may be committed, for instance, by selling indecent magazines in the street. Under the Indecent Displays (Control) Act it is an offence to display indecent matter in public, for instance in a shop window.

indecency with children Unlawful sexual activity with children. Under the Indecency with Children Act 1960 it is an offence to commit an act of **gross indecency** with a child under 14. Under the Protection of Children Act 1978 it is an offence to take an indecent photograph or film of a person under 16, or one who appears to be under 16, or to keep, distribute or show such a photograph or film.

indecent assault Physical interference, which is of a sexual nature or which contravenes normal standards of privacy, with a person without the consent of that person. Such behaviour in relation to children under the **age of consent** is an indecent assault even if the child actually consented; in law that consent is disregarded. Indecent assault is an offence under the Sexual Offences Act 1956 ss.14–15.

indecent exposure Exposure of part of the body which would normally be clothed in the interests of decency. Under the Vagrancy Act 1824 s.4 it is an offence for a man to expose his genitals, whether in public or private, with intent to insult a woman. Indecent exposure by either a man or a woman is an offence at **common law** and it may also be prohibited by local **bye-laws**.

indemnify To promise to compensate another person for any loss, damage or liability which the other might incur. For instance, a man who borrows a lawnmower might indemnify the owner of the mower for any damage caused to it while it is in his possession.

indenture Type of **deed** made between two or more parties which is in two or more parts depending upon the number of parties to it. Such a deed used to be made on a single sheet of paper and the individual parts were ripped from it to leave a jagged edge. It could later be proved who the parties were by matching the edges. This procedure is no longer used, but a deed in two parts is still frequently referred to as an indenture.

indictable offence Criminal offence which may be tried on **indictment** before a jury in the Crown Court. *See also* **offence triable either way**; **summary offence**.

indictment Formal document by which a Magistrates' Court charges a person with a criminal offence, which is the necessary initial stage before trial by **jury** in the Crown Court. The terms of the indictment are governed by the Indictments Act 1915 and the Indictments Rules 1971. It must state the defendant's name, the court which will try the case, the alleged offence and brief details of it such as date and place. *See also* **duplicity**.

industrial action Action taken by a group of employees in pursuit of a dispute over wages or conditions of work with their employer, in which the employees either **strike** or refuse to fulfil their contract of employment in some other way.

industrial injury Personal injury or disease that arises from the performance of a job. Persons suffering industrial injuries (or their relatives, if death occurs) may qualify for industrial injury benefits paid under the Social Security Acts. A worker may qualify for this benefit even if he had ignored safety procedures.

industrial tribunal Court with powers to hear and decide disputes between employee and employer that relate to **unfair dismissal**, **redundancy** and **sex discrimination**. Tribunals operate throughout the country and consist of a legally qualified chairperson and two others, who will frequently be drawn from the ranks of employers or trades unions. The losing side may appeal to the **employment appeals tribunal**.

inevitable accident *See* **accident**.

infanticide Criminal offence which is committed by a woman who kills her child or causes its death through neglect within 12 months of its birth and while the balance of her mind is affected through not having fully recovered from giving birth (Infanticide Act 1938). The woman will be punished as for **manslaughter**. If the woman is charged with murder, she may argue as a defence that the crime was infanticide.

inferior court Court whose decisions may be appealed to the High Court. The category includes **Magistrates' Courts** and **County Courts**. The powers of inferior courts are limited by statute.

information Document by which criminal proceedings in the Magistrates' Court are started. An information must be "laid" before the court will issue a **summons** or **warrant of arrest**. The information must state who is charged and give details of the alleged offence.

informer Person who gives information to the police that a certain person has committed a crime, but who does not give evidence in court. The courts normally refuse to require the police to identify their informer because of the public interest in encouraging a flow of information to the police.

infringement Breach of the law or violation of another's right. For instance, to publish a book without the author's consent would be an infringement of the author's **copyright**.

inheritance Process by which the property of a deceased person passes to that person's heirs, either under the terms of a **will** or, if dying intestate, under the law of succession.

The term inheritance may also describe the property which is inherited.

inheritance tax Tax on inherited property introduced by the Finance Act 1986 to replace capital transfer tax.

inhibition Entry in the land register by order of a court to prevent dealing with **registered land** until a particular time or event. For instance, an inhibition may prevent a piece of land from being sold while its ownership is being contested in court.

injunction Court order which restrains a named person from doing a particular thing. The High Court may issue an injunction to restrain an illegal act such as the erection of a building without **planning permission**, or to prevent a **tribunal** from deciding a case over which it has no **jurisdiction**.

County Courts have power under the Domestic Violence and Matrimonial Proceedings Act 1976 to issue an injunction which bars a man from his home, when he has been guilty of violence against his wife or female partner.

injurious falsehood Deliberate lie told with the intent to harm another person's trade or business interests. Injurious falsehood is a

tort and may be compensated by **damages**. For instance, it is an injurious falsehood for a food manufacturer to spread the lie that a competitor's product is infected with salmonella.

injury Term with two applications.
First, violation of a legal right.
Second, actual harm to a person or property.

Inner Temple One of the four **Inns of Court** in London.

innkeeper Person who holds himself out to the general public as providing accommodation for any passing traveller at a reasonable rate. This status was recognized at **common law** and is now regulated by the Innkeepers Act 1878. The innkeeper cannot refuse to accept a guest who is in a fit state if he has a room available. The innkeeper is not liable for a guest's personal property and may sell any property left at the inn after six weeks. Under the Hotel Proprietors Act 1956 hotels are subject to the same rules as inns.

innocent misrepresentation *See* **misrepresentation.**

Inns of Court Four independent professional associations of **barristers** – namely Lincoln's Inn, Inner Temple, Middle Temple and Gray's Inn. Every barrister must be a member of one of them. The governing body of each Inn consists of senior barristers called **Benchers**. The Inns are responsible for discipline among barristers and admission to the profession, although examinations are now set by the Council for Legal Education on behalf of the Inns. *See also* **Senate of the Inns of Court**.

innuendo Meaning of a statement which is not its natural meaning, but which may be implied by the hearer or reader who knows of other relevant facts. For instance, in one case a chocolate company used a picture of a well-known amateur sportsman in its advertising. This carried the innuendo that the sportsman had violated his amateur status and accepted a fee from the company.
    In proceedings for **defamation** the **plaintiff** may support his claim that a statement is defamatory, by arguing that it carries an innuendo.

inquest Proceeding presided over by a **coroner** (with or without a

jury of between seven and 11 jurors) to determine the cause of death of a person who has died in suspicious circumstances (Coroners Act 1988). Common inquest verdicts are **suicide**, death by **misadventure** and unlawful killing. An open verdict is recorded when the cause of a violent death cannot be precisely ascertained.

Formerly, in cases of unlawful killing the jury could name the person whom they believed to be responsible. This is no longer permitted as it might prejudice a later criminal trial.

inquiry Body of commissioners appointed by Parliament to investigate a matter of public concern such as a riot, rail crash or public corruption. The commissioners may exercise powers to summon witnesses and hear evidence on oath under the Tribunals and Inquiries Act 1971.

insanity Defence to a criminal charge, governed by the **M'Naghten Rules** laid down by a panel of judges in 1843. Under the rules a person is presumed sane until proved otherwise. A person is considered to have been insane at the time of an offence if he suffered a defect of reasoning caused by disease of the mind, so that either he did not know what he was doing or did not know that it was wrong.

If the defence of insanity is successful, the **jury** deliver a **verdict** of not guilty by reason of insanity. The defendant is not released, but is ordered to be detained in a secure hospital such as Broadmoor until the Home Secretary, on medical advice, decides to release him or her.

insider dealing Offence under the Company Securities (Insider Dealing) Act 1985, committed when somebody with access to confidential information relating to a company, by virtue of his or her position within the company or as adviser to the **company**, uses that information to profit by dealing in that company's **shares**.

insolvency Inability to pay debts as they fall due. Personal insolvency is called **bankruptcy**. Insolvency of a **company** is dealt with by **winding-up** the company. Both are regulated by the Insolvency Act 1986.

instalment One part of a debt that has been divided into a number of parts under an agreement that the debt may be paid off by payment in these parts at specified intervals. *See also* **hire-purchase agreement**.

instructions Term with two applications.

First, directions given by a client to his **solicitor** or **barrister** in relation to the conduct of a case in court.

Second, directions given by a solicitor to a barrister on behalf of the client. In this case the barrister refers to his instructing solicitor.

insurance Contract by which one party (the insurer or underwriter) agrees to compensate another party (the insured) in the event of certain losses specified in the contract. The sum which the insured must pay for this service is the **premium**, which is calculated by an **actuary**.

intellectual property Rights in relation to ideas, designs, musical compositions, artistic works and literature which are protected by law, primarily by the laws of **patent, copyright** and **trade marks**. In each case the law gives the author, composer, artist or designer the right to exploit the work commercially, and this creates a form of intangible property.

intention That which a person decides to bring about. Intention is relevant in a number of areas of the law.

A **contract** comes into existence only when the parties to an agreement have an intention to create legal relations.

A number of **torts**, such as **deceit, malicious prosecution** and **injurious falsehood**, require intention.

Many criminal offences are committed only if the defendant acted intentionally. In criminal law intention is proved, not only when a person desired a particular result, but also when he or she chose to cause that result, whether or not it was desired.

interest Payment made by a debtor to a creditor in **consideration** for being given credit. Interest is normally calculated as a percentage of the sum owed and is payable at periodic intervals. *See also* **consumer credit**.

interim order Provisional order of the court, which ceases to have effect when that court or a higher one has made a final decision in the case.

interim payment Sum which a court orders the losing party in civil proceedings to pay to the winning party on account of **damages**

before the court has calculated the final damages which should be paid.

interlocutory injunction In civil proceedings, an injunction which is issued by the court during the preliminary stages of the proceedings. It operates only until the court has finally determined the case. An interlocutory injunction is commonly issued to prevent one party from pre-empting the court's final decision. For instance, if one parent is seeking an injunction to prevent the other from taking their child abroad, the court may issue an interlocutory injunction to prevent the child from being removed before the case is decided.

interlocutory order During **interlocutory proceedings** an order made by the court in relation to the conduct of the case. Examples are orders for **discovery of documents, Anton Piller orders,** and **interlocutory injunctions**.

interlocutory proceedings In civil cases, any proceedings that take place between the issue of the **writ** or **summons** which starts the proceedings, and the actual hearing of the case. *See also* **interlocutory injunction; interlocutory order; pleadings**.

International Court of Justice Court set up by the United Nations in 1946 to hear disputes of **international law**. It consists of 15 judges and sits in The Hague. It may hear cases only if the states involved agree and it has no power to enforce its judgments.

international law Body of rules that relate to the relationships between states and are generally considered binding by them. Important areas of international law are the law of war, law of boundaries, law of the sea and law of space. The sources of international law are the custom of nations and international conventions. There is no international lawmaking body, but the United nations and other international organizations use political pressure to enforce international law and disputes may be referred to the **International Court of Justice**.

interpleader Process by which a person who holds property claimed by two parties may force the two parties to dispute the matter between themselves. In doing so the person incurs no personal expense. For instance, the process might be used by a bank which holds money in a joint account that the joint holders claim independently.

interpretation Process by which a legal document is understood. *See* **statutory interpretation**.

interrogatories Written questions, about relevant matters at issue, from one party in civil proceedings to the other. Permission of the court is required before interrogatories may be served.

intervener Person who voluntarily intervenes in court proceedings after receiving the permission of the court to do so – for example, to answer an accusation of adultery with a spouse who is being petitioned for **divorce**.

intestacy Dying without having made a will or having made a will that is invalid. Rules of intestacy, laid down in a number of Acts of Parliament, determine which relatives inherit the property of a person who dies intestate. Immediate family (spouse and children) inherit first, followed by more distant relatives such as nephews, nieces and cousins. If there are no relatives, the Crown inherits the property.

The court appoints an **administrator** to distribute the property to the **beneficiaries**.

intimidation Making threats or using violence in order to force a person to do or refrain from doing a certain act. It is an offence under the Conspiracy and Protection of Property Act 1875 s.7. It may also amount to the **tort** of inducing a **breach of contract**. There is a specific offence of procuring a woman to have sexual intercourse by intimidation (Sexual Offences Act 1956 s.2). It is **contempt of court** to intimidate a witness or juror. *See also* **blackmail**.

intoxication Being under the influence of drink or drugs. Certain specific offences relating to intoxication exist (*See* **drink and driving**; **drunk and disorderly**).

Intoxication may be a defence to certain criminal offences. It is an acceptable defence if the intoxication is involuntary (for instance, if a person were induced to drink alcohol without his or her knowledge or consent) or if the offence requires a specific **intention** and the offender was too drunk to form that intention.

invasion of privacy *See* **privacy**.

invoice Statement addressed to a customer by the supplier of goods or services in which the goods or services supplied and their price are described.

involuntary manslaughter Criminal offence of causing the death of another person as a result of gross negligence or recklessness or as a consequence of committing an unlawful and dangerous act. The offence is described as involuntary because the accused did not intend death. *See also* **manslaughter**.

irregularity Failure to follow the proper formalities in a legal proceeding.

irretrievable breakdown of marriage Circumstances in which the relationship of a married couple has completely broken down with no possibility of its being revived. It is the only ground for divorce under the Matrimonial Causes Act 1973. The marriage is considered to have broken down irretrievably if any one of five facts can be established: **adultery**, **unreasonable behaviour**, **desertion**, **separation** for two years with consent to divorce, separation for five years. *See also* **divorce**.

issue Term with three legal applications.
    First, the natural children of a person or couple.
    Second, a point in dispute which must be resolved.
    Third, all paper money in circulation.

J

jeopardy Condition of a person who is at risk of being convicted of a criminal offence. A person may not be put in double jeopardy – that is, a person who has been tried and acquitted of a criminal offence may not be charged again with the same offence. Nor may a person who has been convicted of a criminal offence be charged a second time for that offence.

jetsam Goods thrown from a ship into the sea which sink and remain submerged. *See also* **flotsam**.

joinder of causes of action Plaintiff's act of joining several different claims against one defendant together in one **action**. The court has the power to order separate **trials** if appropriate.

joinder of parties Joining together a number of people either as **plaintiffs** or **defendants** or both in any one **action**. For instance, joinder may be ordered when several people are injured in one incident due to the alleged negligent driving of one person.

joint and several obligation Relationship in which two or more people are liable for their obligations to third parties both individually and as a team. For instance, a **creditor** of a **partnership** which goes into liquidation may choose to sue any of the partners individually or all of them jointly, since the partners have joint and several obligation to third parties.

joint custody Mutual right, after a divorce or separation, of both parents to take the long-term decisions that affect a child. In such circumstances one of the parents will also be responsible for the day-to-day **care and control** of the child.

joint obligation Obligation entered into by two or more people together, so that in any legal proceeding the parties must **sue** or be sued together.

joint tenants Two or more people who own property jointly. The form of ownership may be a joint tenancy or tenancy in common.

Under a joint tenancy, there is a single interest in the property, which passes to the other joint owners on the death of one party. Eventually the last survivor becomes the sole owner of the property.

Under a tenancy in common, each person owns a share in the property and has individual ownership of that share. Each person may sell his or her share or give it away on death, thus creating a new tenant in the arrangement.

joint tortfeasors People who share responsibility for the damage caused by a **tortious** act. For example, an employer and employee are joint tortfeasors in an action by a **plaintiff** who has been injured because of the negligence of the employee while acting in the course of employment. In this instance both the employer and the employee are responsible for the injury caused. They have **joint and several obligation**.

jointure Estate held by **joint tenants**.

joyriding Riding in or driving a stolen vehicle without intending to deprive the owner of it permanently. Joyriding is the common name for the criminal offence of taking a conveyance without the owner's consent (Theft Act 1968 s.12). It is an offence to drive the vehicle or to ride in it as a passenger knowing that it is stolen.

The offence is tried in a **Magistrates' Court** and the endorsement of the offender's driving licence or **disqualification from driving** may be imposed if appropriate.

judge Person who adjudicates in disputes before a court and determines appropriate penalties. Judges are officers of the Crown, and the most senior judges of the House of Lords and **Court of Appeal** are appointed by the Queen after consultation with the Prime Minister and the **Lord Chancellor**. High Court judges, **circuit judges** and Recorders are appointed by the Lord Chancellor from senior barristers of many years experience.

Judge-Advocate General Adviser to the Secretary of State for Defence on matters of **military law**.

judge in chambers Term used to describe a judge when he or she is dealing with court business which does not have to be conducted in open court. *See* **chambers**.

judge-made law *See* **common law.**

Judges' Order Order made by a **judge in chambers**.

Judges' Rules Formerly, rules of practice developed by the **judiciary** which were intended to act as guidelines for the police when interrogating suspects. The rules specified when cautions should be given to the suspect and emphasized the importance of informing the suspect of his or her legal rights and the need to provide adequate refreshment and periods for rest.

Police questioning is now governed by **codes of practice** issued by the **Home Secretary** under the Police and Criminal Evidence Act 1984.

judgment Formal decision or sentence in a court of law. It may include the reasons for the decision.

judgment in default Judgment given to a **plaintiff** in circumstances in which the **defendant** has failed to take the necessary procedural steps to defend an action. The defendant may, for example, have failed to acknowledge the service of a **writ** within the allocated time.

judgment summons Summons issued against any person or persons who have been found liable by a court to pay a **debt** but have not paid it. The summons orders them to appear before a court to be questioned about their financial circumstances. *See also* **summons**.

Judicial Committee of the Privy Council Committee created by the Judicial Committee Act 1833 for the purposes of hearing appeals from courts in the Commonwealth countries, British colonies and dependent territories. Today it is less important as an appeal court, since most Commonwealth countries have abolished appeals to the Privy Council.

The court sits in London and at least three members of the Committee must hear the appeal. Most appeals are in civil cases. The Committee does not deliver a judgment but gives advice to the Sovereign, who in practice acts upon them by approving an appropriate **Order in Council**.

judicial immunity Freedom of judges from being sued for **damages** for judicial acts committed in good faith, even if done mistakenly, so that judges may perform their tasks without fear of repercussions.

It is, however, possible to **appeal** to a higher court if it is believed the judge made a mistake in the conduct of a trial.

judicial notice Knowledge which a judge is assumed to possess and which therefore does not have to be proved in a court case. Examples of matters of which judicial notice is taken are the legal process, the system of government or meanings and usages of the English language.

judicial precedent Previous decisions of a court, followed by judges. *See* **binding precedent.**

judicial review Process in which decisions of lower courts, **tribunals** and administrative bodies are reviewed by the High Court, which may provide a remedy if there has been a mistake of law or an error in procedure, such as a breach of **natural justice.** Remedies available in judicial review include *certiorari, mandamus,* **prohibition, injunction** and **declaration.**

judicial separation Alternative to divorce, by which the obligations of marriage, including the duty to live together, are terminated by court order. The marriage, however, still exists, so that neither party can remarry. The grounds for judicial separation are the same as for **divorce.**

judiciary All professional judges in a legal system.

jurat Notice attached to an **affidavit** which provides details of when, where and before whom the affidavit was sworn.

jurisdiction Scope of authority of a court or legal system.

The jurisdiction of a court is measured in terms of geographical area and the type of case with which it may deal. The jurisdiction of a legal system is normally co-extensive with a country's boundaries.

jurisprudence Legal science, which may be subdivided into legal philosophy, legal history, analytical jurisprudence and the sociology of law.

juristic person Synonym for **artificial person**.

juror Person who serves on a **jury**. Jurors are selected from the electoral register and must be aged between 18 and 65 and have lived in the United Kingdom, Channel Islands or Isle of Man for at least five years (Juries Act 1974). Certain people are unable to serve on a jury. *See also* **disqualification from jury**.

jury Group of people selected to listen to the **evidence** in a legal dispute and reach a verdict. The jury must decide upon the facts of the case, not the law, which is a matter for the judge.

Juries normally sit in the **Crown Court** to hear trials of defendants accused of serious criminal offences, but they may also sit in the **High Court** for certain civil cases such as **defamation** and **fraud**. Juries are also used to determine **cause of death** in a **coroner's** court.

In criminal cases, the verdict should be unanimous, although a majority verdict of no less than 10–2 is allowed if the jury has deliberated for at least two hours. If the jury is unable to reach a verdict, it is dismissed and a **retrial** may be ordered with a new jury. *See also* **challenge of jurors; disqualification from jury**.

jury bailiff Court officer whose duties are to keep the jury in isolation while considering its verdict, to protect the jury from interference and to carry communications between the jury and the judge.

justice Upholding rights, enforcing duties and punishing wrongful acts. To achieve justice is the ultimate aim of the law.

justice of the peace (JP) Member of the community who decides cases in the **Magistrates' Courts**. Also known as a magistrate, a JP is an unpaid, part-time judge who need have no legal qualifications.

Local advisory committees interview and recommend suitable candidates to the **Lord Chancellor**, who appoints JPs.

JPs are given some training in legal procedure and sentencing powers. During a case they are advised on the law by the **clerk to the justices**, but the clerk can have no say in the actual verdict. JPs usually sit as a **bench** of three to hear cases. *See also* **juvenile court; stipendiary magistrate**.

justifiable homicide Killing of one human being by another in circumstances in which the act is not unlawful – for instance, executing a convicted criminal with the authority of the State. Justifiable homicide also occurs when a person who is charged with **murder** proves that the killing was in **self-defence**. *See* **homicide**.

justification Plea of a **defendant** in a court case who admits that the allegations made by the **plaintiff** are true, but claims that what was done was legally justified. For example, in an action for **defamation**, the defendant may admit making the defamatory statement, but claim that it was substantially true and therefore justifiable.

Justification may also be claimed by a defendant in criminal law. For instance, a person accused of **assault** may admit the offence, but plead that it was done in **self-defence** and was therefore justified.

juvenile Children and young people under the age of 17.

juvenile court Court that deals with criminal offenders who are under the age of 17 at the time of the court appearance. The court is usually attached to a **Magistrates' Court** and the hearing, which is in private, is conducted by a **stipendiary magistrate** or by three **justices of the peace**, at least one of whom must be a woman and one a man.

If the juvenile is found guilty of the offence the magistrates will decide upon an appropriate sentence after consulting social reports on the child. Under the Criminal Justice Act 1988 the only custodial sentence that may be imposed on a juvenile by the juvenile court is a period of detention in a Young Offender Institution.

juvenile offender Person under the age of 17 who has committed a criminal offence. A juvenile offender is normally tried in a **juvenile court**, unless the crime is really serious (for example, **homicide**) or is a serious offence which was committed with adults who are also being tried. In such circumstances, the offender is tried in the **Crown Court**.

K

kangaroo court Unofficial court, the procedure of which does not comply with the rules of natural justice.

keeping a disorderly house Using premises as a **brothel**, a criminal offence under the **common law** and, since 1956, under the Sexual Offences Act ss.33−36. It is an offence to keep, manage or assist in the management of a brothel, or to allow premises to be used for such purposes. *See* **disorderly house.**

keeping the peace Being of good behaviour. A **magistrate** has the power to bind over any individual to keep the peace. *See also* **binding over**.

kidnapping Criminal offence under the **common law** of carrying away or hiding any person against his or her will by force or threats. The motive is usually to obtain payment of a ransom demand in return for the release of the victim. More recently, kidnapping has been used by political extremists against governments as a means of obtaining the release of political prisoners from detention. *See also* **abduction; false imprisonment**.

kleptomania Mental disorder which expresses itself in an individual as a compelling urge to steal. The property stolen is frequently of little value and the motive for the theft is not gain.

knock-for-knock agreement Agreement between motor insurance companies after a collision between vehicles, in which each company agrees to pay for the damage to its own client's vehicle.

know-how Knowledge and skills used by a person in doing his or her job. It includes industrial techniques used in the manufacturing and processing of materials. Know-how may be sold. If a skilled person sells know-how in the course of a business, the proceeds are treated as income for tax purposes (Income and Corporation Taxes Act 1988, ss.530−531).

knowingly Certain criminal offences are committed only if the act is done knowingly. For instance, the offence of living off the earnings of prostitution is committed only if the money is received knowingly. The man charged with the offence must know that the money was earnings from prostitution.

L

labelling Criminological theory that the criminal law operates to attach the status of criminal to individuals. It is argued that to label somebody a criminal may lead that person to look upon himself or herself as a criminal and, in consequence, to lead a life of crime. Those who favour caution rather than **prosecution** for young offenders argue that this avoids labelling.

laches Unreasonable delay or negligence in bringing a legal claim. Under the rules of **equity**, if there has been considerable delay, amounting to laches, the court will not allow the **plaintiff's** claim. In addition, under the Limitation Act 1980 there are time limits relating to specific types of civil action, after which a claim may not be brought. *See also* **limitation of actions**.

land The whole of the earth's surface except for the oceans and the seas. For legal purposes all land is owned by somebody, either an individual or a group of people, the State or the community.

Ownership of land in England and Wales is governed by the Law of Property Act 1925. Ownership includes the airspace above the land and the subsoil below, subject to the right of aircraft to pass through the airspace. The term land also includes all trees and crops in the soil and all permanent **fixtures** and buildings.

land certificate Certificate, provided by the Land Registry, that records details of **registered land** and is given to the owner of the land as a document of title. *See also* **land registration**.

land charges Rights and interests relating to land that must be registered with the Land Registry or, if relating to unregistered land, with the Land Charges Registry. Land charges include **restrictive covenants** and **easements**. The rules governing land charges are contained in the Land Charges Act 1972. If a charge that requires registration is not registered it will not affect any person who subsequently buys the land.

landlord and tenant Relationship that exists between the owner of land or buildings and a person who is permitted to occupy them by the owner. The relationship is created by **contract**. It is called a **lease** if it is for a long period of time and a **tenancy** if for a short period. The tenant is entitled to exclusive possession of the premises.

land registration System of registering ownership of land with the Land Registry. An entry in the Registry that relates to a particular piece of land takes the place of title deeds as proof of ownership. Registration simplifies the process of transferring property from one person to another. The register includes the name of the owner of the property, details of the type of ownership, a description of the property and any **land charges** over it. This system, introduced in 1925, is now regulated by the Land Registration Act 1966. *See also* **land certificate**.

lapse Term used to describe what happens when a gift of property in a will fails because the person who is bequeathed the property has died before the **testator**. Under the Wills Act 1837 ss.32−33 a gift to a child or other descendant of the testator does not lapse if that person has children that are alive at the time of the testator's death. The gift passes to these children.

larceny Former offence of **theft** under the Larceny Act 1916. The offence was either petty larceny if the theft was small, or grand larceny if the property stolen was more valuable. Theft is now governed by the Theft Act 1968.

law Body of rules that are accepted as obligatory by the community to which they apply and which carry sanctions if broken. In the United Kingdom, law is both written and unwritten and is derived from **Acts of Parliament, common law, custom** and **Community law**.

Law Commission Body set up in 1966 to produce a systematic programme of law reform. It has a full-time staff headed by five commissioners − two academics, two lawyers and a judge. Issues may be referred to it by the Government, but it can investigate any question that is in need of reform. After consulting interested parties, it produces reports, often with draft legislation for the Government to introduce into Parliament.

Law Latin Terminology borrowed from Latin, but understood by lawyers in a technical legal sense.

Law List Annual list of all barristers, solicitors and public legal officers.

Law Lords Judges who sit in the Appellate Committee of the House of Lords, which is the final **appeal** court in the country. The Law Lords include the **Lord Chancellor**, the **Lords of Appeal in Ordinary** and ex-Lord Chancellors.

law merchant Body of laws and customs that regulate commerce and trade. It was formerly administered in special courts, but it has now become part of the **common law**.

Law Officers Two Government officials, the **Attorney-General** and his assistant, the **Solicitor-General**, who are appointed by the Government in power to represent it in legal proceedings. The law officers may also be called upon by the Government for legal opinion.

Law of Property Acts Series of statutes passed between 1922 and 1925 by which the whole of the **common law** and the rules of **equity** relating to ownership of property were reformed and consolidated. The major Acts were the Law of Property Act 1925, the Settled Land Act 1925, the Trustee Act 1925, the Land Registration Act 1925, the Land Charges Act 1925, and the Administration of Estates Act 1925. These Acts still largely regulate the law of property.

law reform Alteration of the rules or system of law in order to improve it. The Government receives recommendations for law reform from three permanent advisory bodies: the **Law Reform Committee**, the Criminal Law Revision Committee, and the **Law Commission**. It also receives recommendations from *ad hoc* bodies established to consider particular areas of the law.

Law Reform Committee Committee, consisting of **judges, solicitors, barristers** and **academic lawyers,** that investigates problems in the **civil law** and recommends improvements. It is a part-time committee and can only investigate issues that are referred to it by the **Lord Chancellor**.

law reports Authorized reports of decisions made by the courts. Since 1865, reliable law reports have been produced by the Incorporated Council of Law Reporting, which publishes both the Law Reports and the **Weekly Law Reports**. Private law reports are also published, the best known being the **All England Law Reports**.

The law reports provide details of the facts of the case and the reasons on which the judge based the decision. They are frequently referred to during court cases by **barristers** in order to establish a particular rule of law. A reliable system of law reporting is essential if the system of **binding precedent** is to function properly.

Law Society Professional body that controls and regulates the solicitors' profession. It was created in 1831 and is responsible for enrolling solicitors, prescribing qualifications, setting examinations and preserving standards of behaviour. It also operates a compensation fund for people who have suffered at the hands of a corrupt solicitor.

lawful Something that is within the boundaries of the law, either authorized by it or not contrary to it.

lay assessor *See* **assessor.**

lay client Person who is represented by a barrister, described as a lay client in order to distinguish him or her from the solicitor who briefs the barrister, who is also the barrister's client.

Leader of the House Government minister responsible for organizing the timetable of business in the House of Commons in association with the chief **whips** of the Government and the Opposition. *See also* **Parliament**.

leading case Judgment in a case that represents the existing legal position on a particular point of law. It is not necessarily the most recent case, because other cases may have come afterwards which simply apply the rules established in the leading case. *See* **binding precedent.**

leading question Question, asked by a barrister in court of a witness, that suggests a particular reply. The barrister, in effect, is putting words into the witness's mouth. For instance,"would you agree that the man was looking aggressive?" is a leading question. Generally, such questions are not allowed except in **cross-examination**. The barrister should have asked, "how did the man look?".

leapfrog Procedure whereby an individual whose case was decided in the High Court can bypass the **Court of Appeal** and appeal directly to the Appellate Committee of the **House of Lords**, which is the highest appeal court.

This procedure was introduced by the Administration of Justice Act 1969. It is used only if the case is one of public importance and the issue in dispute is already subject to a **binding precedent** from the House of Lords.

lease Agreement by which the owner of land grants a right to possession of land to a person for a number of years in return for payment of rent. The tenant or lessee is said to own the **leasehold** of the property. *See also* **landlord and tenant**.

leasehold Right to possess land, arising under a **lease**.

leave Permission. A person who wishes to appeal against a decision of a court to either the **Court of Appeal** or the Appellate Committee of the **House of Lords** must first obtain permission or "leave" to do so. Leave to appeal to the Court of Appeal is granted by that court. Leave to appeal to the House of Lords, which may be granted either by the Court of Appeal or by the House of Lords itself, is granted only when the case involves a point of law of general public importance.

In civil proceedings there are a number of procedures that are available to the parties only with the leave of the court.

legacy Gift of goods or personal property under a **will**. A residual legacy is a gift of any goods which have not been disposed of under the will. *See also* **bequest**.

legacy duty Formerly, a tax paid by the **executor** of a will or the **administrator** of the estate of a person who died without making a will, to the State. The sum was calculated according to the value of the legacies bequeathed and the relationship of the persons receiving the gifts to the dead person. It was abolished by the Finance Act 1949 s.27. *See also* **estate duty**.

legal aid State-subsidized provision of legal assistance in the conduct of proceedings. It was introduced by the Legal Aid Act 1949, and is now governed by the Legal Aid Acts 1974, 1979, 1982, 1988.

In civil proceedings, legal aid is available to both the **plaintiff** and the **defendant**. To be eligible, the applicant must satisfy a "means test" based on disposable income and capital. The applicant's case must also have sufficient prospect of success to satisfy a "merits test". Applications are sent to the **Law Society**, which administers the system, assisted by the Department of Social Security, which determines the financial eligibility of the applicant. The merits of the case are considered by a Legal Aid Committee made up of **barristers** and **solicitors**.

In criminal proceedings, legal aid is available to a defendant, but not to a person who brings a **private prosecution**. The applicant must satisfy a means test and it must be in the interests of justice that legal aid should be granted. Legal aid in criminal proceedings is normally granted by the Magistrates' Court in which the defendant first appears.

Legal advice and assistance not related to court proceedings is available under the **green form** scheme.

legal charge Right relating to land or other property which is held by somebody other than the owner. For instance, a **mortgage** creates a legal charge on land in favour of the person who has lent money against the security of the land. *See also* **land charges**.

legal executive Person employed by a solicitor to assist in legal work. The Institute of Legal Executives is responsible for regulating the qualifications of legal executives.

legal personality Status of being subject to duties and obligations imposed by law and of having the capacity to sue or be sued in the courts. Every person has a legal personality unless he or she is a **minor** or is mentally defective. Legal proceedings may be undertaken on behalf of a minor or a mentally defective person by a responsible adult, who is described as the "next friend".

An organization or institution that has a legal personality is a **corporation**.

legal right Claim against others or the State which is enforceable by law.

legal tender Coins or banknotes in amounts which if offered as payment of a debt, the creditor is obliged by law to accept. Gold coins, bank notes and small quantities of silver and bronze coins are legal tender. The creditor is not obliged to give change, so that the exact debt should be tendered.

legal treatise Textbook of law. A term normally used of a book which has been accepted as an authoritative statement of the law for a long period.

legatee Person to whom a **legacy** is left.

legislation Law in written form, contained in an **Act of Parliament** or, in the case of **delegated legislation**, in some other form, such as a **statutory instrument** or **bye-law**, which gains its authority from an Act of Parliament.

legislature Body having ultimate power to create law by **legislation**. In the United Kingdom, the legislature consists of the Sovereign, the House of Lords and the House of Commons.

legitimacy Status of a child born of a couple who were lawfully married at the time of conception. A child is presumed to be legitimate if his or her parents were married at the time of the birth, even if they were not married at the time of conception. The child of a marriage which is **void** or **voidable** is also considered to be legitimate. *See also* **illegitimacy**.

legitimation Rule introduced by the Legitimacy Act 1926 which states that a child may be made legitimate by the subsequent marriage of the parents.

lesbian conduct Sexual activity between women. It is not illegal in the United Kingdom, although it may be evidence of **unreasonable behaviour** that has led to an **irretrievable breakdown of marriage** and therefore grounds for divorce.

lessor Person who grants a **lease** to another, who is called the lessee. *See also* **landlord and tenant**; **leasehold**.

letter before action Letter sent by a **plaintiff** or his solicitor to a **defendant**, before legal proceedings are commenced, in which the claim of the plaintiff is set out. A plaintiff who begins proceedings without first stating his claim by letter before action may have to pay any unnecessary legal expenses incurred.

letter of credit Letter addressed to a particular person, usually written by a banker or merchant, which asks the person to provide goods or credit to another named person. The writer of the letter acts as guarantor for payment of the bill.

letter of request Letter from a court in one country, addressed to the authorities of a second country, which requests the judicial department to obtain the evidence of a witness in that country for the purpose of legal proceedings in the first country.

letters patent Document by which the Sovereign may confer certain honours and privileges. For instance, a barrister is appointed **Queen's Counsel** by letters patent.

levy To raise money by means of taxation.

levy execution To take goods or money to satisfy a judgment or order of a court, as for instance when a **bailiff** seizes goods in order to satisfy a court order that a party to civil proceedings pay **damages**.

liability Legal obligation. A person who is found by a court to have broken a contract or committed a **tort** is said to be "liable" or responsible for the wrong.

libel Statement which amounts to **defamation**, published in a permanent form. The most common form of libel is an untrue statement about a person made in writing. A libel may also be committed in a radio or television broadcast, a painting or a tape recording.

A person who commits libel may be sued under the **tort** of defamation. In certain circumstances a person may be prosecuted for the offence of **criminal libel**. *See also* **absolute privilege**; **apology**; **innuendo**; **justification**; **qualified privilege**.

licence Term with three applications.

First, permission to do a particular act which would otherwise be a civil wrong. For instance, it would be a **trespass** for a person to move into a room in another person's house without a licence to do so. No formalities are required for this sort of licence.

Second, permission to do a particular act which would otherwise be unlawful. For instance, to drive a motor car or to sell intoxicating liquor is unlawful unless licensed by law. The grant of this type of licence normally involves a formal procedure.

Third, a document, such as a driving licence, that records that permission to perform a particular act has been granted.

licensing agreement Agreement by which the owner of a **copyright**, **trade mark** or **patent** permits another person to publish, manufacture or sell the thing or reproduction of the thing that is copyrighted or patented. For instance, beer brewed in the United Kingdom is frequently sold under the trademark of a foreign brewer, because the United Kingdom brewer has a licence to do so from the foreign brewer. Licensing agreements may be exclusive (in which case the licence-holder has a sole right to manufacture and sell a product in a particular region) or non-exclusive (in which case various persons have a right to manufacture and sell the product).

licensing justices Court, consisting of **magistrates**, that has the authority to grant, vary and renew **licences** to sell intoxicating liquors.

lie Of a legal action, to fall under a recognized category of legal claim. Thus, it might be said that, on particular facts, "an action would lie in contract", meaning that the appropriate claim would be under the law of contract.

lien Right of a person in possession of property that belongs to another to retain that property until the owner of it settles a debt. Thus, a car repairer has a right to keep the car until the customer pays for the repairs. The right is simply to keep the property, not to sell it. *See also* **general lien**.

life estate Right of ownership of land for the duration of a person's life.

life imprisonment Maximum penalty for certain criminal offences. Since the abolition of the **death penalty** in 1965 it is the only possible punishment for **murder**. Persons sentenced to life imprisonment may be released on licence by the Home Secretary following a recommendation of the **Parole Board**. The released person may be arrested and returned to prison at any time if he commits further offences or is considered a danger to the community. In very serious cases, a judge may add to a sentence of life imprisonment a recommendation that the convict should serve a minimum number of years.

life peer Member of the public granted the title of peer of the realm for the duration of his or her natural life, and whose descendants do not inherit the title. The title is granted by the Sovereign under the Life Peerages Act 1958. Life peers are entitled to sit in the **House of Lords.** Law Lords and bishops in the House of Lords are life peers. *See also* **Law Lords; peer**.

limitation of actions Rule of law that certain types of legal action will not be dealt with by the courts unless started within a specified period of time. Under the Limitation Act 1980, actions under the law of **contract** and in **tort** must be started within six years. Actions for the recovery of land must be started within 12 years. Actions for negligence that relate to personal injury must be started within three years, unless the court gives leave to start an action "out of time".

limited company Company where the shareholders' liability to creditors is limited to the amount of unpaid capital.

limited partner Person who becomes a partner in a **firm** by contributing money or property of a particular value to the firm and whose liability for the firm's debts is limited to the value of the money or property contributed. Every firm must have at least one partner with unlimited liability.

limited probate Grant of authority, for a limited period, to a person to administer the **estate** of a deceased person. For instance, if the person named as **executor** of a **will** is a **minor** or suffering from mental disorder, another person may be given limited **probate** to deal with the will until the named executor reaches the **age of majority** or regains mental capacity. *See also* **administration pendente lite**.

Lincoln's Inn One of the four **Inns of Court** in London.

liquidated damages Damages corresponding to a fixed, pre-estimated sum of money — for example the costs of repair to a car.

liquidation Process by which an insolvent company is wound-up. An official, the liquidator, is appointed by the court to conduct this process. If no official is appointed the **Official Receiver** will assume control of the liquidation.

listed buildings Buildings of architectural or historic interest, listed under a procedure in the Town and Country Planning Act 1971 and protected from development and demolition.

litigant in person Person conducting his or her own case in court without the assistance of a solicitor or **counsel**.

litigation Court process by which a legal dispute is decided. The parties involved are called the litigants.

Lloyd's List Record of events in shipping, including sailings, sinkings and casualties, published by Lloyds of London, an association of underwriters and insurance brokers mainly concerned with marine insurance.

loan Contract under which one person lends some property to another for a period of time. If the property lent is money then ownership in that property is transferred to the person who receives the loan. He or she may spend the money on condition that an equivalent sum (with or without interest) is returned on a specified date. With other types of property, ownership remains with the lender and the borrower must return the property in good condition when required to do so.

lobbying group Group with an interest in a particular cause whose function is to persuade Members of Parliament to introduce or propose **legislation** to promote that cause. Some lobbying groups, or lobbies, are professional bodies that lobby Parliament in relation to legislation that affects their profession. Others promote particular causes, such as abortion on demand.

local authority Government body created by Act of Parliament. The Local Government Act 1972 created three main types of local authority in England and Wales: county councils (the largest and most powerful), district councils and parish councils. A local authority has powers and obligations within its geographical area relating to matters such as education, housing, public health, recreation, roads, and general town and country planning.

lodger Tenant who occupies part of the house of a landlord in return for the payment of rent, but has no control over the premises. In legal terms, the lodger has a **licence** rather than a **lease**. The landlord usually lives in the house and retains responsibility for the upkeep of the premises.

loitering for purposes of prostitution Criminal offence under the Sexual Offences Act 1959 s.1(1). Prostitutes will be guilty of the offence if they are found either loitering or **soliciting** in a public place. Loitering is committed by lingering persistently in a particular locality. Soliciting involves communication and attempted persuasion. The offence must be committed in a public place such as a road, street or footpath, or from a window overlooking a public road. *See also* **prostitution**.

London Gazette Official publication of the Government which provides details of the acts of the Queen in her political capacity and gives information to the public. All bankruptcy orders and winding-up petitions must be advertised in the Gazette.

Lord Advocate Senior legal officer of the Crown in Scotland, responsible for representing the Government in legal proceedings against it and for conducting Crown prosecutions. The Lord Advocate also advises the Government on all matters that relate to Scottish law.

Lord Chamberlain Officer of the Queen's household, responsible for certain aspects of the running of the household. The functions include maintenance of furniture and pictures and responsibility for all employees who work within the house and its grounds. Before the Theatres Act 1968, the Lord Chamberlain had power to license stage plays and could refuse a licence on grounds of bad taste or immorality.

Lord Chancellor Officer, appointed by the Crown on the recommendation of the Prime Minister, who has judicial, executive and legislative functions to perform.

The Lord Chancellor is traditionally a member of the Cabinet. He or she is also *ex officio* **Speaker** of the House of Lords, participates in debates and reports the **royal assent** to Parliamentary **bills**. As a judge, he or she is the head of the **judiciary**. He or she sits in the House of Lords when it is sitting as a final **appeal** court and often delivers the judgment.

Lord Chief Justice of England Second most important member of the **judiciary** after the **Lord Chancellor**, appointed by the Crown on the recommendation of the Prime Minister. He or she may sit in the House of Lords when it is acting as a final **appeal** court, although in practice he usually presides over the criminal division of the **Court of Appeal**.

Lord Lieutenant Representative of the Sovereign in each of the counties of England and Wales. The chief duty of a Lord Lieutenant is to appoint **Justices of the Peace** for the **Lord Chancellor.**

Lord Mayor *See* **mayor.**

Lord President of the Council Head of the Privy Council office which arranges royal proclamations and **Orders in Council**, the grant or amendment of royal **charters**, and approval of **bye-laws** and statutes of chartered organizations.

Lord Privy Seal Official keeper of the **Privy Seal.** The title is usually attached to the Leader of the House of Commons, as supervisor of the government's legislative programme.

Lords Spiritual Church of England archbishops and bishops who sit in the **House of Lords.**

Lords Temporal Peers of the realm who sit in the **House of Lords**, other than the Lords **Spiritual**.

Lords Justices of Appeal Senior judges who sit in the **Court of Appeal**.

Lords of Appeal in Ordinary Senior judges who are made life peers in order to sit in the House of Lords when it is acting as a final **appeal** court. They are more commonly referred to as **Law Lords**.

loss Term with two applications.

First, adverse financial consequences caused by wrongful action, for which **damages** are payable.

Second, *see* **total loss**.

loss of amenity Loss of the pleasures and enjoyment of life as a result of an accident which has caused physical or mental injury. If the accident was caused by the **negligence** of another person, the victim is entitled to compensation under the **tort** of negligence for loss of amenity. This compensation is in addition to compensation for financial loss which the victim has suffered from medical expenses and time off work.

lost property Property of which the owner does not know the whereabouts, either because he or she has mislaid it or because it has been stolen. The owner continues to have the best claim to the property if it is found, but if the owner cannot be traced the finder has the next claim to the property.

lottery Game of chance in which participants purchase tickets and prizes are awarded by drawing lots. Lotteries are regulated by statute and must generally be held to raise money for charity or a particular group, not simply to make a profit.

lump sum Single sum of money paid instead of instalments. In **divorce** proceedings the court may order one spouse to pay a lump sum to the other instead of **maintenance**.

lunatic Formerly, person suffering mental illness or impairment so as to be unable to take responsibility for his or her own affairs. The modern equivalent is a person suffering **mental disorder** as defined by the Mental Health Act 1983.

M

magistrate *See* **Justice of the Peace.**

magistrate's clerk *See* **clerk to the justices.**

Magistrates' Court Lower court of law, staffed by Justices of the Peace or **stipendiary magistrates,** responsible for dealing with minor criminal offences called **summary offences.** The court has the power to impose a maximum sentence of six months imprisonment on convicted offenders.

The Magistrates' Court may also deal with **offences triable either way.** In addition, proceedings for all serious criminal offences called **indictable offences** start in the Magistrates' Court, which is responsible for determining whether there is sufficient evidence to commit the accused for trial in the **Crown Court.**

The Magistrates' Court also deals with some civil matters, such as licensing applications. *See also* **licensing justice.**

Magna Carta Great charter of liberties which received the royal assent of King John at Runnymede on 12 June 1215. The charter, which was drawn up by the barons of the realm who were dissatisfied with the rule of King John, was intended to protect citizens against abuse by the Crown. It declared a number of fundamental rights of the citizen and set out in writing the limitations of royal power.

maintenance Financial support provided by each spouse for the other and for their children. On marriage both partners accept a duty to maintain each other and if either partner fails to fulfil this duty, the other may apply to a court for a maintenance order. In practice, maintenance orders are usually requested on the **divorce** of the couple, although maintenance may also be requested within marriage when one spouse fails to provide adequate financial support for the other.

If maintenance is requested on divorce, the application will be made to the **County Court,** or the **High Court of Justice** if the divorce is being defended. A quicker and cheaper procedure is available in the **Magistrates' Court** for a spouse who requests maintenance, but does not want a divorce.

Courts follow certain guidelines when deciding on maintenance. The basic rule is that the court will look at the needs of the parties (spouse and children) in the light of the resources available. Under the Matrimonial Causes Act 1973 s.25, the court must consider the following when deciding upon maintenance and the division of the family assets: the house, capital earning capacity, responsibilities of each spouse, standard of living, age, how long the marriage has lasted and the contributions each spouse has made to the welfare of the family. The court will not generally take into account the conduct of each spouse. Adultery, for instance, will not usually affect entitlement to maintenance.

Maintenance which is granted for a child continues until the child reaches school-leaving age. If it considers it to be in the child's interest, the court may order payments to continue until the child is 18, even if the child has left school. The court may also order payments to continue beyond the child's 18th birthday if it continues to receive full-time education or training. Maintenance for a spouse terminates on remarriage.

maintenance pending suit Temporary award of **maintenance** granted to one spouse on the separation of a married couple. It lasts until divorce proceedings are heard and a final award is made.

majority verdict Decision of a jury in criminal proceedings. The court prefers the decision to be unanimous and will not accept a majority verdict unless the jury has considered the case for at least two hours. Under the Juries Act 1974 s.17 a majority verdict will be accepted after two hours' deliberation providing it is by no less than 10–2.

male issue Male descendants through the male line only. The son of a daughter is a male descendant; the son of a son is a male issue.

malfeasance Committing of an unlawful act.

malice aforethought Intention required for the crime of **murder**. A person has malice aforethought if he or she intended to cause either death or **grievous bodily harm** when doing the act that killed the victim. Prior planning is not required and it may be sufficient if the intention was formed on the spur of the moment.

malicious damage Formerly, criminal offence of causing damage to the property of another under the Malicious Damage Act 1861. It was replaced by the offence of **criminal damage** under the Criminal Damage Act 1971.

malicious prosecution Prosecution of a person for a criminal offence which is not founded on sufficient evidence and is motivated by ill will. The person who is wrongly prosecuted may **sue** the person who started the prosecution for **damages**.

mandate Order to do something, particularly a royal order. In politics, if a candidate or party is elected on the basis of certain proposed political reforms, the party or candidate is frequently said to have received a mandate from the electorate to carry out those reforms.

mandatory injunction Court order that requires a person to undertake some action to rectify a wrong. For example, an order that requires a landlord to allow a tenant who has been unlawfully evicted to return to his or her home. *See also* **injunction**.

man on the Clapham omnibus Phrase used by judges to refer to the ordinary, reasonable man. In the **tort** of **negligence** a person will be liable if it can be shown that he failed to foresee and avoid a risk of causing harm which the man on the Clapham omnibus would have foreseen and avoided.

manslaughter Criminal offence of causing the death of another person. All unlawful killings, apart from **murder, infanticide** and causing death by **reckless driving**, are manslaughter, although there are a number of different offences within this classification. *See also* **involuntary manslaughter**; **suicide**; **voluntary manslaughter**; **diminished responsibility**; **provocation**.

Mareva injunction Court order to freeze the assets of a person or company so that they cannot be taken out of the country or otherwise disposed of. It is granted in circumstances in which the court believes that a defendant may try to thwart a claim against him by moving assets abroad or hiding them, so as to avoid having the assets seized to pay **damages**.

marginal notes Explanatory notes written in the margin of an **Act of Parliament**. They do not form part of the Act, but may be referred to by judges when interpreting the provisions of the Act.

market Public place designated by law to accommodate buyers and sellers of goods at particular times. The right to hold a market may be granted by the Crown or acquired by evidence of a long-standing practice. Markets are regulated by various statutory provisions. Towns which are entitled to hold markets are called market towns.

market overt Open market. It is a rule of law that the purchaser of any goods in market overt in England obtains ownership of the goods, even if it later turns out that the seller did not have the right to sell the goods. Providing the purchaser acted honestly he or she will become the lawful owner of the goods, even if they were stolen goods. All **markets** recognized by law are market overt, as well as all shops in the City of London, when they are operating on weekdays.

markets and fairs Public places where permission has been granted to hold a gathering of people for a particular purpose, such as buying and selling specific goods and services. There is no legal distinction between markets and fairs, although in practice markets are usually held weekly and fairs once or twice a year.

marksman Person who is unable to write and so signifies his written authorization by means of a mark such as a cross. To avoid the possibility of fraud it is desirable that a witness signs to acknowledge that the mark belongs to a particular individual.

marriage Process whereby a man and a woman acquire the legal status of husband and wife. This may be a religious ceremony in a church or a civil ceremony in a registry office. The parties must be at least 16 years old and, if under 18, their parents must consent to the marriage. Both parties must be unmarried. The law prohibits marriage between close relatives. The marriage must also be entered into voluntarily. If any of these requirements is not satisfied, the marriage is **void**, even if the partners go through an apparently valid marriage ceremony. *See also* **consanguinity**.

marriage settlement Arrangement, made in anticipation of a marriage, in which the parties to the marriage or others (normally the parents) agree that certain property should be transferred to either the husband or wife.

marshal Personal assistant to a judge while on **circuit**.

martial law Term with two applications.

First, law applicable to foreign territories which are occupied by the armed forces. The law is administered through courts-martial.

Second, rule by the military in times of emergency when the ordinary civil authorities cease to function properly.

Master of the Crown Office Judicial officer of the **Supreme Court of Judicature** who has responsibility for listing **appeals** in criminal cases to the Court of Appeal and also appeals by way of **case stated** from **Magistrates' Courts** to the **Divisional Court** of the **Queen's Bench Division**.

Master of the Rolls Senior judge in the **Court of Appeal**. Originally the Master of the Rolls was responsible for keeping court records. Now, however, he plays an important part in developing the civil law through decisions in the Court of Appeal.

Master of the Supreme Court Officer who is authorized to deal with legal matters that arise after the commencement of a legal action, but before the actual hearing. These matters include the exchange of relevant documents between the parties to the hearing and the setting of a suitable place and time for the hearing.

In the **High Court of Justice** there are Queen's Bench and Chancery Masters, as well as Taxing Masters, who deal with the assessment of costs in court actions.

material fact Fact that is relevant to a particular issue. Thus, in relation to a legal dispute, material facts are those that might influence the outcome. In insurance law, material facts are those which are relevant to determine a particular risk. They must be disclosed by the person seeking insurance.

maternity rights Legal rights, relating to employment, of women who are pregnant or who have recently given birth. Under the Employment

Act 1980 a pregnant woman has the right to be paid for time off work for necessary medical care prior to the birth. Under the Employment Protection (Consolidation) Act 1978 a woman who has been employed for at least two years is entitled to six weeks maternity leave, paid at a rate of 90 per cent of her normal pay. A woman who wishes to take time off work following the birth has the right to have her job held open for 29 weeks after the birth, unless she works in a small firm with six employees or fewer. Some contracts of employment provide greater maternity rights than are provided by the general law.

matricide Killing of one's mother.

matrimonial causes Legal proceedings that relate to marriage, such as **divorce**, **judicial separation** and **nullity** of marriage. Most matrimonial causes are dealt with in the **Family Division** of the **High Court of Justice** or the **County Court**.

matrimonial home Premises shared by a married couple during marriage. If a couple with children obtain a divorce, the court may order that the party who receives custody and control of the children should also either become owner of the house or have the right to live in it until the children are grown up.

matrimonial offence Formerly, misconduct by a spouse which had to be proved in order to obtain a **divorce**. Matrimonial offences included adultery, desertion and cruelty. The Divorce Reform Act 1969 abolished the concept of the matrimonial offence.

matrimonial relief Remedy provided by the courts for the break-down of a marriage. *See also* **matrimonial causes**.

mayor Chief councillor of a local government district which is styled a **borough**. The main duties include chairing and maintaining order at council meetings and exercising a casting vote in the event of a tie. The mayor acts as the borough's chief representative at a variety of civic functions. *See also* **local authority.**

Mayor's and City of London Court London court, abolished by the Courts Act 1971. Under the Act the City of London became a **County Court** district, and the County Court for the City has since been known as the Mayor's and City of London Court.

medical appeal tribunal Panel, composed of a legally qualified chairman and two medical consultants, which hears final appeals against decisions by the Department of Social Security to refuse to pay benefits such as industrial illness benefit or the disability allowance.

medical inspection Examination by a doctor, on behalf of the Department of Social Security, to determine whether an applicant should receive a benefit that is dependent on proof of illness or disability.

medical negligence Failure by a doctor to provide the standard of care which might be expected of a reasonably competent doctor. If injury or loss is caused, the doctor may be sued for **damages** under the ordinary **tort** of **negligence**. If a doctor is employed by a local health authority, the authority may be sued for the doctor's negligence.

Member of Parliament Elected representative of one of the 650 Parliamentary constituencies, who form the House of Commons, and hereditary or **life peers**, who sit in the House of Lords. In strict constitutional theory, the Sovereign is also part of Parliament, but is never called a Member of Parliament. *See also* **Parliament.**

memorandum of association Document that sets out the objectives and powers of a company. By law it must be lodged with the Registrar of Companies when the company is formed. Under the Companies Act 1985 the memorandum must contain the name of the company, including the word "limited" if the liability of the members is limited, the intended place of the registered office, the objects of the company, the nominal capital, and the number and denominations of shares.

memorial Document that contains the relevant parts of a **deed** relating to land, prepared for the purposes of registration of the land.

menaces Threats of violence to a person or property or threats to expose some secret information about a person. A demand for money made with menaces amounts to the crime of **blackmail** under the Theft Act 1968 s.21.

178

mental disorder By the Mental Health Act 1983, "mental illness, arrested or incomplete development of mind, psychopathic disorder, and any other disorder or disability of mind". Special legal rules apply to persons who suffer from a mental disorder. For instance, such persons cannot generally enter into a binding **contract**. Such persons may plead the defence of **insanity** if charged with a criminal offence. *See also* **diminished responsibility; fitness to plead**.

mercantile law Law associated with business or commerce, such as insurance law, **sale of goods**, banking law, company law, cheques, **bills of exchange** and **debts**.

merchandise marks legislation Formerly, Acts of Parliament which prohibited the dishonest marking and sale of products with false trade marks. Such activities are now controlled by the Trade Descriptions Acts. *See also* **trade description**.

mercy killing Deliberate killing for the purpose of relieving physical or mental suffering. Such killings are technically **murder** and the motive of mercy does not provide any defence. However, it is accepted in law that drugs administered to relieve pain may also incidentally shorten a patient's life. Nor does the law require a doctor to take extreme measures to keep alive a severely handicapped new-born child with a very low expectation of quality of life. *See also* **euthanasia**.

merits Major issue in question in legal proceedings. A person is said to have a good defence to an action "on the merits" if the defence relates to the real issue in question, not to some technical point − for example, that the time allowed for bringing an action has expired.

mesne Intermediate. In feudal England, a landlord was described as a mesne landlord if he rented property from a superior landlord (such as the Crown) and then let it out to a tenant.

If a tenant remains on the premises of a landlord after the tenancy has terminated the landlord is entitled to sue for **damages**. The minimum sum of money which may be recovered is equivalent to the rent he would have received if the tenancy had continued, but it is called "mesne profit" rather than rent.

mesne profits *See* **mesne**.

messuage Dwelling-house and any land or buildings attached to it.

Middle Temple One of the four **Inns of Court** in London.

midwifery Art or practice of assisting in the delivery of babies. Midwives must receive a certificate to practise from the Central Midwives Board.

military law Rules to which persons in the armed forces are subject. They include conditions of service, discipline and punishment for specific military offences. The rules of military law operate in addition to the normal rules of law, not as a substitute for them.

Minister of State Deputy minister to a cabinet minister such as a Secretary of State.

minor Person under the age of 18. A minor reaches the **age of majority** at the first moment of the 18th anniversary of his or her birth.

minority group Group of individuals who, for example, belong to a particular race or speak a particular language or have particular religious beliefs or customs which are different from the majority of the population. It is a general legal principle that all persons should be treated equally whatever their race, religion or language. *See also* **race relations**; **racial discrimination**.

misadventure Accident which arises other than by criminal or negligent conduct. A **coroner** may record a verdict of death by misadventure in circumstances in which a person, while doing a lawful act, unintentionally kills another. Other accidental deaths may also be recorded as deaths by misadventure.

misbehaviour in public office Ancient crime in **common law**. In theory the charge might still be brought, but in practice it has been superseded by offences such as **bribery and corruption**.

miscarriage of justice Under the Criminal Appeal Act 1968, a reason for overturning a criminal conviction. For instance, it would be a miscarriage of justice if a person were convicted and it were later discovered that a prosecution witness had lied, or some new evidence were found that proved that the person convicted did not commit the crime. Under the Criminal Justice Act 1988, persons who are imprisoned but later released because there has been a miscarriage of justice are entitled to compensation.

mischief rule Rule used by the judges to assist them in interpreting the wording of a **statute**. When deciding a case, a judge may be required to interpret an **Act of Parliament**, and the judge will often look to see what mischief the Act was introduced to control in order to determine the meaning of particular parts of the Act.

misdemeanour Formerly, any offence which was not a **felony**. The classification of crime into felonies and misdemeanours was abolished by the Criminal Law Act 1967. *See also* **summary offence**; **indictable offence**.

misdescription Error in the description of property which is the subject of a contract of sale. If the misdescription is substantial the purchaser is entitled to be released from his obligations under the contract. Alternatively, monetary compensation is available.

misdirection False or misleading summary of the evidence and the law in a judge's direction to the jury in a criminal trial. If the defendant is subsequently convicted, he or she may apply to the **Court of Appeal** for the case to be reconsidered on the grounds that the judge misdirected the jury.

misfeasance Failure to perform a lawful act correctly. For instance, a company director who defrauds his company, or a trustee the beneficiary of a trust, is guilty of misfeasance.

misjoinder Wrongful joining together of two or more **plaintiffs** or two or more defendants in a single legal action. A mistake of this nature does not invalidate the whole action.

misnomer Wrong name for a person. A misnomer of a person in civil or criminal proceedings does not invalidate the case. The court has the power to substitute the correct name.

misprision Failure to inform the appropriate authorities that an offence has been committed. Formerly, misprision of **felony** was an offence, but this was abolished by the Criminal Law Act 1967. Misprision of **treason** remains an offence.

misrepresentation False statement of fact that induces a party to enter into a contract. If the statement is made dishonestly it is fraudulent misrepresentation; if it is made carelessly it is negligent misrepresentation; and if it is made innocently it is innocent misrepresentation.

The party which has been misled may choose whether to continue with the contract or abandon it and may also be entitled to monetary compensation under the Misrepresentation Act 1967.

missing person Person who is absent without reasonable explanation. Anyone who has been missing for seven years will be presumed dead for all legal purposes.

mistake Error. A mistake of the law is not acceptable as a **defence** to a criminal charge. Everyone is presumed to know the law and will be punished for breaking it, even if the offence is committed in the mistaken belief that it is not against the law.

In contract law a mistake will not normally be relevant.For example, a person who bids for property at an auction in the mistaken belief that it includes a field adjacent to the property will be bound by the contract if the bid is accepted. If, however, the mistake is so fundamental that in effect there is no real agreement between the parties, the court may declare the contract **void**. For instance, there will be no contract if an agreement is made to sell a bicycle which unknown to either party had been destroyed in a fire.

mistrial False trial or a trial in which there is a fundamental defect. For instance, a trial heard in a court which had no authority to hear the case would be a mistrial.

mitigation Statement, presented in a court, intended to minimize the penalty imposed or reduce the **damages** payable. In a **defamation** case, for example, the fact that the defendant has made a public apology may be pleaded as mitigation in an attempt to reduce the compensation which he or she must pay.

In **criminal law**, a plea in mitigation is made by the **defendant** after conviction, in which **counsel** for the defendant gives details of the defendant's circumstances in an attempt to reduce the sentence imposed.

In contract law, a person is meant to take reasonable steps to mitigate loss, and damages may be adjusted in the light of this expectation.

M'Naghten Rules Set of rules that are applied to determine whether a person committed an offence while insane. *See* **insanity.**

mode of address Manner in which a person is addressed.

moiety One of two equal parts.

molest To pester, annoy or trouble a person. A person who is molested by a former spouse, for example, by receiving persistent telephone calls may apply to the court for a non-molestation order to prevent such conduct.

monarchy Form of government in which power is vested in a single, usually hereditary, individual. The United Kingdom has a constitutional monarchy, in which Parliament vests power in the monarch. Almost all the monarch's powers are actually exercised by the Prime Minister and Cabinet.

money Medium of exchange and method of signifying value accepted by a community. It is generally accepted to mean all coins and bank notes of **legal tender**.

money-lender Person who is in the business of lending money. Money-lenders make their profit by charging interest on the loan. The business of money-lending is regulated by the Consumer Credit Act 1974, which lays down the terms and conditions which money-lenders may impose and which requires all such persons to be registered with the Director General of Fair Trading. *See also* **fair trading.**

monogamy State of being married to only one person at any one time. In the United Kingdom the only legally recognized form of marriage is monogamous. A person who goes through a ceremony of marriage while already being married to someone else commits the criminal offence of **bigamy**.

monopoly Exclusive control of the market supply of any product or service. Under the Fair Trading Act 1973 the Secretary of State for Trade and Industry has wide powers to prevent any company or group of companies from gaining control of more than 25 per cent of the supply of a product or service. The minister is advised on this matter by the Monopolies and Mergers Commission.

month At **common law** a lunar month, the period of twenty-eight days from the rising of one new moon to the rising of the next. In most commercial dealings and **statutes**, however, a month is considered to be a calendar month and may therefore be 28, 29, 30 or 31 days.

moot Mock trial that involves a point of law that arises from an agreed set of facts. Formerly, moots formed a compulsory part of legal training before barristers could appear in court. Today law students in universities, polytechnics and bar school practise moots as part of their training.

moral right Claim that most people would consider justified, but which is not necessarily supported in law.

morally wrong Description of an act which is disapproved of by the majority of a society. Most criminal acts are both legally and morally wrong. Murder, for example, is disapproved of by society and prohibited by the law. Some acts, however, are considered to be morally wrong and yet may not be illegal. At one time, for example, living together as man and wife without going through a ceremony of marriage was considered to be immoral, but was not prohibited by the law.

moratorium Postponement of an obligation, authorized by law. For instance, a **statute** may authorize the postponement of debt payments on the outbreak of war.

mortgage Legal arrangement by which the owner of land obtains a loan against the security of the **land**. The mortgage contract specifies the loan, the interest payable and the means of repayment. The owner of the land (the mortgagor) transfers to the lender of the money (the mortgagee) a legal right to take the land if the loan is not paid off, as required. When the loan is paid off the mortgage is said to be redeemed and the lender loses all rights to the property. *See also* **land charge**.

motion Term with two applications.

First, an application to a court for an order directing that some act favourable to the applicant should be carried out.

Second, a proposal made at a meeting for the participants to consider and vote on.

motor insurance Provision of financial protection against injuries and damage to property caused by driving a motor vehicle. The law requires all motorists to insure against the possibility of causing injury to other road-users in order that any person who suffers injury will receive adequate compensation.

In practice, most motorists obtain either third-party or fully comprehensive insurance. Third-party insurance covers any injuries to other road-users and damage to their property. Fully comprehensive insurance also protects the vehicle of the driver.

It is a criminal offence under the Road Traffic Acts to use a vehicle without insurance and there is no defence even if the motorist mistakenly believes that he or she is insured. There is a defence if the offender was driving a vehicle, owned by his employer, in the course of his or employment, with reasonable grounds for believing that the vehicle was properly insured. *See also* **knock-for-knock agreement**.

movable property Personal property, such as jewellery, clothes, automobiles or furniture, that is capable of being moved, as opposed to **real property**, such as land, which is fixed.

municipal corporation Formerly, local authority in a borough. Municipal corporations were replaced by district councils under the Local Government Act 1972.

municipal law Law of a particular state or country, as opposed to **international law**.

muniments Deeds and other documents that prove the ownership of a particular piece of land or property.

murder Most serious form of unlawful **homicide** committed when one person causes the death of another, and at the time intends to kill or cause **grievous bodily harm**. The death must occur within a year and a day of the act that caused it. A person convicted of murder receives a mandatory sentence of **life imprisonment**. *See also* **manslaughter**.

mute by the visitation of God Person who fails to respond to the question whether he or she pleads guilty or not guilty in court as a result of being deaf or dumb. Attempts are made to help the accused understand the charge and make a plea, but if these fail the court will assume that the plea is not guilty and will proceed with the trial.

mute of malice Person accused of crime who deliberately refuses to answer when asked in court whether he or she pleads guilty or not guilty to a criminal charge. The court will assume that the plea is not guilty and will proceed with the trial.

mutiny Crime whereby soldiers or sailors or other members of the armed forces disobey their orders and take command by force from their superior officers.

Mutiny Act Formerly, an annual **statute** which gave legal standing to the army for the following 12 months. Annual orders are now made under the Armed Forces Act 1971. Such an arrangement is necessary because it is illegal to keep an armed force in peace time without the consent of Parliament.

mutual will Will, made by agreement, in which two people leave all or most of their property to each other. Such a will cannot be changed without the consent of both parties.

N

name and arms clause Clause in a **will** or **settlement** of property which specifies that the person receiving the benefit must assume the surname and arms of the person making the gift. The clause contains a provision that the gift will pass to another beneficiary if this condition is not fulfilled.

name, change of *See* **change of name.**

naming a member Procedure in the **House of Commons** whereby the **Speaker** may call on any member of the House to leave the chamber for the rest of the day's session if he or she has offended against the rules of the House − for example, by refusing to withdraw an offensive remark. If the member refuses to obey the order, the House will vote on a motion that the member be suspended from the House.

national insurance Compulsory system run by the State, in which individuals and employers pay a proportion of their income into a fund. In return they receive a pension on retirement and benefits in the event of sickness or disability.

nationality Legal relationship between a person and a state, by which the individual owes allegiance to the state and has a right of abode in it. Under the British Nationality Act 1981 there are various categories of nationality, such as British citizenship, British Dependent Territories citizenship, British Overseas citizenship. Since every state has different rules about nationality, it is possible to have dual nationality. Primarily, British nationality is acquired by being born to a parent who is a British national. Nationality may also be acquired by **naturalization.**

nationalization To bring under national management. It is the government transfer of control or rights of ownership from a private company to the State. *See also* **privatization.**

natural justice Principle embodied in all dispute-resolving mechanisms in order to ensure fairness. The rules of natural justice specify that all persons should be given a fair hearing with the opportunity to present their side of the story. The person who adjudicates over the dispute must have no interest in the outcome, since justice must not only be done, but be seen to be done.

natural law Fundamental, universal laws or truths beyond human creation. These truths are considered to be either God-given or inherent in the nature of mankind.

naturalization Procedure whereby a person from another country becomes a citizen of the country he or she has chosen to live in. Under the British Nationality Act 1981, an applicant for naturalization must have been resident in the United Kingdom for at least five years. Details of all persons who are naturalized are published in the **London Gazette**.

natural person Human being, as opposed to a body such as a **corporation**, with an artificial personality. *See also* **artificial person; legal personality.**

natural rights Fundamental rights which are considered to be inherent in any civilized society, such as the inalienable rights, proclaimed in the American Declaration of Independence, of "life, liberty and the pursuit of happiness".

necessaries Those things which are necessary for the maintenance of life, such as food, drink, clothing and shelter. In contract law, a **minor** is generally incapable of making a binding contract, but if the contract is for the purchase of necessaries then the minor is obliged to pay a reasonable sum for them. Necessaries for this purpose are described as "goods suitable for the condition in life of the minor, and to his actual requirements at the time of the sale and delivery" (Sale of Goods Act 1979 s.3).

necessity Situation in which it is necessary to do an act which causes harm because it is the only means of avoiding a greater harm. It may be a **defence** to a claim in proceedings in **tort** that the act complained of was committed out of necessity. For example, it is well established

that it is not wrongful to throw cargo overboard in order to save a
ship from sinking.

In **criminal law**, necessity is a defence in limited circumstances
only. For instance, it may be a defence to a charge of **criminal
damage** that some property was damaged to avoid damage to other
more valuable property. It is clear, however, that necessity is never
available as a defence to a serious crime such as murder. This was
decided in the case of *R. v. Dudley and Stephens* (1884), in which the
two defendants killed and ate a cabin boy when a shipwreck left them
floating in a lifeboat for several days without food.

negligence Action in the law of **tort**. It arises when a party who owes
a **duty of care** to another breaks that duty by failing to act reasonably
and as a result causes damage to the other person. A motorist, for
example, owes a duty of care to all other road-users and if the motorist
breaks the duty of care by driving too fast and as a result injures
another road-user, the victim may sue for **damages** in the tort of
negligence.

Neighbourhood Watch Crime prevention scheme whereby neighbours
in an area agree to watch one another's houses and property to
discourage burglary and other offences.

nervous shock Illness brought about by shock, including change of
personality, psychiatric disorders and insomnia. A person who suffers
nervous shock due to the **negligence** of another, perhaps by seeing an
accident involving a close relative, is entitled to claim compensation in
the courts. The claimant must suffer the nervous shock either from
seeing the actual accident or seeing the victims soon afterwards. Claims
are not allowed for sorrow or distress and medical evidence is required
in court to prove that the victim is suffering from nervous shock.

new trial Second **trial** of a criminal charge. It may be ordered when
the first trial either suffered a fundamental defect (such as jurors
accepting bribes) or did not reach a proper conclusion (such as the
jury not being able to reach a **verdict**). It is also ordered if the judge
dies before the end of the case.

next friend Person who brings a court action on behalf of a **minor** or
of a person suffering from a **mental disorder**. The friend, who

should be a close relative, is responsible for paying any court costs.

next-of-kin Nearest blood relative. Although in practice many people refer to a spouse as the next-of-kin, strictly speaking this is inaccurate, since a spouse is not a blood relative. Under the rules of **intestacy**, however, a spouse will benefit before all blood relatives except children.

noise Loud and disturbing sound. A person who is persistently bothered by excessive noise from a neighbour may be able to bring a court action in the **tort** of **nuisance**. The court may impose an **injunction** on the neighbour to stop making noise.

Noise may also be controlled by a **local authority** which may take legal action against any person or company that creates noise above the acceptable levels as registered in the noise level register (Control of Pollution Act 1974).

nominal damages Compensation awarded to a **plaintiff** who has successfully proved his or her case, but who has not suffered any particular financial loss as a result of the act complained of. A small figure, such as £5, is awarded in recognition of the fact that the case has been won.

nondisclosure Failure to perform an obligation to disclose important information.

non-feasance Not doing something. Non-feasance does not generally make a person liable for either a **crime** or a **tort**, unless the individual is under a legal obligation to do that which he does not in fact do.

non-joinder Failure of a **plaintiff** to include a person who ought to be included in a civil claim. Such a mistake will not of itself cause the whole action to fail.

non-molestation order Court order, directed at one spouse (or cohabitant) at the request of the other, to restrain the other from molesting the applicant or any child of the family. *See also* **molest**.

non-suit Formerly, a decision of the judge during a trial that the **plaintiff** had failed to establish a case against the **defendant** and that the trial should therefore be abandoned. The phrase is now used when a judge decides that the case against a defendant has not been established and that the issue should therefore not be put to the jury. A verdict in favour of the defendant is granted.

notary/notary public Officer, normally a solicitor, who is required to witness the signing of certain deeds and legal documents to prove that they are authentic.

notation Addition to a formal legal document which indicates the circumstances in which it was made.

not guilty Term with two applications.

First, a **plea** made in a criminal trial by a **defendant** who denies the accusation and who in effect is challenging the **prosecution** to prove the case.

Second, a **verdict** returned by a **jury** which has decided that the prosecution has not proved the case and that the defendant should be acquitted.

not guilty by reason of insanity Special **verdict** returned by a **jury** which has decided that the accused is insane and therefore cannot be held criminally responsible for the offence that he or she has committed. Although this amounts to an acquittal, the court has the power to detain the accused in a special secure hospital for an indefinite period, until the Home Secretary decides that the individual may be safely released. *See also* **insanity**.

notice Knowledge of a particular matter. Many types of contract are brought to an end by one party giving notice to the other of a wish to withdraw. In some legal contexts a person is **deemed** to have notice of something if reasonable steps were taken − for instance, delivering a letter to the person's last known address − to bring that thing to his or her attention.

notice of abandonment Communication by the owner of something to his insurers that, following some accident, the thing is so badly damaged that he wishes to receive compensation for the full value and does not wish to salvage or repair it. In this case the insurer becomes the owner of the damaged thing.

notice of additional evidence Communication by the **prosecution** to a person who is accused of a crime and who has been committed for trial at the **Crown Court**. It states that the prosecution intend to call some **evidence** against the accused at the trial which was not introduced in the earlier **committal** proceedings.

notice of motion Formal notification which must be given to any person who may be affected before an individual can apply to court for a **motion**.

notice to admit Request by one party in civil proceedings to the other party that a particular item of evidence or document be accepted by both sides without having to be proved.

notice to proceed Notification by one party in civil proceedings to the other party, required by law when the first party wishes to take a further step in the proceedings after no action had been taken in them for a period of at least 12 months or more.

notice to produce Request by one party in civil proceedings to the other party that the other party produce before the court a particular document in his or her possession.

notice to quit Notification given by a landlord to a tenant that the tenancy is brought to an end on a particular date and the tenant should leave the premises on that date. The minimum term of notice is four weeks.

notice to treat Notification which must be given to the owner of land when a body such as the Ministry of Transport wishes to exercise powers of **compulsory purchase** and negotiate a price for the land.

notifiable disease One of a number of serious infectious diseases which, if diagnosed in a patient by a doctor, must be reported by the doctor to the local Medical Officer of Health. The purpose of this requirement is to help monitor and prevent the spread of infectious diseases.

noting Process by which a notary attaches a note to a **bill of exchange** to indicate in what way the bill has been dishonoured and is therefore valueless.

novation Binding agreement by which an existing contract is abandoned and a new contract on the same terms is entered into.

novelty Originality, required to be present in an invention, before the inventor will be granted a **patent**.

nuclear family Social unit consisting of a man, a woman and their offspring as contrasted to the extended family of grandparents, cousins, etc.

nuisance Cause of action in the law of **tort**, either a public or a private nuisance.

An action in private nuisance may be brought when a person's use or enjoyment of his or her property is interfered with. For example, neighbours may play loud music regularly throughout the night and interrupt sleep or they may store foul-smelling manure close to the dividing boundary so that their neighbour cannot enjoy sitting in the garden. The courts may award monetary compensation to the **plaintiff** and may impose an **injunction** on the neighbour to stop the activity complained of.

Public nuisance arises when a person commits an act which interferes with the public generally. Such acts include obstructing the road, causing an explosion and throwing fireworks in the street. Public nuisance is a crime as well as a tort, so that the offender may be prosecuted. To sue in tort the **plaintiff** must show that he or she suffered some damage which was greater than that suffered by the general public.

nullity Legal invalidity. If a couple has entered into a **void** or **voidable** marriage, either spouse may apply to a court for a decree of nullity, which will declare that the marriage is null and void.

nuncupative will Will made orally in front of witnesses. Such a **will** is valid only if it is made by a soldier, sailor or airman on actual military service. The witnesses will be required to provide evidence of the provisions in the will; and that they are not entitled to inherit anything themselves.

O

oath Promise before God to make true statements or to perform a particular task. In theory, a statement or promise made under oath is more credible because the maker will fear divine retribution if it is untrue. Oaths are required in many circumstances. A **witness** must take an oath before giving evidence in court and jurors take an oath to decide the case according to the evidence. There is no set form of oath. Christians usually swear by Almighty God while holding a Bible. Others take whatever form of oath is appropriate to their religion. Under the Oaths Act 1961 any person who has no religious conviction may make an **affirmation** instead.

objection in point of law Argument in the course of legal proceedings that even if the facts alleged by the other party are true, the claims made by that other party cannot be supported in law.

obligation Legal duty to perform some task. It may be imposed on individuals or undertaken voluntarily.

obscenity Material which has a tendency to deprave or corrupt the reader, viewer or hearer. This may include pornography or material which involves violence, drug abuse or alcoholism. Under the Obscene Publications Acts 1959 and 1964 it is an offence to sell, display or distribute obscene material. It is a defence to show that the publication was justified in the interests of science, literature, art or learning. Material may be seized under **warrant** and, if found to be obscene by a **Magistrates' Court**, destroyed.

obstruction Act or obstacle that impedes or hinders progress. *See also* **obstruction of the highway**; **obstruction of the police**.

obstruction of the highway Criminal offence of blocking a road or pavement so that it cannot be used for the normal purpose of travelling from one place to another. Whether a blockage amounts to an obstruction depends upon the purpose of the blockage, its extent and duration. Thus, stopping to chat to a friend would not normally be an obstruction, but a mass **picket** or demonstration which completely blocked the road would be.

obstruction of the police Criminal offence committed when a person hinders a police officer who is acting in the course of his or her duty. The offence is found in the Police Act 1964 s.51 and includes any act which makes it more difficult for the police to carry out their duties, such as providing a police officer with a false name and address, as well as physical obstruction.

obtaining goods or services by deception Criminal offences of dishonestly deceiving a person into handing over goods or providing a service. For instance, an art dealer obtains goods by deception if he pretends that a reproduction painting is a genuine Constable in order to extract payment from a customer (Theft Act 1968 s.15). Similarly, a woman who enters a hairdressing salon without any money, pretending that she intends to pay, and allows her hair to be cut, obtains a service by deception (Theft Act 1978 s.1).

occupation Term with three applications.
First, a person's trade or profession.
Second, acquisition of territory by the armed forces of a foreign power.
Third, possession and use of land or buildings.

occupier's liability Obligation on the owners and occupiers of premises to ensure that the premises are reasonably safe for any visitors permitted to be on them. *See also* **common duty of care**; **dangerous premises**.

offence triable either way Criminal offence that may be tried either on **indictment** in the Crown Court or as a **summary offence** in the Magistrates' Court under the Criminal Law Act 1977.

offensive weapon Article made or adapted or intended to be used for the purpose of causing injury to a person. It is a criminal offence to possess such an article in a public place. A flick knife is an obvious example of an offensive weapon. The offence may also be committed by carrying an apparently innocent article, such as a screwdriver, if it can be shown that the carrier intended to use it to cause injury to another (Prevention of Crime Act 1953). Under the Criminal Law Act 1988 it is an offence to carry any instrument with a point, or with a blade more than three inches long, without a reasonable explanation.

offer of amends Public apology and a statement of the true facts made by a person who innocently published a defamatory statement about another, in the belief that the statement was true. An offer of amends must be supported by an **affidavit** that sets out the facts that had been relied on for the original statement in order to show that the publication was innocent. If proceedings in **defamation** are still taken against the maker of the statement, he or she may raise the offer of amends as a **defence**.

office Post carrying rights and responsibilities. It may be a post in employment, such as the office of a judge, or it may be a voluntary, unpaid position of responsibility, such as the office of **trustee**.

Official Petitioner Person whose duty it is to seek a **criminal bankruptcy order** in appropriate cases. This office is held by the **Director of Public Prosecutions.**

Official Receiver Officer of the court who is appointed by the Secretary of State for Trade to manage the affairs of any person who has been declared **bankrupt** or any company that has gone into **liquidation** until a **trustee in bankruptcy** or liquidator is appointed.

Official Referee High Court judge to whom the court refers questions concerning detailed examination of technical matters (such as building disputes) for trial.

official solicitor Officer of the **Supreme Court of Judicature** who can be called upon by the court to act in his capacity as a **solicitor** in a variety of circumstances. In particular, he or she represents any person involved in High Court proceedings who is under some disability. The official solicitor will appear as **next friend**, for example, for a mentally disabled person.

off-licence Permission granted by **licensing justices** to a named person to sell alcoholic drinks from particular premises for consumption off the premises. *See also* **on-licence**.

Old Bailey *See* **Central Criminal Court.**

ombudsman Official appointed by the **Crown** to investigate complaints made by members of the public against administrative procedures in government departments. The official title is the Parliamentary Commissioner for Administration.

onerous Laborious or burdensome. A **lease** or other **contract** is described as onerous if it involves burdens or obligations that outweigh the advantages.

on-licence Permission granted by **licensing justices** to a named person to sell alcoholic drinks for consumption in particular premises, such as an hotel, a club or a public house. *See also* **off-licence**.

onus of proof Obligation to prove an accusation in legal proceedings. *See also* **burden of proof**.

open contract Contract in which not all the terms are fully stated, but in which certain terms are implied by law. For instance, in a contract for the sale of land the law implies that the seller has the legal right to sell, even if this is not expressly stated in the contract.

operative mistake Mistake which has some legal effect, such as a **mistake** which is shared by both parties to a **contract** and which causes the contract to have no effect.

operative part That part of a **deed** of **conveyance** that has the effect of transferring the property in law. Other subsidiary sections, called the **recitals**, describe the purpose of the deed and any history of the property being conveyed.

opinion Written advice given, usually by a barrister, on the law in relation to case.

oppression Conduct by a person in authority calculated to harass, intimidate, demoralize or sap the will of another person. Confessions to criminal offences obtained by the police as a result of the oppression of the suspect are inadmissible as evidence in court against that suspect.

option Formal opportunity to do something within a particular period. For instance, under contract law, if one party makes an offer to another party and agrees to hold it open for a stated time, the other party has an option to accept the offer within that period. Generally, an option may be withdrawn within the stated period, but not if the other party has given something, often money, in return for the option.

oral agreement Agreement made by word of mouth. In most cases, so long as all other requirements of a **contract** are satisfied, an oral agreement is legally binding. The difficulty arises in proving what was agreed in a court since it is often one person's word against another.

Some types of contract, especially a contract for the sale of land or buildings, must be made in writing to be legally binding.

oral evidence Evidence given by witnesses in a court of law by word of mouth.

ordeal Ancient method of trial in which the accused underwent an ordeal, such as walking on hot coals. If unhurt, he was considered to be innocent.

order Authoritative direction given by a court, such as an order for **damages**, an **injunction**, or a **sentence**.

Order Paper List showing the order of that day's Parliamentary business.

Order in Council Form of **delegated legislation**, in which the Government introduces law without the need to undertake the formal procedures involved when creating **Acts of Parliament**. Orders in Council are used to bring Acts of Parliament into operation and for other purposes authorized by Parliament.

ordinance Declaration of the **Crown** made without the authority of Parliament.

originating application Method of commencing legal proceedings in the **High Court of Justice**. It is generally used when a person wishes to appeal against the decision of an **arbitrator** or when a person is making an application for **judicial review**. *See also* **originating summons; writ.**

originating summons Method of starting certain types of legal proceedings, especially in the **Chancery Division** − for example to force a sale of land on behalf of a mortgagee.

ostensible authority Apparent authority. For instance, if circumstances make it appear that one person has the authority to act as an **agent** for another in a particular transaction, any agreement that is made may be binding on the **principal**. If, therefore, a board of directors of a company imposes restrictions on the spending power of its managing director and the director ignores these restrictions and enters into a contract with a third party, the managing director has ostensible authority, since the third party does not know of the restriction. The contract will be binding on the company.

ouster Act by which a person is deprived of something which he owns or is entitled to. Generally, ouster implies an unlawful act. However, an ouster order under the Matrimonial Homes Act 1983 has the effect in law of depriving a husband or wife of the right to occupy their home. This order is used in cases of domestic violence.

Ouster of jurisdiction occurs when a statute provides that a particular type of administrative act should not be open to question in the courts.

outstanding Term with three applications.

First, a **debt** is outstanding if it has not been paid.

Second, when sentencing an offender for a criminal offence the court, with the agreement of the defendant, may take into consideration any outstanding offences against him. These must be of a similar nature to the offence he has been convicted of such that the court would have the power to try the outstanding offences.

Third, in relation to a **lease** or other **contract** for a specified period, the outstanding period is the period which is still to run.

overreaching Process by which rights that relate to land are extinguished so that the land may be sold. The person whose rights are extinguished is then given equivalent rights in relation to the money raised by selling the land.

overreaching conveyance Transfer of land by which **overreaching** occurs.

overriding interest Rights that relate to land, enjoyed by persons other than the owner which the owner is bound to respect even if they have not been registered in the Land Registry. Typical examples are the right of occupation and the right of an adjoining land-owner to receive water flowing in a stream across the land in question.

overriding trust Any **trust** that extinguishes and replaces an earlier trust relating to the same subject matter.

overrule To set aside. A legal decision or principle may be overruled either by a more senior court or by an Act of Parliament. Since 1966 the House of Lords, when it sits as the most senior appeal court in the country, has had the power to overrule previous decisions made by itself. Overruling has the effect of changing the law so that all subsequent judges must follow the new principle. *See also* **judicial precedent**.

overt act Open act as opposed to an intention conceived in the mind.

ownership Right to use and enjoy something and to prevent others from using it. Restricted ownership has certain limitations on its use, perhaps because the article or piece of land is owned by two or more people. If there are no restrictions, the ownership is described as absolute and the owner may sell, alter or destroy the property as he wishes.

oyer and terminer To hear and determine. Before the reorganization of the court structure in 1971, **assize** judges were required to hear and determine accusations of criminal offences brought against members of the public. Since the abolition of assizes under the Courts Act 1971 such cases are now heard in the **Crown Court**.

P

panel List of people called to serve as members of a **jury** for a particular session of trials. When a jury is sworn in, 12 members are chosen from the panel.

parcel Portion or small plot of land. In a **conveyance** of land the term is used to indicate the clause of the agreement that describes the property being conveyed.

pardon Release from punishment by the Crown of any person who has committed a criminal offence. A pardon may be granted either before criminal proceedings have begun or after a defendant has been convicted and sentenced.

parental rights and duties Legal consequences of being the parent of a child. Parental rights include the taking of major decisions about such matters as education and medical treatment. A dispute between parents may be settled by the courts either by awarding **custody** to one parent or by making the child a **ward of court**. Parental duties are to maintain the child. The duty to maintain can be enforced by law. Failure to care for a child may amount to the offence of wilful neglect under the Children and Young Persons Act 1933. If parents neglect or fail to control a child or expose it to moral danger, the child may be taken into the care of the local authority by order of a **juvenile court**. In that case, the parental rights and duties are passed to the local authority. Parental rights and duties may be transferred by **adoption**. *See also* **maintenance**.

parish Term with two applications.

First, geographical area attached to a church in relation to which the parson or vicar has responsibilities.

Second, the lowest administrative level of local government. Parish councils are elected and have responsibilities over matters such as footpaths and street-lighting.

parking offence Parking a motor vehicle in a restricted place. Illegal parking is generally controlled by traffic wardens, who leave a ticket that gives details of the offence on the vehicle. The motorist may choose to pay a fixed penalty fine, which must be paid within 21 days of the offence. This does not amount to a criminal conviction.

Alternatively, the motorist may deny the offence and choose to be tried before a **Magistrates' Court**. If convicted, he or she will be fined. This amounts to a criminal conviction and must be reported to insurers before the insurance policy is renewed.

Parliament The United Kingdom's highest legislative authority, comprising the elected House of Commons, the non-elected House of Lords, and the hereditary monarch. The Commons exercises the effective legislative power.

Parliamentary agent Person, usually a Member of Parliament, who is employed to manage any parliamentary business of a private group.

Parliamentary Bar Group of **barristers** who represent parties who are either promoting or opposing private bills.

Parliamentary committee *See* **select committee; standing committee.**

Parliamentary Draftsman Person responsible for drawing up proposed legislation for discussion by Parliament.

Parliamentary franchise Right to vote in an election for members of the House of Commons, extended to almost all United Kingdom nationals and citizens of the **Commonwealth** or the Republic of Ireland resident in the United Kingdom. Excluded from the franchise are people aged less than 18, the sovereign, peers of the realm, and prisoners convicted of serious crime.

Parliamentary privilege Sum of the special rights and privileges of **Parliament** collectively and of individual Members of Parliament. The rights and privileges are designed to ensure that Parliament can fulfil its democratic function without obstruction. The most important right is immunity from prosecution or civil proceedings for things said in Parliamentary debate. *See also* **contempt of Parliament**.

Parliamentary sovereignty Exclusive right of Parliament to make, amend or **repeal** any law that it wishes. By joining the **European Community** in 1972 some of the sovereignty of Parliament has been temporarily surrendered since European Community institutions have power to make law in certain areas. However, Parliament has not surrendered this sovereignty permanently, because the United Kingdom could choose to leave the Community at some date in the future.

parole Permission granted by the Home Secretary to a prisoner to be released during the period of his or her sentence. A prisoner becomes eligible for parole after one-third of the sentence has been served, so long as at least six months have been served, and the prisoner has been recommended for parole by the **Parole Board**. Parole may be granted for limited periods of time in order to gradually reintroduce a prisoner to society. Conditions, such as the need to report regularly to police stations or social workers, are usually attached to parole and the prisoner may be recalled at any time if he or she fails to respond successfully. *See also* **licence**; **remission**.

Parole Board Panel of people who consider whether a prisoner is eligible for release on **parole** and make recommendations to the Home Secretary.

parricide *See* **patricide.**

partly suspended sentence Prison sentence of which the first part is served in prison, but the second part is suspended for a specific period of time and will be served only if the convict commits any further offences during that period. *See also* **suspended sentence**.

particular lien Right of a **creditor** to hold on to goods of a debtor when the money owed relates to those goods. For example, a garage may hold the car of a person who has failed to pay a bill for repairs to it. *See also* **general lien**.

particulars Details of the facts and legal arguments relied upon by a party to civil proceedings. They must be disclosed to the other party before the trial as part of the **pleadings**. If insufficient details are given, the other party may request "further and better particulars", and the court may order that these be provided.

partition Legal process by which **land** owned jointly by a number of persons may be divided up so that each person receives a part equivalent to his or her share of the whole. Any joint owner of land may compel partition, however inconvenient that may be for the others.

partnership Relationship between persons who have agreed to run a business together. The agreement between the partners, which sets out their obligations to each other, is usually contained in the articles of partnership or a partnership deed. Partnerships are regulated by the Partnership Act 1890. By law the act of each partner is the act of them all, so that if one partner performs work negligently and causes loss or damage all the partners may be liable to pay damages.

part performance Rule of law, under the Law of Property Act 1925, by which any party who has partly performed a **contract** relating to land may obtain a court **order** for the contract to be completed, even though there is no written evidence to prove the agreement. For instance, if a tenant has been allowed to move into a house under an oral agreement to **lease** it, this will be considered an act of part performance and the tenant's right to occupy the premises will be protected by law. This rule is an exception to the general principle that all contracts relating to land must be made in writing.

party and party costs Formerly, a basis of taxing court costs. *See* **taxation of costs**.

passing off Carrying on a business in a manner intended to deceive members of the public into believing that it is the business of another. An example is to use a name and image similar to a well-known business in a particular field so that customers mistakenly believe that they are dealing with the well- known business. The established business may take legal action to obtain compensation and to secure an **injunction** against the person passing off.

passport Document issued by the Foreign Office to citizens of the United Kingdom required as proof of identity when passing from one country to another.

patent Right of an inventor to exploit his or her invention commercially for a period of 20 years if he has registered the invention under the Patents Act 1977. Patents are also protected internationally by various **treaties**.

paternity Being the father of a particular child. The husband of the mother is presumed to be the father of her child unless some other man is proved to be so. Courts may have to decide paternity in order to decide who must pay **maintenance** for a child. A **blood test** may be ordered for this purpose.

Paternity leave is time off work granted by an employer to a father at the time of, or following, the birth of his child. There is no legal requirement that this should be granted, but it is provided for in some employment contracts.

patricide Act of killing one's father, also known as parricide. *See also* **homicide**.

patrial Formerly, person who had rights of **abode** in the United Kingdom by virtue of having a parent or grandparent who was born in the United Kingdom. The category was abolished by the British Nationality Act 1981.

patronage Right to nominate a cleric to a **benefice**.

Patronage Secretary Colloquial term for the Government Chief Whip. *See* **whip**.

pawn Article given as security for a loan. The debtor, who is called the pawnor, retains ownership of the article although the **creditor**, who is called the pawnee, is entitled to keep hold of it until the debt is paid. If the debtor fails to pay the debt, the pawnee may sell the property to recover the loan and any interest that has accrued, but any profit must be returned to the pawner.

pawnbroker Any person licensed by the Director General of Fair Trading under the Consumer Credit Act 1974 to carry on the business of taking articles in **pawn**.

pay as you earn (PAYE) *See* **income tax**.

Paymaster General Government minister in charge of the Treasury office who acts as a paying agency for government departments.

payment into court Payment of a sum of money into the court by a **defendant** who is being sued in civil proceedings for compensation. It amounts to an offer of money to the **plaintiff** in settlement of the claim. The amount of money paid in is not made known to the trial judge, and if the plaintiff rejects the offer and is subsequently awarded less by the judge, he or she will usually be required to pay all court costs which have arisen since the date of the payment into court.

pecuniary advantage Any of several financial benefits specified in the Theft Act 1968 s.16. These are: (i) insurance or annuity contracts, (ii) employment, and (iii) an overdraft. It is a criminal offence to obtain a pecuniary advantage by **deception** − for example, obtaining an overdraft from a bank by giving false information about one's financial circumstances, or gaining employment by lying about one's qualifications.

pedlar Person who moves from place to place or house to house selling goods.

peer Term with two applications.

First, a person of equal social standing. The right to be tried by one's peers is the basis, for untitled people, of trial by jury.

Second, a person who has been granted a title of nobility and is entitled to sit in the House of Lords. Such peers may be tried only by the House of Lords.

penal servitude Former criminal penalty that combined imprisonment with compulsory labour. It was abolished by the Criminal Justice Act 1948.

penalty Term with two applications.

First, punishment prescribed by law.

Second, compensation payable under a term in a **contract** that specifies what should happen if one party is in **breach of contract**. For instance, building contracts often contain a penalty clause that the builder should pay a certain sum in compensation per day for late completion of the work.

penalty points Points recorded on a driving licence, imposed by the **Magistrates' Court** on motorists who are found guilty of certain motoring offences. A motorist who receives 12 penalty points in three years loses his or her licence for a minimum period of six months. Most offences carry a fixed number of penalty points. Dangerous parking, for example, carries three points. For other offences, such as careless driving or failing to stop after an accident, a range of points exists and the court will decide the number to allocate after considering the full circumstances of the offence.

pending action Legal proceedings that have been started, but are not finished. For instance, a civil case is pending from the time that the **plaintiff** issues a **writ** against the **defendant** until the day that the case is decided in court.

penology Study of the sentencing of criminal offenders. Penology includes the aims and philosophy of the various methods adopted and their success rates particularly in terms of the reconviction rate of offenders.

pension Periodic payment made to a person who has retired from employment. A weekly state benefit is paid to women of 60 and over and men of 65 and over, provided that they have paid sufficient **national insurance** contributions during their working life. In addition, many employees contribute to a pension fund during their working life in order to provide some security on retirement.

peppercorn rent Nominal rent of a very small sum which it is not intended that the landlord should collect. It is recorded in a **lease** of land in order to make it clear that the landlord owns the property.

peremptory Not capable of being denied or contradicted.

performance right Form of **copyright** whereby the writers or composers of drama or music reserve the right to perform the work publicly or to licence others to perform it. Granting licences and collecting fees for performances is centralized in the Performing Rights Society.

periodical payment Payment of a specific sum of money on a regular basis, usually weekly or monthly. In claims for **maintenance** one spouse may be ordered by the court to make periodical maintenance payments to the other.

periodic tenancy Tenancy that is not for a fixed length of time. The tenant pays rent periodically e.g. weekly or monthly, and the tenancy continues until either party decides to terminate the arrangement by informing the other and giving sufficient notice. *See also* **tenancy**.

perjury Telling a lie in the course of giving evidence under oath in court. An offence under the Perjury Act 1911.

perpetual injunction Injunction which is not issued for a temporary period but which goes on indefinitely unless the injunction is later lifted by a court. *See also* **injunction**.

perpetuity Unlimited duration. Under the Perpetuities and Accumulations Act 1964 any attempt to regulate the ownership of land for either more than 80 years or for more than 21 years after the death of a named person will have no legal effect.

persistent offender Person who regularly commits criminal offences. A person who has been convicted of an imprisonable offence on more than three occasions since reaching the age of 21 may, on a subsequent conviction, be given an **extended sentence**.

personal action Civil action in which the **plaintiff** requests a remedy that requires the **defendant** to do something. For instance, in a claim for **breach of contract** the plaintiff seeks a court order that the defendant complete the contract.

personal injury In the law of **tort**, physical or mental injury, as opposed to damage to property or reputation.

personal property All property other than **freehold** ownership of land or buildings. Personal property therefore includes movable objects such as cars, jewellery and books, intangible property such as ownership of **copyright** or the right to payment of a **debt**, and **leasehold** ownership of land.

personal representative Person who administers the **estate** of a deceased person. A personal representative who is nominated in the **will** is called an **executor**. A personal representative who is appointed by the court is called an **administrator**. *See also* **administration of estates**.

personalty Personal property. **Personal property** which has no connection with land is called pure personalty, whereas interests in land such as **leaseholds** are called **chattels** real.

personation Pretending to be another person. Personation may be a criminal offence if the motive is improper. For instance, it is a criminal offence to vote as someone else at local or general elections under the Representation of the People Act 1983 s.168. It is also an offence under the Sexual Offences Act 1956 s.1 for a man to induce a woman to have sexual intercourse with him by impersonating her husband.

persuasive precedent Decision of a court that need not be followed in subsequent cases, but that may persuade other judges to adopt the same approach. Decisions reached in senior courts in the system create **binding precedents**. Judges may, however, be persuaded to follow decisions made in lower courts or in foreign courts.

perverse verdict Decision of a **jury** completely contrary to the evidence presented in the trial or to the **direction to jury** given by the judge.

perverting the course of justice Performing any act intended to obstruct, or corrupt or interfere with the course of legal proceedings, or to prevent legal proceedings from being started. It is an offence at **common law**. Examples include hiding evidence of crime, threatening witnesses to prevent their giving evidence, or interfering with accounts in order to cover up a fraud and frustrate a police investigation. *See also* **contempt of court**.

petition Request or application made to a court or other authority. For instance, a person may request a court to grant a divorce by a **divorce** petition. An application to have a person made **bankrupt** is a bankruptcy petition.

The document in which such an application is made is also known as a petition.

petition of right Formerly, a procedure by which a person might obtain a legal remedy against the **Crown**. It has been obsolete since the Crown Proceedings Act 1947, which allows the Crown to be sued in the normal way.

Petty Sessional Division Geographical area in relation to which a particular **Magistrates' Court** has authority.

petty sessions Courts that formerly held the power to try minor crimes known as **summary offences**. Petty sessions are now called **Magistrates' Courts** and are presided over by **justices of the peace** or **stipendiary magistrates**.

picketing Workers on strike standing outside their place of work in order to remind fellow workers that there is a strike in progress in the hope of persuading them to join in. Under the Trade Union and Labour Relations Act 1974 s.15 picketing is lawful providing that the picketers are workers behaving peacefully outside their own place of work. It is not lawful for anyone else, such as family or friends of workers, to join in, nor for workers to undertake secondary picketing by picketing at a place of work other than their own. If these rules are breached, the employer may use the civil law to obtain an **injunction** that orders the picket to stop.

Even if the picket complies with the Trade Union and Labour Relations Act, the picketers may be prosecuted under the criminal law if a criminal offence such as **obstruction of the highway** or **breach of the peace** occurs.

place of safety order Order made by a **juvenile court** that a child be removed from its parents or from anybody else with custody of the child and placed in the temporary care of the local authority. The order is used in an emergency, when there are grounds to believe that the child is in physical or moral danger. *See also* **care order; custody of children**.

plaint Action started usually in the County Court.

plaintiff Person who initiates legal proceedings to claim a **remedy**, such as **damages** or an **injunction**, against another person, the **defendant**.

plaint note Document issued when proceedings in the **County Court** are started. The plaint is on a standard form available from the court and contains the names of the person or persons to be sued, the person suing and the case number.

planning blight Circumstances in which the value of premises or land is reduced, making them difficult to sell, because development plans that would entail the compulsory purchase of the property are under consideration. The property is said to be blighted and the owner may compel the authority that is seeking to develop the area to buy the property at a reasonable market valuation.

planning permission Legal procedure to grant permission for the proposed development of land, or for changes in the use of land or buildings, under the Town and Country Planning Acts. Planning permission is primarily the responsibility of the local authority. However, an appeal may be made to the Secretary of State for the Environment, who may overrule the local authority's decision. For important, large-scale developments, the Secretary of State may appoint an inspector to hold a public inquiry and advise him or her. *See also* **planning blight**.

plea Response made to the charge by the **defendant** in criminal proceedings. The defendant may plead either **guilty** or **not guilty**; refusal to plead is taken as a plea of not guilty. *See also* **unfit to plead**.

plea bargain Deal made between a person charged with crime and either the **prosecution** or the **court**, by which the **defendant** agrees to plead **guilty** in return either for a promise of a particular type of **sentence** from the **judge** (for example, a fine rather than imprisonment) or a reduction in the seriousness of the charge by the prosecution (for example, reducing a charge of attempted **murder** to one of **wounding with intent**). The practice is objectionable because it is coercive and reduces the defendant's freedom of choice relating to **plea**. It is also unlawful, but it is nevertheless an everyday feature of the English criminal justice system.

plea in mitigation Address to the court, normally by the lawyer representing a **defendant,** made after the defendant's **conviction**. The purpose is to influence the court to give a lower rather than a higher **sentence**. A plea in mitigation might seek to minimize the seriousness of the crime, emphasize the defendant's previous good character, or express the defendant's remorse.

plea of the jurisdiction Defence to either civil or criminal proceedings that the court does not have jurisdiction to try the case, either because the events occurred outside the geographical limits of the court's jurisdiction or because the case is of a type which the court does not have authority to decide.

pleadings Procedures that take place before a trial in civil proceedings, chiefly the exchange of documents in which each side sets out its case. The purpose of pleadings is to allow each party to get a clear idea of the other party's argument.

pleas of the Crown Obsolete term for criminal proceedings, so called because all criminal proceedings are undertaken in the name of the Crown.

pledge Deposit of goods or other property as security for a loan of money, or for the fulfilment of some other obligation. *See also* **pawn**.

plenipotentiary Person or body given full authority and power to carry out a particular act on behalf of another.

poaching Offence of trespassing in order to take wild fish or **game** on the land of another person. Poaching is distinguished from **theft,** because the wild creatures do not belong to anybody. Rather, the offence infringes the landowner's right to hunt and fish on his own land. *See also* **trespass**.

poison Substance harmful to the taker. The sale and distribution of poisons is regulated under the Poisons Act 1972. Offences of poisoning are found in the Offences Against the Person Act 1861. Under section 22 it is an offence to administer a stupefying drug such as chloroform. Under section 23 it is an offence to administer any noxious substance with the intention to cause harm or the knowledge that there is a risk of causing harm.

police Organization responsible for maintaining law and order. A member of the police force is an officer of the Crown and a public servant. *See* **constable**; **constabulary**.

Police Complaints Authority Body established under the Police and Criminal Evidence Act 1984 for the purpose of investigating complaints from the public against police officers. The Authority also has the power to supervise the investigation of a crime alleged to have been committed by an officer, although the decision whether to prosecute is made by the **Director of Public Prosecutions**. The Authority may recommend that disciplinary proceedings be taken against an officer, but final adjudication is normally by the Chief Constable of the police force involved.

police, obstruction of *See* **obstruction of the police.**

political asylum Refuge given by one country to a national of another who claims that if he were forced to return to his own country he would face persecution on political grounds. Political asylum may be granted in an embassy abroad. The final decision whether asylum be granted is made by the **Home Secretary**.

political offence Crime is committed by holding or expressing certain political views or by taking political action which would not amount to an ordinary crime. Under **extradition** treaties between states, it is normal practice that one state will not extradite a person if the offence which he or she is alleged to have committed is a political crime.

political participation Methods by which people participate in the political process − for example, by voting in elections and referenda, and by membership of political parties.

political parties Organized groups of people who share a common interest or common ideals, and seek to achieve political power by contesting elections.

political uniform Dress or uniform signifying association with a political organization. It is an offence to wear such a uniform in public under the Public Order Act 1936 s.1.

poll tax *See* **community charge.**

polygamy Marriage to two or more people at the same time. Polygamy is impossible for any person with **domicile** in the United Kingdom, because only the first marriage ceremony (unless former spouses are dead or divorced) is valid in law. However, under the Matrimonial Proceedings (Polygamous Marriages) Act 1972, a marriage entered into under a foreign legal system that permits more than one spouse, when the person in question has not taken a second spouse, is treated as if it were a lawful marriage for the purposes of family law. *See also* **bigamy**; **monogamy**.

popular culture Culture of the masses as contrasted to the "high culture" of the educated elite. In the 20th century it has been largely communicated through the media of television, radio, electronically recorded music, film and video.

port Place where, by law, goods are allowed to pass in and out of the country and where **Customs and Excise** officials control the flow of goods and charge relevant import and export duties. Ports may be on the coast or inland − for example, airports and container ports.

portion Gift to a child of part of a parent's **estate** either under the parent's **will** or under the law of **intestacy**.

positive law Law made by human institutions such as courts or legislatures. Positive law is neither inherent in human nature, nor God-given. It is whatever human societies choose to make it. *See also* **natural law**.

positive vetting Procedure by which an applicant for a job involved with the defence or security of the state is investigated in order to determine whether he or she might be disloyal, have criminal tendencies or might be vulnerable to **blackmail**.

possession Custody and control of a thing or piece of land. Mere custody without control is not possession. For instance, a worker who holds a tool that belongs to his or her employer and uses that tool under the employer's directions does not have possession of it.

possession of drugs *See* **drugs, controlled.**

possession, order for Court order by which a tenant is required to vacate **land** or premises and hand **possession** back to the landlord. It is appropriate when the tenant is in breach of the terms of the **lease** or when the period of the lease has expired.

possession, writ of Document that authorizes an officer of the court to seize possession of land on behalf of a person adjudged by the court to be entitled to it.

possessory lien *See* **lien.**

post-industrial society Society whose economy is no longer dominated by basic manufacturing industry (termed an industrial society), but rather by service industry. Most of the countries of Western Europe can be described as post-industrial societies.

post mortem Physical examination of a corpse, carried out by a pathologist under the directions of a **coroner**, for the purpose of determining the **cause of death**. *See also* **inquest**.

post-nuptial settlement Contract by which the parties to a marriage or others agree between themselves to make specified gifts to the couple following the marriage.

pound Place where goods seized under legal powers are stored. Historically, cattle which strayed from one farmer's land on to the land of a neighbour and caused damage might be seized and kept in a pound until the owner paid compensation. In modern times, a car seized by the police for **obstruction of the highway** is kept in a car pound until a fixed fee is paid to regain it.

poverty Condition of being without reasonable minimum income or resources; the condition of wanting for goods or services that most others take for granted.

power of appointment *See* **appointment, power of.**

power of arrest *See* **arrest.**

power of attorney Grant of authority by one person to another to act on his or her behalf, either generally or in relation to specified matters. Under the Power of Attorney Act 1971, the grant must be made by **deed** and can be revoked at any time by the person who makes it. Generally, a power of attorney is automatically revoked if the grantor becomes mentally incapable. However, under the Enduring Powers of Attorney Act 1985, it is possible for a person to grant a power which will continue after the grantor becomes mentally incapable. This is particularly useful for elderly people who wish to arrange for someone to act on their behalf in the event of mental disability.

power of entry to premises Authority to enter another person's premises without that person's permission. Normally, such an entry is a **trespass,** but the law confers power to enter in a number of circumstances. Under the Police and Criminal Evidence Act 1984, premises may be entered to make a lawful **arrest**. If a person is arrested elsewhere than at his or her normal home, the police may then enter and search the home. However, there must be grounds to believe that it might contain stolen goods or other prohibited things, such as drugs, connected to the offence for which the suspect was arrested. A **search warrant** also allows for entry to named premises.

Under **common law** the police may enter premises to prevent a serious crime or to prevent a **breach of the peace**.

Public utilities that supply services such as water, electricity and gas have statutory powers to enter premises in specified circumstances in the interests of safety or to protect their own property and prevent fraud.

power of search of premises *See* **power of entry to premises.**

power of seizure Power of the police to take and retain stolen or prohibited articles found in the course of exercising a **power to stop and search** a person or a **power of entry of premises** under the Police and Criminal Evidence Act 1984.

In **civil law, bailiffs** have a power to seize the goods of a person who has not paid money due under a court order or judgment.

power to stop and search Authority given to a police officer, under the Police and Criminal Evidence Act 1984 s.1, to stop and search any person in a public place when there are reasonable grounds for believing that the person has possession of stolen goods or other prohibited articles such as **offensive weapons**.

practice Term with two applications.

First, the provision of legal services to clients. A solicitor may not practise without a practising certificate, issued yearly by the Law Society, nor without insurance against claims made by clients.

Second, the partnership of solicitors providing legal services.

preamble Words of explanation and introduction which go before the operative part of a legal document. Thus, the preamble to an **Act of Parliament** does not create law, but explains why the Act was passed and what it seeks to achieve. Other legal documents have preambles that serve a similar function.

precatory trust Trust not expressly established, but created because particular words (called precatory words) in a **will** or other legal document call upon a particular person to deal with property in a particular way. It is implied that the person who receives that property should hold it in **trust** for another. Thus, if, in a will, a man leaves his car to his brother and asks the brother not to use it, but to keep it for the first man's son, this would imply that the brother should in fact hold the car in trust for the son.

precedent Court decision that may influence the decisions of other courts in future cases that raise similar issues. *See also* **binding precedent; persuasive precedent**.

precept Demand to pay **rates** to a **local authority** or water authority.

preference Something done that is of greater advantage to one person than to others. Thus, a preference **share** in a company entitles the holder to receive a fixed dividend, whereas holders of ordinary shares receive a dividend only if profits are available after the preference shareholders have been paid. *See also* **fraudulent preference**.

prejudice Prejudgment of an issue before it is properly decided. For instance, if a newspaper describes a man awaiting trial for murder as a murderer, that prejudices the later trial and amounts to **contempt of court**. *See also* **without prejudice**.

preliminary act Document that gives details of a collision between ships. It must be submitted to the court by any party to legal proceedings that arise from such a collision, at the beginning of the case.

preliminary enquiries Investigation, usually conducted by a solicitor who is acting for the purchaser of a house or other property, that seeks to discover relevant matters about the property and its immediate environment. Relevant matters include the physical condition of the property and legal questions such as whether any other person has a right to occupy the property or has a **right of way** over it.

premises Term with two applications.
First, buildings and land.
Second, the first part of a **deed**, which sets out the names of the parties and the nature of the transaction with which the deed is concerned.

premium Term with two applications.
First, the cost of something over and above the stated or nominal cost. Thus, a premium paid by a tenant is an extra sum, which must be paid in order to obtain a **lease**, above the figure actually quoted in the lease itself.
Second, the annual cost of an **insurance** or **assurance** policy.

prerogative of mercy Power of the **Crown**, exercised by the Home Secretary, to **pardon** a person convicted of a criminal offence and, as a consequence, cancel any **sentence**.

prerogative order *See* **prerogative writ**.

prerogative writ Formerly, a writ issued at the discretion of the High Court for the purpose of controlling mistakes and abuses of power by lower courts and public officials. Prerogative writs have been replaced by prerogative orders, of which the most important are *certiorari*, *mandamus*, and **prohibition**.

prescription Legal right to something by virtue of having used that thing for a long period. For instance, a squatter who occupies premises for 12 years without interruption gains a right of ownership of the premises by prescription. Other rights, such as **rights of way**, may be obtained by prescription.

presiding judge Judge who hears a case in court.

pressure group Organized group of people with a common interest who try to influence public opinion, bureaucrats or politicians.

presumption Willingness of a court to accept a fact until the contrary is proved. For instance, in law, all people are presumed to be sane and it is not necessary to prove that somebody is sane before that person may be convicted of a criminal offence or that person's will be accepted as valid. Anything which is presumed by a court may be rebutted, but the party that wishes to disprove has the **burden of proof**.

presumption of death Legal acknowledgement that a person who has been absent for seven years, without being seen or heard of and without reasonable explanation, may be presumed dead. The major consequences are that the missing person's spouse is free to remarry and that the missing person's property and goods are distributed as if he or she were dead.

presumption of innocence Rule of evidence that a person accused of crime is presumed to be innocent unless the **prosecution** prove guilt beyond reasonable doubt.

presumption of legitimacy Rule of evidence that for all legal purposes a child born to a mother who was married at the time of conception or birth is presumed to be the natural child of her husband (and thus legitimate), unless it is proved on a balance of probabilities that the child was fathered by another man.

presumption of marriage Rule of evidence that a couple that lives together as man and wife is presumed to be lawfully married, even if there is no positive evidence of this, unless it is proved that they are not married. A presumed marriage may be described as a **common law marriage**. This rule allows one of a cohabiting couple to inherit on the death of the other under the rules of **intestacy**, unless somebody else contests the **estate** and proves that the couple were not married.

219

pre-trial review Preliminary hearing in court between the parties involved in legal proceedings (or their legal advisers) before the hearing of the case. The purpose of the review is to establish what issues are agreed and what the points of contention are, to determine which witnesses must be called and the probable length of the proceedings. A pre-trial review is standard procedure in the **County Court** and is held before a **Registrar**. It is also used in criminal cases in **Magistrates' Courts** or **Crown Courts** in some parts of the country.

previous conviction *See* **criminal record**.

prima facie case Sufficient evidence against a person accused of crime, such that if a **jury** or **magistrates** believed the evidence they could convict the accused person of the crime. Originally a prima facie case was the standard of evidence which the police required before they would charge somebody with crime. Now that prosecution is the responsibility of the **Crown Prosecution Service** the test is whether there is a reasonable prospect of convicting the accused. At **committal for trial**, the Magistrates' Court must be satisfied that there is a prima facie case against the accused before committing him to the **Crown Court**.

primage and average Payments made by owners of goods for having the goods loaded on to a ship (primage) and for the care of the goods during voyage (average).

primary evidence Evidence from the best available source. *See also* **best evidence**.

Prime Minister Head of the government. The monarch appoints the Prime Minister, who is usually the leader of the party with the greatest number of seats in the House of Commons. The Prime Minister has the power to choose ministers and is responsible for all actions of government. The Prime Minister alone may ask the Sovereign for a dissolution of Parliament, followed by a general election.

primogeniture System of inheritance in which the father's title or property passes to his first-born son on the father's death.

Primogeniture applied to land in English law until it was abolished by the Law of Property Act 1925.

principal Term with three applications.

First, a person on whose behalf a second person acts. Thus, an **agent** may enter into and perform **contracts** on behalf of his or her principal.

Second, in **criminal law**, a person who commits acts prohibited by law (as opposed to persons who aid and abet crime).

Third, original sum of money invested or loaned, not counting any **interest** which it earns.

priority Going before or being dealt with before something else. For instance, under the law of **bankruptcy**, certain debts have priority. This means that they are paid first out of the bankrupt person's funds.

prison Institution, controlled by the Home Office, designated as a place where adult offenders may serve sentences of imprisonment. The relevant law is contained in the Prison Act 1952.

prisoners' rights Prisoners retain all rights that are not expressly or by implication taken away. Civil and criminal law applies to prisoners. Prisoners with a grievance can complain to the governor or a member of the prison board of visitors; they may also petition the Secretary of State.

privacy Freedom from intrusion upon one's personal life and from public discussion of one's personal affairs. Privacy is protected under the **European Convention on Human Rights**. In English law it is not directly protected, but it receives some protection under the laws against **trespass** and **defamation** of character and under the Data Protection Act.

Private Bill Office Parliamentary office to which any proposed private bills must be submitted.

private company Company that does not offer shares for sale to the public. It must have at least two members. *See also* **company**.

private international law System of legal rules that indicate which country's law should be applied to a legal issue which has links with more than one country. It is also called the conflict of laws. *See also* **foreign judgments; foreign law.**

private law All law concerned with dealings between individuals and between institutions other than institutions of the State. It includes contract, tort, family law, company law, land law and all other areas of law which are not part of **public law** or **international law.**

private member's bill Proposed **legislation** introduced in Parliament by a private Member of Parliament, not the Government. Such a bill may not be designed to affect the law in general, but merely to deal with some matter of particular interest to the person or body on whose behalf it is introduced. For example, the original railway network was established under private Acts of Parliament arising from private bills. Or it may be concerned with a matter of general importance, but not introduced with Government backing.

private nuisance *See* **nuisance.**

private prosecution Prosecution of a person for a criminal offence undertaken by someone in a personal capacity, as opposed to prosecutions undertaken by the police, the **Crown Prosecution Service**, or other official bodies, such as water authorities, which have a responsibility to prosecute relevant offences. Normally a private prosecutor bears the expense of the action, although, if the prosecution succeeds, the judge may order that the costs be paid out of **central funds**. The most common private prosecutions are brought by shops for **shoplifting**. A private prosecution which is unfounded may be taken over and discontinued by the **Attorney-General** by a procedure called *nolle prosequi.*

privatization Term with two meanings.

First, the transfer of control or rights of ownership of a State owned company to private buyers. *See also* **nationalization.**

Second, the tendency of people to keep their lives private as opposed to making them public.

privilege Term with two applications.

First, right not to have some matter disclosed or not to disclose some matter in evidence in court. For example, communications between a lawyer and his or her client are privileged and may not be used in evidence unless the client agrees.

Second, right not to have what one has said questioned in any legal proceedings. *See also* **absolute privilege**; **Crown privilege**; **qualified privilege**.

privity Rule of the law of **contract** that only the individuals who make a contract by entering into obligations towards each other can sue for **breach of contract** if the agreement is broken. Thus if two men agree to give £100 each to a woman and one of the men later goes back on the agreement, the other man can sue the defaulter for breach of contract because he is a party to the contract, but the woman cannot sue, because although she is to benefit from the contract, she was not in a relationship of privity with the other parties.

privy Being a party to, or having knowledge of, something which is not generally known. Thus, if three persons jointly **sue** another person, each of the three is privy to the action. A person is privy to confidential information if it has been lawfully communicated to him.

Privy Council Honorary council, comprising politicians, senior judges, and other outstanding public figures from the United Kingdom and the Commonwealth. Its Lord President is usually a Cabinet Minister. *See also* **Lord President of the Council**; **Judicial Committee of the Privy Council**.

Privy Purse Allowance granted by Parliament for the private expenses of the Sovereign, part of the civil list which covers all royal expenses. The Sovereign's treasurer is called the Keeper of the Privy Purse.

Privy Seal Official stamp used on public documents of the United Kingdom until 1884. *See also* **Lord Privy Seal**.

probate Process by which a **will** is proved to be genuine and the **executors** are authorized to dispose of the **estate** of the deceased person. The grant of probate is the grant of authority to the executor. If there is no dispute about the will, probate may be granted by the Probate Registry of the High Court. If there is a dispute, probate may be granted by the **Chancery Division** of the High Court.

probate in common form Probate granted by the Probate Registry when there has been no dispute about a **will**, and proof is by sworn **affidavit**.

probate in solemn form Probate granted by the **Chancery Division** of the High Court, after proceedings in which a dispute about a **will** or who should be the **executor** has been determined by the court.

probation Procedure by which a person who has been convicted of a criminal offence may be placed under the supervision of a probation officer, instead of being sentenced. Probation may last for between six months and three years. A probationer who does not comply with the instructions of the probation officer may be brought back to court and sentenced for the original offence.

probation order Court order by which a convicted person is placed on **probation**.

procedure Practices by which legal proceedings are conducted and the rules which govern all aspects of the conduct of these proceedings.

process Formal documents that inform a person that either civil or criminal proceedings have been started against him or her and that require him or her to attend court or to make a formal response. These documents include a **summons** and a **writ**.

procession Body of people moving along a route. Under the Public Order Act 1986 s.11, details of any proposed public procession must be given to the local police at least six clear days before the procession. Under section 12 a senior police officer who fears public disorder, risk to life, damage to property or intimidation may impose conditions on the route that the procession may take. It is an offence for an organizer of a public procession not to comply with these conditions. *See also* **public assembly**; **public meeting**; **public order**.

proclamation Public pronouncement by the Sovereign.

Procurator Fiscal In Scotland, officer with responsibility to supervise the conduct of police investigations and to prosecute on behalf of the Crown.

Procurator General Officer who conducts **litigation** on behalf of Government departments in Scotland.

procurer Person who may be liable as an **accomplice** to crime, although not present at the scene, by encouraging or causing another to commit the crime. For example, it has been held that a person procures the offence of driving with excess alcohol by secretly putting alcohol into the drink of a person who is about to drive a car.

There are also, under the Sexual Offences Act 1956, specific offences of procuring unlawful sexual intercourse in relation to mentally defective women and **minors**. They are also offences of procuring a woman for **prostitution** and procuring sexual intercourse by threats or intimidation.

product liability Nature of the liability of a manufacturer or supplier of goods for losses suffered by reason of defect(s) in the goods. The most important provision is the Consumer Protection Act 1987 passed to give effect to the European Community Directive on Product Liability. This establishes liability for defects without the need to prove negligence or fault on the part of the manufacturer, known as **strict liability**.

prohibited article Thing or substance, the possession of which is either generally prohibited or prohibited in a public place. Under the Police and Criminal Evidence Act 1984 s.1, a police officer may search a person in a public place whom he or she reasonably suspects to be in possession of a prohibited article.

prohibition Order issued by the High Court that directs a lower court or administrative authority not to decide a particular case, or not to take a particular action, when what the lower court or administrative authority proposes is unlawful. The order may be made in the course of **judicial review**.

prohibitory injunction Court order addressed to a particular person or body directing them not to do a specified illegal act. *See also* **injunction**.

proletariat Class of manual workers, usually industrial, whose revenue is derived solely from the sale of its labour. It is more commonly referred to as the working class.

promise Expression of an intention to do a particular act in the future. Generally, promises are not binding in law unless some consideration is given for the promise, in which case a **contract** is formed. A promise may, however, be binding if in the circumstances a **promissory estoppel** is created.

promissory estoppel Promise by one person to reduce or **waive** a legal obligation due from another person. If relied upon by the other person it will be treated as binding in law. *See also* **estoppel**.

promoter Term with two applications.

First, a person who presents a **private member's bill** to Parliament.

Second, a person involved in setting up a **company**, especially one who is responsible for offering shares for sale to the public.

proof Term with three applications.

First, process by which a court is persuaded by evidence presented in court that alleged facts are true.

Second, as in **proof of evidence**, the collection of statements taken from witnesses for each side before a trial which represent the evidence which each side hopes to produce in court in order to prove its case.

Third, as in **proof of service**, the means by which a court is satisfied that a **writ** or **summons** has been formally served (delivered) to a party to legal proceedings. Normal means of proof of service are the sending by registered letter to a company's registered office; or the reply to the court by the recipient of the writ to confirm that the writ has been served; or the signing of an **affidavit** by the deliverer of the writ to say that this it has been delivered.

property Term with two applications.

First, anything which may be owned, including, not only land and physical things but also intangible property such as a copyright or a **debt**.

Second, the right of ownership of the above mentioned things.

property adjustment order Court order, made under the Matrimonial Causes Act 1973 following a divorce or judicial separation, to transfer property between husband and wife.

Property Register One of three separate registers kept by the Land Registry. It describes the various plots of land by reference to a map.

prorogation of Parliament Ending of a Parliamentary session, at which time any bill that has not reached the stage of Royal Assent automatically lapses.

proscribe To prohibit in law. Under the Prevention of Terrorism (Temporary Provisions) Act 1989 a number of organizations are listed as proscribed. Membership of these organizations or the provision of assistance or finance to them is illegal.

prosecution Term with three applications.

First, the process by which representatives of the Crown seek to prove that a person charged with a criminal offence is guilty **beyond reasonable doubt**.

Second, the persons responsible for the prosecution (the **prosecutors**).

Third, the process of bringing or continuing any legal proceedings. A plaintiff who fails to prosecute his action may have it struck-out by the court.

prosecutor Person who initiates and conducts criminal proceedings against another. All **prosecutions** are initiated in the name of the Crown. Most prosecutions are conducted by the Crown Prosecution Service.

prospectus Document issued by a **company** by which it offers **shares** for purchase by members of the public.

prostitution Practice of a person who regularly offers his or her body for sexual acts with others in return for payment. Prostitution is not a criminal offence, but many activities associated with it are illegal. *See also* **brothel; keeping a disorderly house; soliciting**.

protected tenancy Tenancy that is fully protected by the Rent Act 1977, so that the landlord is not free to raise the rent or to evict the tenant. It may be a protected shorthold tenancy, which is for a fixed term of between one and five years, a **regulated tenancy** or an **assured tenancy**.

protection order Order, issued by a Magistrates' Court, that permits alcoholic drinks to continue to be sold from licensed premises even though the premises have changed hands. It is a temporary measure, valid until **licensing justices** have fully considered whether the new proprietor should be granted a licence.

protective trust Trust designed to guard against a particular eventuality. For example, a person may be given a right to the rent from particular property for the duration of his life, but with the provision that, if that person should become bankrupt, the rent should be paid to trustees, who are entrusted to use the money for the benefit of that person. The object of this provision is to prevent the income from the property being lost and therefore unavailable to pay creditors under the bankruptcy.

protocol Document that sets out the procedures to be adopted and the agenda for diplomatic meetings between states.

provocation Partial **defence** to the crime of **murder** which, if successfully pleaded, has the effect of reducing murder to **manslaughter**. Under the Homicide Act 1957 s.3, provocation is established if a person has killed another after losing self-control as a result of such provocation as would make a reasonable man do as the defendant did.

Provocation is not a defence to any other charge, but it may have weight in a **plea in mitigation**.

provost marshal Officer appointed under **military law** to command military police and have custody of any prisoners.

proxy Person authorized to act or vote on another's behalf, for example, at meetings of **company** shareholders.

psychopathic disorder Mental disorder, defined in the Mental Health Act 1983 s.1(2) as "persistent disorder or disability of mind (whether or not including significant impairment of intelligence) resulting in abnormally aggressive or seriously irresponsible conduct".

public analyst Officer, appointed under the Food Act 1984, with responsibilities in a particular area for analysing food, for example, for the purpose of tracing the cause of an epidemic of food poisoning.

public assembly Gathering of at least 20 people in a public place, wholly or partly in the open air. If a senior police officer reasonably believes that such public assembly may result in serious public disorder, damage to property, serious disruption to the life of the community, or intimidation, he or she may give directions relating to the siting and duration of the assembly and the numbers attending. An organizer of the assembly who knowingly fails to comply with such directions commits an offence under the Public Order Act 1986 s.14.

publication Communication of ideas or information to others by any means whatsoever, including orally.

public bill Parliamentary **bill** which, if passed, changes the general law of the land.

public document Record made for public purposes and authenticated by a public officer, admissible in court proceedings as evidence of the facts stated in it. Examples are court records and public registers.

public domain Public ownership. Literary, artistic and musical works come into the public domain when the **copyright** period has expired.

public examination Procedure under the Insolvency Act 1986 by which, following a petition for **bankruptcy**, the means of the person in question are examined by the court.

public inquiry Proceedings held before a chairman or inspector, who will normally be legally qualified, in which all interested parties are given the opportunity to present their views on some matter of public significance. Many public inquiries are set up under statutory schemes relating to **compulsory purchase**. Public inquiries have power to call witnesses, and persons giving evidence may be cross-examined.

public health Legal protection of health by powers and duties given to local authorities in the Public Health Acts, in relation to the design, construction and state of repair of buildings, sewers and drainage and other matters.

public law Law that concerns the functions of public authorities and the relationship between public authorities and citizens. This category traditionally includes **administrative law, constitutional law, criminal law** and planning **law.**

public lending right Right of the author of a book under the Public Lending Right Act 1979 to receive payment from a central fund because his or her book has been lent to members of the public by public libraries.

public meeting Meeting to which members of the public are invited. It is an offence to disrupt a public meeting under the Public Meetings Act 1908. *See also* **procession; public assembly; public order**.

public mischief Offence under **common law** that may be committed in a variety of ways, such as by making hoax telephone calls to the police or by assisting compulsorily detained mental patients to escape. It has been held, however, that the offence cannot be extended to any new form of behaviour which is prejudicial to the community, but must be confined to those actions which have already been recognized as falling within it.

public nuisance *See* **nuisance.**

public officer Any person, employed by the Government or by a local authority or some other body set up under statutory powers, with a duty to carry out tasks for the public good.

public order Circumstances in which members of the public can go about their lawful business without fear of **breach of the peace**. Public order is primarily protected by the Public Order Act 1986. *See also* **procession; public assembly; public meeting**.

public policy Notion of what is in the public interest as expressed by the law. Public policy has been used as a means to express the law's understanding of society's moral views, and also to express free-market economic theories. The courts will not enforce any contract which is against public policy. This category includes contracts relating to **prostitution** and **gambling** and also contracts which have the effect of inhibiting trade.

Public Prosecutor *See* **Crown Prosecution Service; Director of Public Prosecutions.**

public records Documents relating to the administration of the Government and the courts, housed in the Public Records Office and protected by the Public Records Act 1837.

Public Trustee Official, appointed under the Public Trustee Act 1906, whose functions include holding **trust** funds administered by the courts and administering **estates** of people who have died without a personal representative.

puisne Junior. All judges of the High **Court of Justice**, except those holding higher office, are called puisne judges.

A puisne **mortgage** is a second or subsequent mortgage by which the lender does not have the security of having possession of the **title deeds** because these are already deposited with the lender under the first mortgage. A puisne mortgage must be registered as a **land charge**.

punitive damages Award of **damages** designed to punish the wrongdoer, not simply to compensate for any injury or loss caused. Punitive damages may be awarded if the wrong done is deliberate and is calculated to make a profit for the wrongdoer – for instance, when a newspaper publishes an untrue defamatory story about a public figure in order to boost its circulation.

pupillage Period of apprenticeship with a qualified barrister which all aspiring barristers must serve before being permitted to practise in the courts. It is normally of one year's duration, but it may be divided into two six-month periods with different barristers to give the apprentice broader experience.

purging contempt Making amends for a **contempt of court** in a manner which is acceptable to the court. If the contempt involves refusal to pay a fine or to obey an order of the court, the contempt is purged by paying the fine or agreeing to obey the order. Other forms of contempt, such as **scandalizing the court**, may be purged by an acceptable apology.

purveyance Ancient right of the Royal Household to enforce the purchase of necessary food, fuel and transport in times of shortage.

purview That part of an Act of Parliament which establishes the law, as opposed to the **preamble**, which does not.

putative father Man who is alleged to be the father of a child, in proceedings by which it is sought to make the putative father pay **maintenance** for the child.

Q

qualified privilege Defence to an action for **defamation**, available to the makers of certain types of statement, provided that the statement that is alleged to be defamatory was made in the belief that it was true. Statements covered by qualified privilege include fair and accurate reports of Parliamentary and court proceedings, reports of public meetings, and any statement that is made by a person under a legal or moral duty to make it to a person who has a genuine interest in receiving the statement. An example of the last is a statement made about a person in a letter of reference from a previous employer to a prospective employer. *See also* **absolute privilege**.

qualified title In **land registration**, the appropriate entry in the register when a person seeking to register an interest in land cannot trace the right to the land to a root of title which is sufficiently old. A qualified title is generally similar to an **absolute title**, except that it may be overridden by claims to ownership which pre-date the root of title on which the qualified title was based.

quango Acronym for quasi-autonomous non-governmental organization. Any body set up by the Government to perform a particular task and designed to be independent of the Government in its day-to-day workings may be described as a quango. Examples include the Arts Council and the Commission for Racial Equality.

quarantine Period during which a person or animal entering the United Kingdom is required to be isolated as a precaution against the spread of infectious diseases. All animals (including pets and livestock) imported live into this country are subject to six months' quarantine. Evasion is a criminal offence.

quarter sessions Formerly, criminal courts which sat four times a year to hear more serious criminal cases. By the Courts Act 1971 quarter sessions were abolished and their functions transferred to the **Crown Court**. *See also* **assize**.

quarter-day Day on which rent was traditionally due on land held under a **tenancy** for a year. The quarter days are 25 March, 24 June, 29 September and 25 December.

quash To overturn or nullify. If an **appeal** court quashes the decision of a lower court, that decision is nullified. In criminal cases, the quashing of a **conviction** is equivalent to an **acquittal** and the person cannot be retried for the offence.

quasi-contract Circumstances in which the law puts one person under an obligation to another as if a **contract** had been made between them. For example, if money is paid by one person to another under a contract which, because of some legal technicality, is **void**, the payer cannot get his money back by basing a claim on the contract because in law there is no contract. However, he or she will be able to claim the money under the quasi-contractual duty of the receiver of the money to repay it.

quasi-judicial In a manner similar to that of a judge. If a local authority or other body which exercises powers given by law is required to make a particular type of decision after hearing evidence and arguments offered by various parties, that decision may be described as quasi-judicial. The decision-maker is bound by the rules of **natural justice** and the decision may be reconsidered by the courts by the process of **judicial review**.

quasi-trustee Person who takes on the role of a **trustee** without having the authority to do so, and consequently assumes responsibility as if he or she had been officially appointed to act as trustee. *See* **trust**.

Queen's Bench Division One of three divisions which together form the **High Court of Justice**. It is headed by the Lord Chief Justice and hears a wide range of cases including civil claims for **breach of contract** or actions in **tort** when the compensation claimed exceeds a specified amount. It also has the power to hear some civil **appeals** against decisions made in the **County Court** and some criminal appeals against decisions made in the **Magistrates' Court**.

The **Admiralty Court** and the **Commercial Court** are two sub-divisions of the Queen's Bench Division.

Queen's Counsel (QC) Senior **barrister**, appointed by the Sovereign on the recommendation of the **Lord Chancellor**. A QC is identified by the silk gown that he or she wears in court; hence the phrase "to take silk" when a barrister is appointed as a QC.

Queen's evidence Evidence given to support the **prosecution's** case in a criminal trial by a person who has been accused with others of the offence. A person who turns Queen's evidence admits the offence but obtains an agreement that he or she will not be prosecuted in return for providing evidence against the others at trial. The judge must warn the **jury** about the dangers of convicting a person on the basis of Queen's evidence that is not substantiated by other witnesses.

Queen's Proctor Solicitor who may intervene on behalf of the Crown in **divorce** cases in which it is suspected that the parties may be colluding to mislead the court. Before a divorce is made absolute either the court or any interested individual may refer a case to the Queen's Proctor for investigation. The office of Queen's Proctor is always held by the **Treasury Solicitor**.

Queen's Speech Speech prepared by the Government and read by the Sovereign at the opening of a new session of **Parliament**. The purpose of the speech is to outline the programme of proposed new **legislation** for the forthcoming session.

question of law Issue about what is the law applicable to the particular facts of a case. In many circumstances it is necessary to distinguish questions of law from questions of fact. For instance, in a criminal **trial** before a **jury**, the judge must decide questions of law (whether particular behaviour would amount to crime), but it is for the jury to decide questions of fact (whether the defendant actually behaved as alleged). In a **criminal appeal** from a trial by jury, the **Court of Appeal** may **quash** a **conviction** if the trial judge made a wrong decision on a question of law, but may not generally reconsider the **verdict** of the jury on a question of fact.

Question Time Period at the start of most sittings in the House of Commons or House of Lords. Members question ministers, either orally or in writing, on any subject.

quiet enjoyment Right to hold property without being subject to claims by other persons to the property. **Contracts** of sale of land or other property and **leases** contain an **implied term** that the buyer or tenant of the property will have quiet enjoyment from the vendor or landlord respectively. For example, if the purchaser of a house takes possession and finds that another person is living in the house and has a lease with three months to run, the purchaser does not have quiet enjoyment of the property, and the vendor is in **breach of contract**.

quit, notice to Document requiring a person to leave land or premises. It is usual for a notice to quit to be given before proceedings are commenced for possession of residential premises.

quorum Specified number of members of any body who must be present before that body is legally entitled to make any decision or undertake any action.

R

race relations Relations between members of different racial groups. Discrimination on the grounds of race is controlled by the Race Relations Act 1976. *See also* **racial discrimination**.

racial discrimination Treating a person less favourably because of his or her racial group. The Race Relations Act 1976 makes it illegal to discriminate on the grounds of race in employment, education and the provision of goods, facilities or services. Certain exceptions exist. For example, it is acceptable to employ a member of a particular racial group for a part in a play in which race is important. *See also* **Commission for Racial Equality**.

racism Acts, values and policies motivated by beliefs in the significance of inherited racial characteristics and in the superiority or inferiority of particular races. *See also* **racial discrimination**.

rack rent Rent at the full market value for the property in question.

rape Unlawful sexual intercourse with a woman who does not consent by a man who either knows that the woman does not consent or is reckless as to whether or not she consents (Sexual Offences (Amendment) Act 1976 s.1). It is a criminal offence punishable with **life imprisonment**. Unlawful sexual intercourse means any intercourse apart from that between husband and wife. Thus a man cannot commit rape against his wife while the marriage continues. However, a wife may be raped by her husband after **judicial separation**, or **decree nisi** of **divorce**, or after obtaining a **non-molestation order.** In the late 1980s the rule that a man cannot rape his wife was criticized widely, and the Criminal Law Revision Committee and the **Law Commission** have recommended that the rule should not apply if spouses have ceased to live together. *See also* **molest**.

rates Taxes levied locally under legal powers by local authorities and water boards on occupiers of premises. Local authority rates were replaced by the **community charge** on 1 April 1990.

ratification Confirmation or approval of some act after the event. Thus, if an employee of a **company** who does not have authority to do so enters into a **contract** on the company's behalf, the company will not be bound by the contract. However, the company may later ratify the contract and become bound by it.

In **international law** it is common for a **treaty** between states to be negotiated by diplomats, but not to take effect until the governments of the countries involved ratify it.

rationalization Term with two applications.

First, the reduction (of, for example, a company) to an economically productive size by the cutting away of unprofitable elements.

Second, the use of false reasons to defend improper actions.

reading In Parliament, a stage in consideration of a **bill**. The first reading is formal notification of the bill, the second reading is a debate on the bill's principles, and the third reading, following committee discussion and amendment, is the final consideration and either approval or rejection of the bill.

real action Alternative term for an **action in rem**.

realm Kingdom, or area of rule. The term is little used, occurring notably in the term peers of the realm (members of the House of Lords) and in the Defence of the Realm Acts 1914, 1915 which imposed a form of martial law during World War I.

real property Freehold ownership of land.

realty Alternative term for **real property**.

reasonable man Hypothetical figure used in the law to indicate that the lawfulness of conduct should be judged according to the current standards of conduct accepted in society. Thus, the legal test for **negligence** is whether a person's conduct fell below the standard to be expected of the reasonable man. *See also* **man on the Clapham omnibus**.

rebut To contradict evidence or an argument raised in court by other evidence or a counter-argument.

receipt Written statement by which a person acknowledges that he or she has been paid a certain sum of money or received and paid for goods and services.

receiver Term with two applications.

First, a person appointed by the court or a **debenture** holder to receive and manage property belonging to a person who is under some legal disability. Thus, under the Insolvency Act 1986 a receiver may be appointed to take over and manage (normally by selling) the property of an insolvent **company** in order to raise money to pay the debenture holder, usually a bank. Under the Mental Health Act 1983 a court may appoint a receiver to manage the property of a person found to be mentally disordered and not capable of managing his or her own property.

Second, a person who commits the offence of **receiving stolen property**.

receiving stolen property Formerly, an offence under the Larceny Acts, committed by a person who came into possession of property knowing it to have been stolen. The offence is now **handling stolen goods**.

recess Period of closure of Parliament for vacation.

recidivism Tendency of discharged convicts to commit further crimes and be reconvicted.

reciprocal enforcement Enforcement of judgments given by courts in foreign countries when a reciprocal arrangement exists between the two countries. *See also* **foreign judgments**.

recitals Part of a **deed** that explains the purpose of the deed but does not have any legal effect. In a deed of **conveyance** of land, the recitals normally describe the property in question and its history. *See also* **operative part**.

reckless driving Offence under the Road Traffic Act 1972 s.2, committed when a person drives so as to create an obvious risk of causing injury to people or damage to property. Causing death by reckless driving is also an offence under the Road Traffic Act 1972 s.2.

recklessness Running an obvious risk of causing harm or giving no thought to such an obvious risk. Recklessness is an element in many offences, such as **criminal damage**, **manslaughter** and **reckless driving**.

recognizance Acknowledgement to a court of an obligation to do something. For instance, before the Bail Act 1976 a person charged with a criminal offence might be granted **bail** only if he or she agreed to enter into a recognizance to forfeit a certain sum of money to the court if he or she failed to return to court to face the charge at the appointed time. *See also* **binding over**.

reconciliation Process of settling disputes and remaking the relationship between a married couple whose relationship has broken down. **Divorce** proceedings may be adjourned for a period if the judge is not satisfied that the parties have had sufficient opportunity to attempt to reach a reconciliation.

reconveyance Process by which a person who has mortgaged property regains the full rights of ownership of the property upon paying off the **mortgage** debt. *See also* **equity of redemption; redemption**.

record Written account of the proceedings of a higher court.

Recorder Formerly, a part-time judge who presided over **quarter sessions** in a borough, but in modern times a part-time judge appointed under the Courts Act 1971 to try less serious cases in the **Crown Court**. A recorder must be a **barrister** or a **solicitor** of at least ten years' standing.

Recorder of London The senior permanent judge at the **Central Criminal Court** in London.

Records Office *See* **public records**.

recovery Receipt of **compensation** for a harm done, or the return of property to which one is entitled by order of a court.

rectification Legal proceedings by which a formal document, such as a **deed**, that contains an error or omission may be altered by order of the court so that it expresses the true intentions of the parties who made it.

rector Clergyman in charge of a Church of England parish, formerly entitled to receive the **tithes**.

The term is also used as the formal title of the head of some schools, colleges and universities.

redemption Regaining full rights of ownership to mortgaged property when the **mortgage** debt is paid off according to the terms of the mortgage. *See also* **equity of redemption; reconveyance**.

redundancy Dismissal of an employee because there is no longer any work for him or her to do. Under the Employment Protection (Consolidation) Act 1978, workers (apart from Crown employees and some other categories) are entitled to redundancy payments if they have either worked at least 16 hours per week for at least two years, or at least eight hours per week for at least five years. However, the employee will lose his right to the payment if he is offered another reasonable job and refuses it. The payment is calculated on the basis of half a week's pay for each year worked before the age of 22; one week's pay for each year worked between the ages of 22 and 40; and one and a half weeks' pay for every year worked between the ages of 41 and 65 (60 for women). *See also* **unfair dismissal; wrongful dismissal**.

re-examination Further questioning of a witness in a court by the party who called that witness, after the completion of the initial questioning (**examination-in-chief**) and questioning by the other party (**cross-examination**). Re-examination is not normally permitted, but it may be allowed if the witness has substantially contradicted what he or she said in examination-in-chief, during the cross-examination or introduced significant new information during the cross-examination.

referee Term with two applications.

First, a person who gives an opinion as to the character and abilities of another person, at the request of that person, to a third person. The **reference** given is protected by **qualified privilege**.

Second, a person to whom parties to a dispute may refer a disputed question of fact for a decision. The parties are bound to accept the referee's decision. *See also* **official referee**.

reference Term with two applications.

First, opinion as to the character and abilities of another person, supplied at that person's request, to a third person. It is protected by **qualified privilege**.

Second, the process by which a dispute is passed to a **court** or **arbitrator** for a decision.

referendum Special election to record formally voters' opinions on important issues. Britain's only full referendum was in 1975, when the vote was two to one in favour of membership of the European Economic community. In 1979, referenda were held in Scotland and Wales, but did not produce the majority required to lead to the setting up of Scottish and Welsh assemblies.

refreshing memory Reminding oneself of what one had observed on an earlier occasion by reference to a written record made by oneself very soon after the events in question. In the law of **evidence**, although a witness is not allowed to produce such a document as evidence, he or she may refer to such a document while giving oral evidence in court. The most common example is the police officer referring to his or her notebook.

refugee Person who flees from his or her country of residence because of a fear of persecution on racial, religious or political grounds or because of hardship brought about by natural disaster or famine. In **international law**, the conduct of states towards refugees is regulated by the United Nations Convention on the Status of Refugees 1951.

regent Person appointed to rule in place of the rightful Sovereign under the Regency Act 1937.

regicide Killing of a king or queen. It amounts to the crime of **treason** as well as **murder**.

registered land Land, the ownership of which is recorded at the Land Registry under the system of **land registration**. The entry in the register conclusively determines who owns the land and the title deeds become irrelevant for legal purposes.

registered office Address nominated by a limited **company** as the place to which all official correspondence relating to the company may be addressed. The registered office of a company may be discovered by inspecting the register maintained by the **Registrar of Companies**.

registered user Person or body in possession of a licence under the Data Protection Act to hold personal information about individuals for particular purposes on a computer data bank.

registrar Term with two applications.

First, an officer with legal responsibility to maintain a register, such as a Registrar of Births, Marriages and Deaths.

Second, a judicial officer who may make rulings on procedure and may exercise some judicial powers. In the **Family Division** of the **High Court** the registrar may make any decision relating to a case except those which must be made by a judge in open court. In the **County Court**, the registrar has administrative functions, but may also sit as a judge in cases tried in the County Court.

Registrar of Companies Officer appointed to scrutinize the documentation produced by a **company**. He certifies **incorporation** by issuing a certificate to the company, and supervises the filing of documents such as accounts and **debentures**. *See also* **articles of association; memorandum of association**.

Registrar of Criminal Appeals Officer of the **Court of Appeal** (Criminal Division) who has administrative responsibility for **appeals** and who deals with matters such as arranging the schedules of the court, getting all relevant papers from the trial court and giving all parties notice of when cases will be heard.

Registrar of Shipping Person appointed to keep the register of British ships under the Merchant Shipping Act 1894. British ships must be owned either by British subjects or by a **company** incorporated in the United Kingdom.

Registrar of Trade Marks Officer with the responsibility for registering **trade marks** under powers in the Trade Marks Act 1938.

registration of births, deaths and marriages Recording, legally required, of all live births, still births, deaths and marriages with a local **registrar**. The information is centralized in the General Register Office.

registration of maintenance orders Process by which orders for **maintenance** issued by the **High Court** are notified and registered with the **Magistrates' Court** so that they may be enforced locally.

registration of vehicles System of registration of vehicle ownership operated by the Department of Transport. The keeper of a motor vehicle must register the fact with the Driver and Vehicle Licensing Centre (DVLC). The keeper will receive a registration document which must be passed to the next owner if the vehicle is sold. If the car is sold the DVLC must be informed by both the seller and the buyer. It is a criminal offence, punishable by a fine, to fail to do so.

regulated agreement Agreement for a loan or the purchase of something on credit or **hire-purchase**, regulated by the Consumer Credit Act 1974. *See also* **consumer credit**.

regulated tenancy Tenancy under which the tenant may register the rent, which cannot be increased, and under which the tenant is fully protected from **eviction** by the landlord.

Regulation Form of law created by the **European Community** which is issued by the administrative bodies of the Community. It has direct effect on all member states. In theory, a regulation automatically becomes law in the United Kingdom when it is issued, but in practice some legislative action is usually taken to implement the change.

rehabilitation of offenders Rule of law embodied in the Rehabilitation of Offenders Act 1974 that any person who has not been convicted of a serious offence for a specified period of time may consider any earlier convictions to be spent and will be treated as if he or she was never convicted. The period of time for rehabilitation varies according to the age of the individual, the offence committed and the severity of the sentence imposed. The rule does not apply to any person who has served more than three months' imprisonment.

re-hearing New hearing of a case which has already been heard and decided upon in a previous hearing – for example, an **appeal** from a decision made in the **Magistrates' Court** to the **Crown Court**.

reinstatement Remedy that may be granted by an **industrial tribunal** when a former employee has successfully proved that he or she has been the victim of **unfair dismissal**. The employer is required to re-employ the employee in the same position and under the same conditions as before.

relation back Principle that an act is assumed to have taken effect from an earlier date. For instance, when a court grants **probate** of a **will** it is assumed to have been granted from the moment the maker of the will died.

relator Person at whose request the **Attorney-General** commences legal proceedings. For instance, in cases of public **nuisance**, criminal proceedings may be taken by the Attorney-General against an individual or organization after a complaint has been received by a member of the public.

release Act of a person who, owed an obligation by another, discharges the other from performing the obligation. For instance, if an employee is required by **contract** to give three months' notice if he or she wishes to resign, this is an obligation owed to the employer. The employer may, however, release the employee from the obligation.

relevant Having a significant bearing on a particular question. In legal proceedings **evidence** may not be given unless it is relevant.

relief Term for the remedy requested by a **plaintiff** in civil proceedings.

remainder Right to ownership of land that comes into operation in the future, after a period during which somebody else has a right to the land.

remand Postponement of a criminal trial until a later date. During this period the **defendant** may be remanded on **bail** or in **custody**. The decision to remand a person in custody must be made by a court and should be made only if it is inappropriate in the circumstances to grant bail.

remedy Means by which the law protects an individual's rights or compensates an individual for infringement of a right. In an action for **breach of contract**, for instance, the court may order a remedy of **specific performance** to ensure that the contract is performed as originally agreed. In an action for **negligence**, the court may order a remedy of **damages** to be paid to the victim to compensate for any injury suffered. In an action for private **nuisance** the court may grant an **injunction** to prevent the nuisance from occurring again.

remission Term with two applications.

First, the pardon of an offender by reduction of his or her sentence of imprisonment.

Second, the release of a debtor's obligation to pay the debt.

remoteness Term with two applications.

First, the circumstance in which a transfer of property is designed to take effect in the future beyond the period of time laid down under the rule against **perpetuities**. Such a transfer of property is invalid.

Second, description of loss, injury or damage which would not have been foreseen by a **reasonable man**. **Damages** which are claimed following a breach of **contract** or the commission of a **tort** may be refused by a court on the grounds that the loss or injury are too remote.

rent Payment in money, goods or services which a tenant must make periodically to the landlord under the terms of a **lease**.

rent book Receipt book which records the weekly rent paid by a tenant to a landlord. By law, it must contain details of the tenant's legal rights. Only weekly tenants need be provided with a rent book. Failure to provide it is a criminal offence.

rentcharge Sum of money payable by the owner of land to some other person who has no other legal interest in the land. Under the Rentcharges Act 1977 it is not possible to create new rentcharges and existing rentcharges will be extinguished 60 years after the passing of the act.

rent officer Administrator appointed under the Rent Act 1977 to keep registers of rents and to consider applications in relation to **fair rents**.

rent rebate Reduction in the amount of rent which must be paid by tenants of local-authority housing, calculated according to the tenant's means under the Social Security and Housing Benefit Act 1982. *See also* **housing benefit**.

rent restriction Limit set on the amount of rent which may be claimed from tenants of certain categories of housing. The limits are set under the Rent Acts 1974 and 1977.

rent tribunal Panel of three persons appointed under the Rent Acts to decide disputes about the levels of **fair rent** set by **rent officers**. Either the landlord or the tenant may appeal to the tribunal against the rent set by the rent officer.

renunciation Giving up or disclaiming of something. For instance, it is a renunciation for an **agent** to inform his **principal** that he will no longer act on the principal's behalf. *See also* **repudiation**; **waiver**.

repairing obligations Duty in relation to premises which are let, to keep the structure, roof and installations and services in good repair. In many cases the **lease** will specify whether the landlord or tenant has the obligation to repair. However, if the lease does not specify this and is for less than seven years, the repairing obligations fall on the landlord (Landlord and Tenant Act 1985 ss.13–14).

repatriation Removal of a person from one country to the country in which he or she was born or the country of which he or she is a national. There is no legal power to do this except by **deportation**.

repeal To nullify **legislation**. An **Act of Parliament** may only be repealed by a later Act of Parliament. Express repeal occurs when the later Act clearly states that the earlier Act is repealed. Implied repeal occurs when the later Act makes no mention of the earlier Act, but by its provisions is presumed to repeal the earlier.

replication Formerly, in a **civil action** the answer which the **plaintiff** makes after the **defendant** has submitted his **defence** or **counterclaim**. It is now called the **reply**.

reply In legal proceedings an answer made to the argument made on behalf of the opposing side. At the **pleadings** stage in a **civil action**, the reply is the answer which the **plaintiff** makes to the **defence** made by the defendant. In a criminal **trial**, the reply is the answer made by the **prosecution** after the argument of the defence has been put.

reply, right of In legal proceedings, the right of the **plaintiff** to respond to any points raised by the **defendant**. However, it is not permissible to use the right of reply as a means of launching a new argument altogether.

reporting restrictions Order made by a court that certain evidence disclosed in a trial should not be reported in newspapers or other media. Under the Contempt of Court Act 1981 s.4, a court may impose reporting restrictions when it appears necessary to avoid a risk of prejudice to the course of justice in the case with which the court is dealing or with any other legal proceedings. For example, it may be disclosed that a witness at one trial has a criminal record, and if that witness has been charged with an offence and is awaiting his or her own trial, it would be proper for the judge to prohibit the reporting of his criminal record, because this might have the effect of causing the jury at his own trial to be prejudiced against him before they had heard the evidence.

representation Term with two applications.

First, the role of a person who is authorized in law to dispose of the property of someone who has died according to the law of **succession**. *See also* **personal representative**.

Second, statement of fact or opinion. *See also* **misrepresentation**.

representative Person who acts for another or others, for example as an **agent** or **personal representative** or lawyer.

representative action Special procedure available in the High Court in circumstances in which a number of separate **plaintiffs** have similar claims against a single defendant. The plaintiffs may club together and a single case be tried involving just one of their claims. The decision of the court in that case then becomes the decision in each of the cases. For example, in 20 cases babies have been injured by eating nails found in a particular type of baby food. The parents wish to sue the manufacturer for **negligence**. In each case the sole issue is whether the manufacturer was negligent. The parents may use the representative action procedure and a single claim will be dealt with by the court. If the court decides that the manufacturer was negligent, all the parents will succeed and be entitled to **damages**.

reprieve Postponement or permanent suspension of the carrying out of a sentence imposed by a court.

reprisal Seizure of the goods of an alleged wrongdoer as compensation for the wrong done. This is not lawful, since the proper means of seeking compensation is either through negotiation or legal proceedings.

Reprisal is also used more generally to mean the taking of revenge. Reprisals taken against witnesses or jurors after a trial amount to **contempt of court**, even if the reprisal taken is not itself unlawful – for instance, if the witness is barred from a public house or club because of the evidence that he or she gave.

repudiation Act, by one party to a **contract**, by which he or she indicates to the other party that the obligations under the contract will not be carried out. Repudiation may be by words, or by conduct. Thus, if one party fails persistently to perform his or her obligations under a contract, this may be taken as repudiation (described as a repudiatory breach). If repudiation has occurred, the other party is released from performing his or her obligations under the contract and may **sue** for **breach of contract**.

reputation Esteem in which a person is held in the eyes of others. Reputation is protected by the law of **defamation** of character.

request *See* **letter of request**.

requisitions on title In relation to a **conveyance** of **land**, a request made by the purchaser (or solicitor) to the seller (or solicitor) in which further information is sought in regard to the seller's **title** to the property. It is usually made between the exchange of contracts and completion of the sale.

rescission In contract law, a remedy which is available to a person

who has been induced to enter a contract by **fraud** or
misrepresentation, by which he or she may escape liability under the
contract. In law the parties are treated as if the contract had never
existed. Rescission is not possible if the contract has been partly
performed and it is impossible to put the parties into the position they
occupied before the contract. In that case, the party who has been
wrongly induced to enter the contract must gain a remedy by an action
for **damages**.

rescue Term with two applications.

First, the offence under **common law** of securing the release of a
prisoner from lawful custody − for example, if the person has been
arrested and is being taken to a police station.

Second, a remedy available to a person whose goods have been
unlawfully taken by another, by which he or she is permitted to take
them back.

reservation Limitation placed on the scope of something which is
given. For instance a person might agree to a contractual offer made
by another, but with a reservation. In this case, assent is given to most
of the terms proposed, but not to all of them.

reservation of title Provision of a contract, whereby the seller of
goods remains the owner of the goods until he or she has been paid
for them.

reserve Term with two applications.

First, in relation to auctions, the minimum price which the seller is
prepared to accept. If the auction of a particular item is stated to be
without reserve, then by law that item must be sold to the highest
bidder however low the bid.

Second, the capital of a **company** which is placed in a special fund
and which under the **articles of association** of the company may be
called upon only in the event of the **winding-up** of the company.

residence Place where a person lives or where a company conducts its
business. Residence is important in deciding a person's **domicile** for
taxation purposes and for establishing eligibility to vote at elections.

residential occupier Person who is, or has recently been, the occupant of particular premises as a home. Under the Criminal Law Act 1977 s.7, it is an offence for a trespasser, who has taken occupation of premises and by doing so displaced the residential occupier, to refuse to leave those premises when requested to do so by the displaced residential occupier. *See also* **trespass**.

residuary legatee Person who receives all outstanding property of a deceased person after any gifts specified in the **will** have been distributed or any persons entitled to benefit have received their inheritance. *See also* **legacy**.

residue Remainder of a dead person's **estate** once all debts and funeral expenses have been paid and once all gifts have been distributed. The person who receives the residue is called the **residuary legatee**. If no person is named as the residuary legatee the residue will be distributed according to the rules of **intestacy**.

resisting arrest Criminal offence, committed if a person resists a lawful **arrest**. The offence is committed even if the person is not subsequently charged with any other crime, so long as the arrest was lawful in the first place. *See also* **arrest with a warrant**; **arrest without a warrant**; **citizen's arrest**.

resolution Formal expression of intention or opinion by a meeting. For instance, a declaration that expresses the agreed opinion of the **House of Commons** is made in the form of a resolution. Members of **companies** also pass resolutions when making decisions at a general meeting.

respondent Term with two applications.

First, a person who answers an allegation brought before a court by means of a **petition**. For instance, the person against whom a **divorce** petition is brought is called the respondent.

Second, a person who defends an **appeal** against a decision of an inferior court. For instance, if a case is decided in favour of one party in the High Court and another party appeals against the decision to the Court of Appeal, the latter party is called the **appellant** and the former, who is defending the appeal, is called the respondent.

restitution Return of money or other property, by order of the court, to another. The order may be given if the property was transferred under a mistake or under a transaction which is **void**, or if there is a duty in **quasi-contract** to hand it over.

restraint of marriage Term of a contract whereby one person is restrained either from marrying anyone or from marrying a particular person. Contracts in restraint of marriage are **void** because they are considered to be against the public interest.

restriction order Order that imposes restrictions on an offender who has been committed to a special hospital by a **Magistrates' Court** or a **Crown Court** upon conviction for an offence. The restrictions may be for a specified period of time or of unlimited duration.

restrictive covenant Condition attached to particular land that restricts the use of that land for the benefit of some adjoining property. For instance, a covenant may restrict the erection of fences or the building of extensions. The covenant must be registered as a **land charge** in order to be enforceable against subsequent owners of the property.

restrictive trade practices Agreements in relation to recommended prices of products, terms of supply and manufacturing processes made by persons carrying on similar businesses. They must be registered with the Director General of Fair Trading, who may refer any trade practices to the Restrictive Practices Court for investigation if there is any suspicion that the practices may be against the public interest.

resulting trust Trust which arises when the property in the **trust** reverts to the original owner because the trust fails. For example, if a person leaves £100,000 in trust for another as a wedding present, but the wedding is subsequently declared void, the money would revert to the donor in the form of a resulting trust.

retailer Seller of goods to the public from shop premises. *See also* **wholesaler**.

retainer Engagement of a barrister or solicitor for a fee to take action for a client or to defend the client in legal proceedings. A retainer is necessary before the lawyer can act.

retirement by rotation Provision in the **articles of association** of a **company** by which the directors retire from the board of directors in rotation. For instance, if a company has nine directors, the articles might require that each year the three who have served longest should retire.

retrial New trial of a case. The **Court of Appeal** may order the retrial of a criminal case tried before a jury if significant new evidence becomes available after conviction.

In **civil actions** in which a **jury** has reached a decision and an appeal court is of the opinion that the decision is unjustifiable a retrial may be ordered. *See also* **new trial**.

retribution Punishment. One of the aims of the criminal justice system is to punish people who have committed criminal offences. The most serious form of punishment is imprisonment since this takes away the freedom of the person convicted.

return Formal document, submitted to a court by a **bailiff**, which certifies that he or she has executed the judgment of the court as ordered.

revenue Income, especially income received through taxation or returns on investment.

revenue offences Offences that are related to making false tax returns, fraudulently evading tax liability and failing to pay tax as required.

reversal Decision of an **appeal** court to overturn or set aside a decision reached in an inferior court.

reversion Interest in land or property which remains in the possession of a landowner when he or she transfers part of the ownership to someone else. For instance, a person who owns the **freehold** of a cottage and transfers the land to someone else for life maintains the reversion of the property, since the cottage will revert to him or her on the death of the other person.

revival Renewal of a right after it has been extinguished. For instance, a **will** which has been cancelled may be revived by re-executing it with the correct formalities.

revocation The cancellation of something which has been done. An offer, for instance, may be revoked at any time before it is accepted. A **will** may be revoked at any time before the death of the **testator,** either by destruction or by a document or new will that specifies that the old will is to be cancelled.

revolution Change in a political or social structure — for example, a government. Commonly understood to mean radical or sudden change.

rider Term with two applications.

First, a clause added to a **bill** which is passing through Parliament to amend the contents of the bill.

Second, an additional recommendation attached to the verdict of a **jury,** such as a recommendation of mercy in murder cases when the **death penalty** was in existence.

right Claim which others are bound to respect and which is protected by law.

right of action Right to bring legal proceedings against another. For instance, a person who is run over and injured by a negligent driver has a right of action against the driver.

right of audience Right to appear and conduct cases in court. Any individual is entitled to conduct his or her own case in court, although in practice most people employ a legal representative. **Barristers** have exclusive rights of audience in the superior courts. Solicitors may appear in the **Magistrates' Courts** and **County Courts**.

right of entry Right of taking or resuming possession of land or property. This right usually arises when a tenant has broken one of the conditions of a **lease**. The landlord may exercise the right of entry only if adequate warning of the infringement and adequate time to remedy the situation has been given to the tenant. The right must be exercised peacefully. If this is not possible the assistance of the court must be sought.

right of silence Rule that an individual, suspected of or charged with a criminal offence, is not obliged to answer questions relating to the offence. A person who is arrested must be warned that he or she is not obliged to say anything before being questioned by the police. A person standing trial for a criminal offence may not be forced to give evidence. However, if a person is silent, either in the police station or at trial, a court is at liberty to assume that the silence is evidence of guilt.

right of way Legal right to pass along a specified route across land that belongs to another. The right may relate to a particular means of transport – for example, by foot but not by a motor vehicle, or by a private car but not by a commercial lorry. A right of way may be granted to another person by the owner of the land, or it may become a right after a person has used a particular route for 20 years without interruption. *See also* **bridleways**; **footpaths**.

riot Criminal offence under the Public Order Act 1986 s.1(1), committed when 12 or more people who are present together use or threaten to use unlawful violence for a common purpose. Their conduct, taken together, is such that a person of reasonable firmness who is present at the scene fears for his or her personal safety. The offence may be committed in private or in public.

riparian Adjoining a river. The owner of riparian land acquires riparian rights relating to the river bank such as fishing and irrigation.

road accident An accident on a road requires that the people involved stop and, if requested, supply their names and addresses. In the event of injury, the people involved must in addition either provide insurance details, or report the accident to the police (Road Traffic Act 1972, ss.25 and 166). Liability attaches if the road accident should have been foreseen and avoided.

robbery Criminal offence under the Theft Act 1968 s.8, committed when a person uses or threatens to use force in order to steal. The offence carries a maximum penalty of **life imprisonment**. A common form of robbery, popularly known as mugging, occurs when a person attacks another in the street and steals his or her money or possessions.

rolls Former name for court records.

Roman Law System of law that originated in the Roman Empire and was developed in the Eastern Roman empire, particularly by the Emperor Justinian. Roman Law is still highly influential and forms the basis of law in most continental European countries and Scotland.

rout Former criminal offence, committed when three or more persons gathered together with the intention to do something which, if executed, would amount to a **riot**. The offence was abolished by the Public Order Act 1986.

Royal Assent Formal notice by **letters patent** of Parliament's passage of legislation. The Sovereign ceased to give the Royal Assent in person in 1854, and the current procedure follows the Royal Assent Act 1967.

Royal Commission Group of people appointed by the Government to investigate some issue and recommend legal change. Royal Commissions are frequently used as a means of bringing about legal change.

royalty Periodical payment made by a publisher to an author or a record company to a musician calculated on the basis of the number of copies of the book or record sold.

rule Term with two applications.

First, a particular statement of law, especially in relation to law that governs the procedure of a court. Thus, the procedure of the High Court is governed by the **Rules of the Supreme Court**.

Second, the order of a superior court in relation to a particular issue.

Rule Committee Committee, chaired by the **Lord Chancellor** and consisting of senior judges, **barristers** and **solicitors**, responsible for making the procedural **rules** that regulate the **Supreme Court of Judicature**. These rules have the force of law by virtue of the Supreme Court Act 1984. They are published in the **White Book**.

rule of law Principle embodied in the legal system which implies a number of concepts essential in a free society. The concepts are these: that all men are equal before the law, whatever their rank or station, and as such are all subject to the ordinary law and procedures of the courts; that no man shall be punished unless convicted in an ordinary court for a definite breach of the law; and that the government is subject to the law.

Rules of the Supreme Court Rules relating to procedure in the **High Court of Justice** and the other courts of the Supreme **Court of Judicature**. *See also* **Rule Committee**.

S

sale of goods Contract whereby the owner of goods transfers ownership of goods to another in return for money. Contracts for the sale of goods are controlled by the Sale of Goods Act 1979, which incorporates **implied terms** in the contract that the goods sold will be of merchantable quality and fit for the purpose for which they are intended. *See also* **fitness for purpose**; **supply of goods and services**.

salvage Compensation payable to any person who voluntarily and successfully assists in the rescue of a ship, its cargo or its passengers from danger. Claims for salvage may be made in the **High Court of Justice**, which will assess the amount payable.

sanction Means used to enforce compliance with the law. In criminal cases the **sentence** of the court is the sanction. In a civil action the order of the court at the end of the case, awarding **damages** or ordering an **injunction**, is the sanction.

In **international law**, a sanction is a measure agreed upon by a number of states which is disadvantageous to a particular state and which is designed to force that state to comply with international law.

sanctuary Formerly, place in which a person gained immunity from arrest or punishment by law. Generally, sanctuary was available in churches and monasteries. The right was abolished in 1623. *See also* **abjuration**.

satisfaction Giving of a thing or a service to another person, which is accepted by that person instead of the performance of an obligation which is owed to him. For instance, a motor car may be offered and accepted in place of a money debt, which is then legally extinguished.

scandalizing the court Form of **contempt of court**, committed by publishing something that is either gratuitously abusive of a court or judges, or that suggests impropriety or corruption.

scheme of arrangement Contract between a debtor and all his **creditors** by which the creditors agree not to make the debtor bankrupt provided that the debtor agrees to pay his debts by instalments or to pay each creditor a fixed proportion of the debt owed.

seal Wax or a piece of red paper used to seal a document and which may have a mark impressed into it to indicate the maker of the document. Certain documents are required by law to be under seal. *See also* **deed**.

search *See* **power of entry to premises**; **power to stop and search**.

search warrant Authority granted by a **Magistrates' Court** or individual **justice of the peace** to a police officer to search named premises. The court or magistrate must be satisfied that there are reasonable grounds to believe the premises contain material which would be evidence of a serious **arrestable offence** (Police and Criminal Evidence Act 1984 s.8).

seat belt Belt fitted in a motor vehicle to restrain a person in the event of sudden stopping or impact. It has been compulsory to fit seat belts to new vehicles since 1964. Since 1983 it is an offence for a person in the front seats of a vehicle not to wear a seat belt while the car is in motion. Drivers of police and emergency vehicles, taxi drivers and delivery drivers are exempt. A person who has difficulty wearing a seat belt for a medical reason may obtain an exemption certificate from a doctor.

secondary picketing Being at a place of work, other than one's own place of work, for the purpose of communicating information to workers in relation to an industrial dispute. It falls outside the provisions of the Trade Union and Labour Relations Act 1974, which makes some forms of **picketing** lawful. Secondary picketing is unlawful if it amounts to inciting workers to break their contracts of employment.

Secret Service Organization responsible for part of the United Kingdom's intelligence work, counter-intelligence and national security work.

secret trust Form of **trust**, created by a **will**, in which a person leaves property to another person subject to a duty that the property be held for the benefit of a third person.

Secretary of State Senior minister in the British Government, responsible for one of the major departments of state.

secularization Gradual loss of non-religious functions from religious institutions to secular institutions.

secure tenancy Tenancy of a council house or flat or one leased from a **housing association** that provides the tenant with **security of tenure**, except for non-payment of rent or other breaches of the **lease**.

security for costs Deposit of money or some other valuable security with a court by the **plaintiff** in a **civil action** in order to guarantee that, if the plaintiff loses and is ordered to pay the **defendant's** costs, there will be money available. The court may order that security be provided in the following instances: if the plaintiff is not resident in the United Kingdom; if the plaintiff is a **company** and there is reason to believe that it has insufficient funds to pay the costs; or if the plaintiff has misstated his address, or changed it in order to avoid the consequences of losing the case.

security of tenure Legal protection for something which a person holds, such as a job or tenancy of land or premises.

sedition Criminal offence, consisting of any conduct for the purpose of inciting hatred and contempt of the Sovereign or the Government or stirring up public dissatisfaction with the Government. An exception is made for open discussion of matters of public concern and frank criticism. *See also* **treason**.

seditious libel Criminal offence of publishing seditious material. *See* **sedition; treason**.

seduction Formerly, civil action for **damages** which could be brought by the parent or husband of a woman who had been seduced by another man. It was abolished by the Law Reform (Miscellaneous Provisions) Act 1970.

segregation Cultural, social or geographical separation of different ethnic or social groups within a society.

seisin Actual occupation of **freehold** land. The person in occupation is said to be seised of the land. Seisin is protected by the law unless some other person can show a better right to the land.

seizure *See* **power of seizure.**

select committee Parliamentary committee which investigates matters within its remit by questioning relevant ministers, civil servants and others and issues reports. Most select committees are limited to the work of an individual Government department.

self-defence Lawful justification for the use of force against another person. It is a **defence** to a charge of violent crime against another person that the violence was used in self-defence. The defence is available to any person who uses force to protect himself or any other person from an attack or to prevent another person from committing a crime. The force used must be reasonable. It is not self-defence to use more force than is necessary in the circumstances, nor to use force in retaliation after the initial attack has stopped.

Senate of the Inns of Court and the Bar Governing body of the **Bar**, which represents the four **Inns of Court** on matters of common interest. The Senate operates through a variety of standing committees, such as the Professional Conduct Committee, which deals with complaints and disciplinary matters. The Senate works closely with the Council of Legal Education, which is responsible for setting the examinations for entry to the profession. *See also* **Bar Council**.

sentence Penalty imposed on a person convicted of a criminal offence. Sentences available include **fine, imprisonment**, detention in a Young Offender Institution, **suspended sentence**, and **community service order**. For most crimes maximum penalties are set by statute and the judge will use his or her discretion in selecting an appropriate penalty up to the maximum. For **murder**, however, there is a mandatory sentence of **life imprisonment**. *See also* **probation order**.

separate trial Trial of two or more **defendants**, charged with the same offences, separately. The trial judge has a discretion to order separate trials if one or more of the defendants applies for it. Separate trials will be ordered if it would be prejudicial for one defendant to be tried with his co-defendant – for example, if each defendant asserts that the other was solely responsible for the offence.

separation agreement Agreement between a husband and wife to live apart. An agreement to separate is not generally considered to be legally binding on either party since the courts are reluctant to enforce agreements between husband and wife when the parties have not had the benefit of legal advice. The alternative is to obtain a **judicial separation** order or to formalize the agreement in a **separation deed**.

separation deed Formalized agreement between a husband and wife to live apart, set out in a **deed**. A typical deed contains arrangements for **maintenance**, care of the children, and a mutual agreement to release each spouse from the marital duty to live together. A formal separation is a suitable alternative to **divorce** in cases in which there is a chance of reconciliation or the couple object to divorce for religious reasons. *See also* **judicial separation**; **separation agreement**.

separation of powers Principle of **constitutional law** by which the three branches of State authority, the legislature, the executive and the judiciary, should be independent of each other.

sequestration Remedy for **contempt of court** by which the court gives authority to named persons (the sequestrators) to enter the premises of the person or body which has committed contempt, and seize assets or manage the assets for the benefit of the court. The owner may regain his premises and property by **purging the contempt**.

Serjeant-at-Arms Officer of Parliament responsible for security, and for accommodation and services provided for MPs.

service of documents Delivery of a **writ** or **summons** or other formal document issued by a court to the person to whom it is addressed. Service is necessary before the document has legal effect. If a person has named a **solicitor** to conduct the proceedings, delivery to the solicitor is sufficient. If a person refuses to accept the document it is sufficient to touch that person with the document and to state that service is being made. *See also* **service by post**.

service by post Alternative to **service of documents** by personal delivery. Service may be made through the ordinary post to the **defendant's** ordinary or last known address. Service to a **company** may be made by post to the **registered office**.

session Term with two applications.

First, sitting of Parliament from the date of the opening ceremony to the prorogation.

Second, sitting of a court in its judicial capacity.

set-off Defence to a civil action for compensation that effectively acknowledges the **plaintiff's** claim, but makes a monetary claim against the plaintiff which extinguishes or diminishes the plaintiff's claim. The amount set-off may be a fixed sum, such as an outstanding **debt**, or a claim for **damages** which must be calculated by the court.

settlement Tying land and property up for the future by leaving it to **trustees** to hold it for successive owners who have a limited interest in the land or property.

settle out of court To terminate a legal dispute by arriving at a satisfactory agreement before the case comes to trial. Most civil claims are settled before the proposed date of the court hearing.

several tenancy Tenancy held by a person in his or her own right, and not jointly with any other person.

severance pay Payment made to an employee whose **contract** of employment has been cut short.

severing the indictment Order by a court that different offences included in a **indictment** be tried separately.

sex discrimination Treating a person less favourably because of that person's sex or marital status. The discrimination may be direct, such as only employing men, or indirect, if conditions are imposed on a particular job which effectively limit the opportunities of a particular sex. The Sex Discrimination Act 1975 allows any individual who has been discriminated against, whether in the field of employment or in any other field such as accommodation or education, to take legal action against the person who has practised discrimination. In addition the Act created the Equal Opportunities Commission to monitor general problems of sex discrimination. *See also* **discrimination; equal pay; racial discrimination.**

sexism Doctrine or practice of discrimination on the basis of sex.

sexual intercourse Intercourse by insertion of the penis in the vagina. Under the Sexual Offences Act 1956 s.44, intercourse is complete on penetration. It is not necessary to prove emission of semen. This definition applies for the purpose of **rape** and other **sexual offences** involving intercourse.

sexual offence Crime involving sexual intercourse and other acts done with a sexual motive, punishable under the Sexual Offences Acts 1956–1985. Sexual offences include **rape, indecent assault, incest, abduction** for sexual purposes, **unlawful sexual intercourse** and offences linked to **prostitution**.

share Proportion of the capital of a **company**, owned by a member of the company called a shareholder, who shares in the profits and loss of the company. Members of the public invest money in companies by purchasing shares with the aim of making a capital gain if the company is successful, as well as receiving **dividends** on the shares. There are three types of shares: ordinary shares, in which the dividend fluctuates with the fortunes of the company; preference shares in which dividends are paid at a fixed rate regardless of the success of the company; and deferred shares, in which the holder is entitled to a dividend only after all other shareholders have been paid.

The company must issue shareholders with a certificate that gives details of their shareholdings within two months of their issue.

shareholder Person who owns shares in a **company**. The rights of the shareholder are determined by the size of his or her shareholding and the type of shares held.

sheriff Officer of the **High Court of Justice** with responsibility for **execution** of judgments.

shop Business from which the retail sale of goods to the public by a retailer takes place. The Offices, Shops and Railway Premises Act 1963 lays down standards of health, safety and welfare for employees working on such premises. *See also* **Sunday trading**.

shoplifting Popular term for the criminal offence of **theft** from a shop during opening hours.

Short Cause List List of simple legal actions in the **Queen's Bench Division** of the High Court which can be tried in a short time, usually under two hours.

short committal Procedure whereby **magistrates,** with the consent of the **defendant,** commit him or her to trial in the **Crown Court** without the formal procedure of a full **committal for trial**. By giving consent, the defendant acknowledges that this is a *prima facie* case against him or her. The short committal was first introduced by the Criminal Justice Act 1967 and it is now the most common form of **committal**. It is known as a "section 6(2) committal" since the procedure is now governed by that section of the Magistrates' Courts Act 1980.

shorthand note Note made in shorthand of the evidence, legal argument and judicial decision in superior courts. Transcripts of such notes are made available to **appeal** courts if an appeal against the decision is lodged.

short title Name by which an Act of Parliament is commonly known. Most Acts state their short title in one of the sections of the Act.

shotgun certificate *See* **firearms; firearms certificate**

sick pay Payment made to an employee who is absent from work through illness. Most employees are entitled to statutory sick pay, which is a cash payment payable for up to 28 weeks. It is paid initially by the employer, who later claims a refund from the State. The payment is available only to employees, not to self-employed people.

Some contracts of employment give employees the right to sick pay from their employer in addition to that provided by the State.

signature Name of a person or a mark or sign representing that name, written by the hand of that person. A signature shows an intention to be bound by the contents of the document signed.

sign manual Signature of the Sovereign.

silk Name by which **Queen's Counsel** are commonly known by virtue of the fact that they wear silk gowns.

similar fact evidence At the trial of an alleged offence, evidence relating to other offences. This may be given because the other offences are so similar to the alleged offence as to make it very likely that all offences were committed by the same person. The rule that similar fact evidence may be given is an exception to the general rule that in a criminal trial the court must not hear evidence relating to other crimes allegedly committed by the **defendant**.

simony Corruption in the appointment of a cleric to a **benefice**.

single-parent family Social unit made up of a single parent and his or her child or children. Single-parent families may be entitled to additional income support.

sitting Term with two applications.

First, the period during which the High Court is in session. The legal year is divided into four sittings, called Hilary, Easter, Trinity and Michaelmas. These sittings are roughly equivalent to the four seasons except that there are no sittings at all during August and September, so that Michaelmas starts on 1 October.

Second, meetings of each House of Parliament to conduct public business. Each meeting is called a sitting, which continues until it is adjourned.

slander Publication of untrue statement, usually by spoken word, which tends to lower a person's reputation in the eyes of right-thinking members of society. Slander is the publication of material which amounts to **defamation** in a non-permanent form, as opposed to **libel**, which is publication in a permanent form. The wronged party may sue the maker of the statement for **damages** or an **injunction** or both.

sleeping partner Partner in a firm who takes no part in the running of the business, but who remains equally liable for any debts which the firm may acquire. *See also* **partnership**.

slip rule Rule that any minor or clerical error in the **judgment** or **order** of a court may be corrected by the court at any time upon the application of an interested party.

small claims court Popular name for the **County Court** that sits to hear legal disputes in which the amount claimed is small (currently £500 or less) and in which both parties agree that a more informal procedure known as **arbitration** may be used to resolve the dispute. The **registrar** who is responsible for the day-to-day running of the County Court usually acts as arbitrator. The procedure is quick, cheap and informal and does not require the parties to obtain legal representation to present their cases. Most small claims cases are consumer disputes.

smallholding Holding of agricultural land which is smaller than a small farm. Smallholdings are regulated by various **Acts of Parliament**, including the Agriculture Act 1970 and the Local Government Act 1972.

smuggling Criminal offence, committed when a person imports or exports prohibited goods or imports or exports any goods secretly in order to avoid paying **Customs and Excise** duties.

social contract Explanation, originally put forward by Hobbes, of the origins and implications of common rights and obligations in society. The acceptance by people that they have to give up complete personal freedom to allow social order to be established by society.

social enquiry report Report made available to a court, prepared by probation officers or social workers to provide information on a convicted person's character, domestic circumstances and physical and mental condition. Such reports are considered by the court before sentencing that person.

socialization Process by which a person learns to conform to the social norms of a particular society. It is the process of the communication of 'culture' to an individual.

social justice Fairness and equity in the allocation of material benefits and advantages. The fairness of social organization.

social mobility Movement between different levels of the social hierarchy.

social order Structure and cohesion within a society derived from its members' participation in shared beliefs and values that are usually of a moral or ethical nature.

social security appeal tribunal Appeal **tribunal** which hears applications from individuals who have been refused social security benefits. The tribunal has three members, two of whom must be non-lawyers, one chosen from a panel of local employers and one from a panel of local employees. The third member, who is usually a lawyer, is appointed by the Secretary of State to be chairperson. Appeal against the decision of the tribunal is allowed to a Social Security Commissioner.

social services department Department of a local authority, headed by the Director of Social Services and responsible to the Social Services Committee. The department has statutory duties in respect of social services, such as those relating to children, the mentally disabled and the elderly.

social worker Employee of a local authority responsible for operating the welfare services provided by the authority. These services are designed to alleviate the conditions of the poor and aged and protect the welfare of children. *See also* **social services department**.

society Term with two meanings.
First, a group of human people who share distinctive institutions, language and culture. It is broadly defined by geopolitical boundaries.
Second, a social environment comprising the aggregate total of people insofar as they influence or frame an individual member's behaviour.

socio-economic groups Series of groups categorized by occupation type, and income, education and lifestyle.

sodomy Anal intercourse committed by a man with another man or a woman. It is also known as **buggery**.

software protection Legal protection of the commercial interests of the authors of computer programmes under the law of **copyright**. Breach of copyright in a computer programme occurs if the programme is reproduced without permission or if a completely different programme is produced which performs the same function and appears to the user to be the same as the original.

sole licence Permission to use or exploit something commercially which is given to one person only, to the exclusion of others.

sole proprietor Single owner.

sole trader Single owner of a business. For example, many window cleaners and decorators operate as sole traders, the advantage being that there are no specific legal requirements to set up in business as a sole trader. The disadvantage is that if a sole trader incurs **debts**, the **creditors** are entitled to repayment out of the personal assets of the sole trader if the business does not have sufficient funds to pay the debt. *See also* **company**; **partnership**.

soliciting Personal invitation or inducement. It is an offence under the Street Offences Act 1959 s.1 for a prostitute to solicit in a public place for the purposes of **prostitution**. *See also* **loitering for the purposes of prostitution**.

solicitor Lawyer who advises clients on legal, financial and business matters. The governing body of the solicitors' profession is the **Law Society**, which is responsible for enrolling solicitors, setting examinations and issuing certificates that authorize solicitors to practice. Solicitors advise on a wide range of matters, including **wills**, **conveyancing** and the forming of companies. In addition, a solicitor will help to prepare the defence of a person who is being prosecuted for a criminal offence.

If court proceedings are necessary, whether civil or criminal, a solicitor will **brief** a **barrister** to present the case on behalf of the client. A solicitor may appear on behalf of the client in the **Magistrates' Court** and the **County Court**, but if the case is to be heard in a more senior court a barrister is necessary. *See also* **rights of audience**.

Solicitors' Complaints Bureau Office established in 1986 by the **Law Society**, theoretically independent of it, to deal with complaints by the public about the misconduct of **solicitors**. The Bureau's functions are dealt with by two main committees. The Investigation Committee, which has a majority of non-solicitor members, decides whether the investigation of the complaint warrants further action. If it does, the complaint is forwarded to the Adjudication Committee, which must decide whether the solicitor should be prosecuted for professional misconduct before the Solicitors' Disciplinary Tribunal.

Solicitor-General Second most senior law officer of the Crown after the **Attorney-General**. He is appointed by the Prime Minister and is largely responsible for giving legal advice to the Cabinet and supervising the passage of legal **bills** through Parliament.

Solicitor-General for Scotland Lawyer and member of the Government, the deputy to the **Lord Advocate**.

sounding in damages Legal action brought in order to recover **damages** for some wrong or injury suffered, as opposed to action to recover a **debt**. The **plaintiff** must show that he or she suffered some loss or damage as a result of the behaviour of the **defendant**. The court assesses the amount of compensation to be awarded.

Sovereign Head of state, in the United Kingdom the king or queen. The Government acts in the Sovereign's name for many purposes, but the Sovereign's personal powers are now very limited. In executive action and legislation, Parliament is supreme. Parliament also established the rules for the succession to the throne. *See also* **Parliamentary sovereignty**.

Sovereign immunity Rule of **international law** that the **Sovereign** of one state is not subject to the **jurisdiction** of the courts of another state. Thus, the Sovereign of another state can neither be sued in an English court nor charged with a criminal offence. Sovereign immunity is the basis of **diplomatic immunity**.

sovereignty of Parliament *See* **Parliamentary sovereignty.**

Speaker Person who presides over the main sittings of the House of Commons and is responsible for order and discipline. The title comes from his traditional role as elected spokesman for the House in relation to the Sovereign. In the House of Lords, the Speaker is the **Lord Chancellor**. *See also* **woolsack**.

Special Commissioners of Income Tax Body of persons, including the Commissioners of Inland Revenue, appointed by the Treasury. It is responsible for making income tax assessments or hearing appeals against assessments, especially if a legal point is at issue.

special constable Person appointed by **magistrates**, not a regular member of the police force, who assists the police in carrying out certain duties and may exercise all the powers of a **constable**, for instance, in an emergency that requires additional manpower.

special damages Compensation for losses or injuries that are not assumed to be the inevitable result of a wrongful act, and which must be proved to the court before **compensation** is payable. For instance, damage in the form of repair costs and loss of earnings while recovering from an accident are special damages which must be proved to the court.

In public nuisance, individual members of the public are not generally entitled to sue for **damages** that they have suffered unless they can show that the damage was different from that suffered by the public generally. Such damage is called special damage.

special examiner Person appointed by the High Court to take evidence on oath from a witness outside the court – for instance, if a witness is too ill to attend court.

special jury Formerly, a **jury** which could be requested by the **defendant** in a trial involving certain commercial matters. The jury was chosen from persons experienced in commercial matters such as bankers and merchants, and owners of property that exceeded a certain value. It was abolished by the Courts Act 1971.

special manager Person appointed by a court to run an insolvent **company** (Insolvency Act 1986 s.177).

special order *See* **special procedure list.**

special procedure list List of special procedure orders. A form of delegated legislation in which the procedure allows time for petitions to be lodged against a **statutory instrument** before it becomes law.

special resolution Procedure which must be used to make alterations to the **articles of association** or **memorandum of association** of a **company**. Twenty-one days' notice must be given of a general meeting and the resolution requires the assent of three-quarters of those present who are entitled to vote.

specific bequest *See* **bequest.**

specific performance Order by a court that a party to a **contract** perform his obligation under the contract. It is a **remedy** for **breach of contract**, and is granted only if an order for **damages** does not give adequate compensation. It is typically used when one party refuses to carry out a contract to sell land.

specification Description of an invention which must be submitted to the Patents Office before a **patent** will be granted.

specimen A motorist who is reasonably suspected of drinking and driving can be required to provide a sample of breath for a preliminary test of blood alcohol level. If the preliminary test is positive the motorist will be taken to a police station. He or she will then be asked to provide either two breath specimens or a blood specimen or a urine specimen. The results of tests on those specimens can then be used by the police in further proceedings. It is an offence to fail to furnish specimens without reasonable excuse (Road Traffic Act 1972 s.7–8).

speeding Driving a motor vehicle on a public road at a speed in excess of that permitted by law (Road Traffic Regulation Act 1984 s.89). Two witnesses to the speeding are usually required, but evidence may be accepted from radar machines approved by the Minister of Transport.

spent conviction Under the Rehabilitation of Offenders Act 1974, a conviction which should not be disclosed and which no longer forms part of a person's criminal record, because the relevant period of time since the conviction has expired. *See also* **rehabilitation of offenders**.

spouse Husband of a woman or wife of a man.

squatter Person in occupation of **land** without permission and against the interests of the owner. *See also* **adverse possession**; **residential occupier**.

stakeholder Person who holds the stakes for parties to a **wager**. Also an independent party who holds a sum of money provided by a buyer of property as a deposit, under an obligation to hand it over to the vendor on completion of the contract of sale.

stamp duty Tax paid on legal documents relating to certain types of transaction. The tax is proportionate to the value of the transaction. The document is stamped to prove that the tax has been paid and is invalid without the stamp.

standard of care Degree of care that the law requires a citizen to exercise in particular circumstances in order to avoid harm to other people or their property. *See also* **common duty of care**; **negligence**; **recklessness**.

standing committee Committee of the House of Commons appointed to examine a **bill** clause by clause, consider amendments and report to the House before the third **reading**. A special standing committee may take evidence before the detailed examination of a bill.

standing mute Failure by a person charged with a criminal offence to make any reply, when asked to plead either guilty or not guilty to the charge. *See* **mute by the visitation of God**; **mute of malice**.

standing orders Rules formulated by a body or institution to regulate its own operation.

Star Chamber In Tudor and Stuart times a branch of the King's Council that operated as a criminal court. It was abolished in 1641.

statement of affairs Statement required by law to be made by a **bankrupt** person about his or her financial affairs or by the directors of a company in liquidation.

statement of claim In **civil actions**, statement made by the **plaintiff** in which the relevant facts on which the claim is based are set out.

state of emergency Circumstances in which, because of war, civil disorder, strikes or natural disaster, the normal machinery for running the country is ineffective. A declaration of a state of emergency by the government brings **emergency powers** into operation.

status Particular category of person, to which the law attaches particular rights, privileges and duties. *See also* **age of majority**; **capacity**.

statute Act of Parliament.

statute law revision Systematic process of examining the body of statute law and repealing statutes or parts of statutes which have been superseded or are obsolete. This is the responsibility of the Statute Law Committee, which periodically presents a Statute Law Revision **bill** to Parliament. *See also* **consolidation**; **Law Commission**; **law reform**; **repeal**.

statutory corporation Body, with a legal personality, established by **statute** to perform particular public functions, and having legal personality. Examples include the Civil Aviation Authority and the British Railways Board.

statutory declaration Statement solemnly declared before a **solicitor** or **commissioner for oaths**. Making a false declaration is punishable as **perjury**. Statutory declarations are required for particular purposes when it is important that somebody should tell the truth.

statutory instrument Form of **delegated legislation** made by a minister under powers granted by **Act of Parliament**. A statutory instrument which goes beyond the powers granted to a minister may be held to be invalid by the courts.

statutory interpretation Process by which a court determines the meaning of the words of a statute. Interpretation is governed by a number of rules. The basic rule (the literal rule) is that words should be understood in their normal sense. The other major rules are the **golden rule** and the **mischief rule**. A number of special rules are found in the Interpretation Act 1978.

statutory sick pay *See* **sick pay**.

statutory tenant Person who, having occupied premises under a **tenancy** for a period of years, remains in occupation after the period of years has come to an end. The tenancy is described as statutory because although the original **lease** has come to an end, the tenant retains certain protection from eviction and rent increases under the Rent Acts.

stay of execution Court order that **execution** of a judgment be postponed for a period.

stay of proceedings Court order by which legal proceedings are either postponed or terminated. Proceedings may be stayed if they amount to an abuse of process, if there has been excessive delay by one of the parties, or if it would be more convenient for the case to be pursued in the courts of another country.

stereotype Most common collection of characteristics used by one group of people to define another, often resulting in an exaggerated, unfair description.

stipendiary magistrate Magistrate, appointed by the **Lord Chancellor**, who is legally qualified and who is in the full-time paid employment of the court. *See also* **justice of the peace**.

Stock Exchange Central market for government securities, British and foreign shares, and traded options. The International Stock Market of the United Kingdom and the Republic of Ireland has its headquarters in London, and has administrative offices in various parts of the United Kingdom and Ireland. The Exchange is a self-regulating body under the Financial Services Act 1986.

street offence Criminal act that is punishable by law which is most often committed in public places (for example, mugging).

street trading Offering or displaying anything for sale or actually selling something in a street or public place. It is an offence unless a **licence** has been obtained from the local authority under the Local Government (Miscellaneous Provisions) Act 1984.

strict liability Liability to punishment or to pay damages without proof of fault. For example, an employer may be strictly liable to pay damages for any harm caused by the negligent act of his employee in the course of the employee's duties.

In **criminal law** strict liability is found in many statutory offences. For instance, most offences relating to the safety of motor vehicles, factory safety and pollution are of strict liability. For these offences it must be shown that the defendant did the prohibited act or caused the prohibited consequence, but it need not be proved that the act was intentional, reckless or negligent.

strike Cessation of work by a group of employees in order to coerce the employer into settling an industrial dispute in a particular way. A trade union may be sued for inducing its members to strike, unless the strike follows a ballot in accordance with the Trade Union Act 1984. A striking worker is in **breach of contract** of employment and may be dismissed. However, if the employer does not dismiss all the strikers, but selects particular workers for dismissal, this is victimization and amounts to **unfair dismissal**.

striking out pleadings Deleting part of the **pleadings** in a **civil action**. It may be ordered by the judge if the pleadings in question are frivolous and would waste the time of the court. It may also be ordered as a means of punishing a party for undue delay.

subculture Shared values, beliefs and practices of a group in disagreement with the dominant culture.

subject to contract Temporary, to be replaced in due course by a **contract**. An agreement to sell something subject to contract is not binding, but simply expresses the parties' intention that a contract will be made in due course.

submission Argument as to the facts of a case or the law relating to a case which is put to a court.

subornation of perjury Offence of attempting to persuade another person to commit **perjury**.

subpoena Order of a court addressed to a particular person who is required to attend court to give oral evidence or to produce other evidence, such as documents, to the court. Failure to comply with the order may be punished as **contempt of court**.

subrogation Legal process by which an insurer or other person who has paid compensation to an insured person takes over that person's rights. Thus, if insured goods have been lost or damaged and the insurer compensates the owner in full, the insurer takes over all of the owner's rights in relation to the goods. If the goods are then found or repaired the insurer may sell them to recoup the compensation paid out.

subsidiary Stemming from and dependent upon. In company law, one company is a subsidiary of another if the other company holds a majority of the **shares** in the first company; or if the other company holds some shares and controls the appointment of directors of the first company.

substantial damages Damages which compensate for a substantial loss suffered, as opposed to **nominal damages**.

substantive law Body of laws which contains rules regulating human behaviour, as opposed to the law of **evidence** and **procedure**, which regulates the adjudication of disputes by courts.

sub-tenant Person who occupies land or premises under a **lease** granted by a person who himself or herself holds the land or premises under a **lease**. It is technically incorrect to describe a **lodger** as a sub-tenant, since a lodger normally holds a **licence** to occupy premises, not a lease.

succession Legal process by which rights of ownership pass from one person to another. Succession may take place by **gift** or **contract**. However, the term is most commonly used in relation to succession following upon a person's death. The dead person's property passes according to a **will** or, if there is no valid will, under the law of **intestacy**.

successive actions Two or more distinct legal claims based upon the same facts. Generally successive actions are barred by the courts and the **plaintiff** must make all claims relating to an incident at once. Thus, if a man assaults another person, the victim cannot sue for a black eye, and then subsequently for damages for a broken nose suffered during the attack.

sue To bring a **civil action** against another.

suicide Deliberate self-killing. Formerly, suicide was a **felony** (also known as self-murder) and a person who attempted suicide might be tried and punished, as might someone charged with **aiding and abetting** another to commit suicide. By the Suicide Act 1961, suicide ceased to be a crime, although it remains an offence to assist suicide.

   A person who kills another under a suicide pact is not guilty of **murder**, but only of **manslaughter** (Homicide Act 1957 s.4). A suicide pact is an agreement entered into by two persons that both shall die together. A person may plead a suicide pact only if at the time of the killing he or she had a settled intention to die.

suing and labouring clause Term in the standard contract of marine insurance which is appended to the Marine Insurance Act 1906. The clause guarantees that if the owner of an insured ship incurs expenses in preventing loss or damage to the ship, or in suing for its recovery, these expenses will be borne by the insurers.

suit Legal proceeding tried in court.

summary judgment Procedure in which the **plaintiff** in a **civil action** obtains a decision in his or her favour from the court without being fully argued, because the **defendant** enters no credible defence to the claim made against him. The procedure is often called "Order 14", after the order under which this can be done from the **Rules of the Supreme Court**.

summary jurisdiction Power of the **Magistrates' Court** to try certain less serious criminal offences (**summary offences**) without sending them for trial at the **Crown Court**, and to hear cases **triable either way** if the defendant elects to be tried summarily.

summary offence Crime which is triable only by a **Magistrates' Court**. *See also* **indictable offence**; **offence triable either way**.

summary proceedings Trial of an offence in the **Magistrates' Court**, or proceedings in other courts when the court makes its own decision to act without its process being set in motion by another. An example of the latter occurs when a court summarily finds a person present in court guilty of **contempt of court**.

summary trial Trial of a **summary offence** or an **offence triable either way**.

summing-up Address by the judge to the **jury** at a trial in the **Crown Court** before the jury retires to consider its **verdict**. It contains a summary of the evidence and the arguments of prosecution and defence and a direction on the relevant law and **burden of proof**.

summons Term with two applications.

First, order from a **Magistrates' Court** to a named person to appear before the court and answer a criminal charge.

Second, notice to appear before any court on the hearing of an application.

summons for directions In a **civil action** in the High Court a method of applying to the court to give directions in relation to pre-trial proceedings, such as **discovery of documents**.

Sunday trading Carrying on retail business on a Sunday. Under regulations made under the Shops Act 1950 shops generally should be closed all day Sunday. However, there are many exceptions that permit, for example, the sale of newspapers, petrol, certain foodstuffs, alcoholic drinks and tobacco.

supervening impossibility New circumstances which make a **contract** impossible of performance, after it has been made but before it has been carried out. If the impossibility goes to the root of the contract, then the contract will be discharged by **frustration** – for instance, if the hall in which a concert is to be given burns down before the appointed day. However, the contract will not be discharged if the supervening event merely makes it more difficult for one party – for instance, a builder who goes bankrupt – to carry out a contract.

supervision order Sentence available to a **juvenile court,** under which the juvenile remains at home but is subject to supervision by a **probation** officer, or a social worker, and may be required to attend courses for certain types of training.

support Right which a landowner has in relation to neighbouring land. If a man digs a quarry next to his neighbour's and the neighbour's land begins to slip into the hole, this may amount to a breach of the neighbour's right to support from the adjoining land. Similarly, occupiers of terraced and semi-detached houses owe each other a right of support in relation to the buildings.

supply of goods and services The Supply of Goods and Services Act 1982 provides protection to the consumer in contracts for the hire of goods, the transfer of goods other than for money and the provision of services. In a contract for services it is implied that the service will be carried out with reasonable care and skill and within a reasonable time. If this is not done the consumer has the right to sue the supplier of the service for **damages** under the 1982 Act.

suppression of documents Offence under the Theft Act 1968 s.20, committed by destroying, defacing or concealing any valuable security, or will, or government record, dishonestly, with an intent either to gain by doing so or to cause loss to another.

Supreme Court of Judicature Superior court created by the Judicature Act 1873 and modified by various Acts since then. It consists of the **High Court of Justice,** the **Court of Appeal** and the **Crown Court.**

surety Person who agrees to pay a sum of money to a court if a particular person does not appear on the appointed day to answer a criminal charge. A person charged with a criminal offence may be required to provide a surety before being released on **bail** while awaiting trial.

surrender To give up something or to give oneself up. If a tenant under a **lease** for a period of years accepts a new lease from the landlord before the original lease has expired, the old lease is said to be surrendered by operation of law. The original lease is in effect rendered void by the new lease.

surrender value Sum, payable to a person who holds an **insurance** policy or an **assurance** policy, which is surrendered before the end of the period during which the policy has to run.

survivorship Rights which were shared between two or more parties and which have passed by process of law to the survivors on the death of one of the parties. *See also* **joint tenants**.

"sus" Slang term for the former offence under the Vagrancy Act 1824 of being a person suspected of loitering with intent to commit an offence. This offence was abolished by the Criminal Attempts Act 1981.

suspended sentence Sentence of imprisonment which the court orders shall not be served immediately, but suspended for a stated period. The term of imprisonment is activated if the individual concerned commits further offences within that period (s.22 Powers of the Criminal Courts Act 1973). Only sentences of less than two years may be suspended. *See also* **partly suspended sentence**.

synod Church council. The General Synod of the Church of England includes a House of Bishops, a House of Clergy, and a House of Laity. Meeting two or three times a year, the General Synod makes decisions on Church legislation and administration, as well as on faith, doctrine, and Church ceremonies.

T

Table Office Part of the department of the Clerk of the House of Commons, responsible for administrative services relating to order papers, written and notice questions, and the provision of clerks to work on bills.

Table of the House Table in the House of Commons, placed in front of the Speaker, at which sit members of the department of the Clerk of the House of Commons. The printing of bills, motions and questions is organized by the clerks. The table is the origin of the expression "tabling a bill".

tacking Process by which, if a single lender, such as a building society, lends money by way of **mortgage** and at a later date makes a further loan by way of mortgage, the two mortgages are said to be tacked together and treated as a single mortgage. The practical effect of this is that if another party has lent money by way of mortgage against the same property before the second loan, the first lender will have first claim on the property for the whole of its combined loan, unless when it made the second loan it had notice of the other mortgage.

Takeover Panel Unofficial body established by the **Stock Exchange** to regulate takeovers and mergers between companies. It operates a voluntary code of practice called the City Code on Takeovers and Mergers.

taking motor vehicles *See* **joyriding.**

taking offences into consideration Practice of criminal courts that, following a verdict of guilty, the defendant may admit other offences and ask that they be taken into consideration in calculating the sentence for the offence with which he or she has been found guilty. The defendant may not be later charged with offences taken into consideration.

tariff Standard scales of sentences which are understood by those working in the criminal courts to apply to certain categories of offence. The tariff is informal and unofficial, but its development is encouraged by judgments of the **Court of Appeal** (Criminal Division), which provide sentencing guidelines, and by the Magistrates Association, which offers guidance on the sentencing for certain common offences.

taxation Raising of funds by the State by requiring payment to be made relating to, and in proportion to the value of, particular transactions. *See also* **income tax; inheritance tax; value added tax**.

taxation of costs Process by which an officer of the **High Court**, called a Taxing Master, determines what **costs** should be payable by a party who has been ordered to pay the other party's costs.

tax avoidance Arrangement of one's affairs so as to minimize the amount of tax payable by law.

tax evasion Unlawful failure to disclose transactions on which one would be liable to be taxed.

Taxing Master *See* **taxation of costs.**

tenancy Generally, holding of land under a **lease** from another person (the **landlord**). The exception is a **statutory tenancy** under which by law a person holds land as if under a lease.

tenancy at sufferance Continued occupation of land after the end of a **tenancy**, by the person who had previously been the tenant, without the **landlord's** permission.

tenancy at will Occupation of land by a tenant under an informal arrangement which may be terminated at any time by either **landlord** or tenant.

tenancy in common Arrangement by which two or more persons hold land in equal shares, and under which either is free to sell or give away his or her share. *See also* **joint tenancy.**

tenant for life Person who is entitled to occupy certain land for the duration of his life under the terms of a **settlement** relating to the land.

tenant from year to year Person who holds land under a tenancy of indeterminate duration, which is stated to run from year to year and which by law may be terminated by six months' **notice** on either side.

tenant pur autre vie Person who holds land for the duration of another person's life. Such arrangements are only possible if the land is held on **trust** for the tenant.

tender Term with two applications.

First, to offer money or something else in payment of a debt or **satisfaction** of some other obligation.

Second, a contractual **offer** to supply particular goods or services at a stated price. *See also* **legal tender**.

tenement House or land which is held under a **tenancy**.

ten-minute rule Parliamentary procedure under **House of Commons** Standing Order 19, which gives individual backbench MPs an opportunity to introduce a bill of their choice in a speech lasting up to ten minutes.

tenure Legally recognized possession of something.

tenure, security of *See* **security of tenure**.

term Term with three applications.

First, formerly, one of the periods in the year during which the superior courts were in operation, now called a **sitting**.

Second, part of a **contract** which specifies an obligation under the contract.

Third, period of time. *See also* **implied term**; **term of contract**.

term of years Term with two applications.

First, period of a number of years.

Second, **tenure** of land, normally by **lease**, for a fixed period of a number of years.

terms of contract Distinct parts of a contract which define the various obligations of the parties. *See also* **implied terms**; **unfair contract terms**.

territorial waters Area of sea adjacent to the coast of a country, in **international law** considered part of the territory of that country. The law of that country operates in that area. Under the Territorial Seas Act, the territorial waters of the United Kingdom extend 12 nautical miles from the coast. For this purpose the coastline is taken to stretch unbroken across large estuaries and bays.

terrorism Use of violence or the threat of violence for political means. Under the Prevention of Terrorism (Temporary Provisions) Act 1989 terrorist organizations may be proscribed, making it a criminal offence to be a member of or to finance or support such an organization. The Home Secretary may also make an **exclusion order** in relation to a person suspected of terrorism.

testament Person's **will** in relation to the disposition of his or her personal property after death.

testate succession Disposal of a person's property after death according to a **will**.

testator Male person who makes a **will**.

testatrix Female person who makes a **will**.

test case Legal proceeding brought in order to determine how the courts will interpret the law in relation to particular circumstances. For instance, if the **Crown Prosecution Service** is not certain whether particular behaviour amounts to an offence, it may bring a single prosecution as a test case, in order to obtain a ruling from the court before embarking upon further prosecutions.

A civil test case may be brought in order to determine the legal position on behalf of a number of potential **plaintiffs**. For instance, if a ship sinks and a number of persons are drowned, all the persons who might sue the shipping company may agree to bring a single test case to determine whether **negligence** could be proved. The outcome of the test case would then normally be used as the basis for settling further claims without **litigation**.

testimonium clause Concluding part of a **deed** or **will**, which states that the parties have signed the document in witness of its contents. This means that by their signatures the parties acknowledge the contents.

testimony Oral **evidence** given on **oath** in court.

theft Dishonest **appropriation** of property belonging to another, with an intent permanently to deprive the owner of it (Theft Act 1968 ss.1–6). Appropriation includes taking property, destroying it, or hiding it so as to deprive the owner of it.

theft by finding Finding property which has been lost and keeping it without making any attempt to discover the real owner. Simply to appropriate the property for oneself may amount to the crime of **theft**. It will not be theft, however, if the finder believes that the owner could not be traced by taking reasonable steps. For instance, it would be impossible to trace the owner of a pound coin found in a street.

third party Person brought into proceedings by the **defendant** because the defendant believes him or her to be liable to the **plaintiff**.

third party notice Document by which a thitd party is joined in proceedings between the **plaintiff** and the **defendant**.

third-party insurance Insurance against liability in respect of damage or injuries caused to the person(s) and property of others by the insured. It is an offence to drive a motor vehicle that does not have valid third party insurance (Road Traffic Act 1972 s.143).

third-party liability proceedings Process by which, in a **civil** action between two parties, the **defendant** may obtain a court order to include a third party within the proceedings because the defendant seeks a **remedy** or **indemnity** against that third party. For instance, if a householder sues a builder who has built a defective extension for him and the builder claims that the extension was defective because of some fault in the materials used, he may seek to bring the merchant who supplied those materials into the action.

threat Declaration of intention to inflict injury on a person or damage to property. In criminal law, a threat of immediate violence amounts to the offence of **assault**. It is an offence to threaten to kill a person under the Offences Against the Person Act 1861 s.16. Threats are also an essential ingredient in the crime of **blackmail**.

In civil law, the victim of a threat which causes fear of immediate physical injury may sue for compensation under the **tort** of **trespass**.

threatening behaviour Criminal offence of using threatening, abusive or insulting words or behaviour towards another person, with the intent to cause that person to believe that violence will be used against him or her, or in order to provoke that person into using violence (Public Order Act 1986 s.4(1)). The offence may be committed in either a public or a private place.

tied house Term with two applications.

First, a public house in which the **lessee** is obliged under the terms of the **lease** to sell only the beer of the brewer who is the **lessor**.

Second, a house or cottage which is rented out to the **tenant** for as long as the tenant remains employed by the landlord.

time immemorial *See* **immemorial existence.**

tipstaff Officer of the **High Court** who carries out court orders to arrest persons guilty of **contempt of court**.

tithe Formerly, a levy, equivalent to 10 per cent of the annual produce, paid by the owners of agricultural land to the Church of England. By the Tithes Act 1836 the levy was converted into a cash payment related to the price of crops. By the Tithes Act 1936 tithes were replaced with taxes on land called tithe redemption annuities, payable to the Crown. These tithe redemption annuities will cease to exist in 1996. If the land in question is sold before that time the buyer must by law pay a fixed sum which extinguishes the duty to pay the tithe annuity.

title Right to ownership of property.

title-deeds Deeds which provide evidence of the ownership of land over a long period. The title-deeds are transferred to the buyer when the land is sold. If the title-deeds are deposited with a lender as security for a loan this creates a **mortgage** under the rules of **equity**. The ownership of **registered land** is proved by the entry on the register rather than by the title-deeds.

toll Payment which must be made by persons who pass along certain stretches of road or bridges. The roads and bridges in question are privately maintained by their owner. The collection of the toll is normally authorized by a private **Act of Parliament**.

tontine System of life **assurance** in which a number of persons subscribe money which is invested. Subscribers receive an annual payment until death. As each subscriber dies, the shares of those that remain increase proportionately, until the longest surviving subscriber takes the benefit of the whole fund.

tools of the trade Implements required for a person to be able to ply his or her trade. Tools of trade to the value of £50 are exempt from distraint. *See also* **distress**.

tort Wrongful act that causes damage or harm to others, for which **compensation** or other **remedy** may be obtained in a **civil action**, apart from **breach of contract**. Examples of a tort are **breach of confidence, defamation, negligence, nuisance, trespass**. A single act may amount to both a **crime** and a tort. Dangerous driving that causes a crash, for example, may lead to a **prosecution** for **reckless driving** and a claim for **damages** for the tort of negligence.

tortfeasor Person who commits a **tort**.

tortious act Conduct that amounts to a **tort**.

totalitarianism Absolute and undemocratic control of the life and thought of individuals and communities by government. A totalitarian state allows no opposition.

total loss In marine insurance, loss of or damage to a ship for which the insurers are liable to pay full value. If the ship is so badly damaged that it would not be economic to repair it, this is called constructive total loss.

town and country planning *See* **planning.**

trade To buy and sell for profit.

trade description Any description or statement attached to goods offered for sale to indicate their size, weight, quantity, quality, fitness for a particular purpose, composition, mode or place of manufacture, or price. A person who is responsible for attaching a false trade description to goods commits an offence under the Trade Descriptions Act 1968. It is also an offence falsely to claim that an item is being sold at a reduced or sale price.

trade dispute Dispute between employees and their employer relating to terms and conditions of employment, allocation and supervision of duties at work, discipline at work, trade union membership or facilities for trade union officials. Workers or unions who take action in a trade dispute, for example, by calling a **strike** and **picketing** the workplace, will not, under the Trade Union and Labour Relations Act 1974, be liable in **tort** for interfering with the business of their employer. This exemption does not apply to **secondary picketing**.

trade mark Any design, name, signature, word, letter or numeral or combination of these, attached to goods to indicate a connection between the goods and a particular person or **company** entitled to use the trade mark. Trade marks may be registered under the Trade Marks Act 1938, and the owner of the mark may take legal action against anybody else who uses a similar mark on goods.

trade plates Special number plates, which motor traders may purchase from the Department of Transport, that permit the vehicle to which they are attached to be used on the public roads as if it were registered and had a road fund licence. Trade plates are used especially on moving vehicles that have not yet been registered in the name of their first owner. They are white with red lettering, numbering and border.

trade union Organization of workers, the principal purpose of which is to secure favourable terms and conditions of employment by negotiation with employers or associations of employers. *See also* **picketing**; **strike**.

trading certificate Under the Companies Act 1985, a certificate which must be issued by the **Registrar of Companies** before certain types of **company** may commence business.

tradition Belief or practice, established over time by use.

transcript Full written account of everything said in the course of a legal proceeding or meeting. It is prepared from the **shorthand note**.

transfer Passing of something from one person to another or from one place to another.

transfer of action Transfer of a legal proceeding from one court to another. This may occur, for instance, when a case that is being heard in the **County Court** appears to involve a difficult point of law that might be better dealt with in the **High Court**. Or a case might be transferred from the High Court to the County Court if the sum claimed were reduced so that the case fell below the lower financial limits of the High Court.

traverse Denial in the defence of an allegation made by the **plaintiff**.

treason Offence involving treachery to the **Sovereign** or an attempt to bring down the constitutional government of the country by unconstitutional means. The offence, defined by the Treason Act 1351, includes the following: planning or attempting to murder the king or queen or the heir to the throne; rape of the queen or the Sovereign's eldest daughter or the wife of the heir to the throne; waging war against the country or helping enemies of the **Crown**; murdering the **Lord Chancellor** or one of the judges. Treason may be committed only by a person who owes **allegiance** to the Crown. Hanging is the penalty for treason.

treason felony Alternative form of **treason** under the Treason Felony Act 1848 which provides a penalty of life imprisonment rather than death by hanging. This offence largely overlaps treason under the 1351 Act and is committed by planning to depose the Sovereign or by inciting foreigners to invade the country.

treasure trove Money, gold, silver, or gold or silver plate which is found after being deliberately hidden in the earth or somewhere else by a person unknown. Treasure trove belongs to the **Crown,** although compensation is payable to the finder. When there is doubt, the **coroner** may hold an inquest to decide whether valuables found are treasure trove.

Treasury Government department responsible for raising revenues through taxation, for expenditure, for efficiency in the public sector, for monetary policy and for international financial management. The head of the Treasury is the Prime Minister, but day-to-day management is under the direction of the Chancellor of the Exchequer, under whom serve the Chief Secretary, the Financial Secretary, the Economic Secretary and the Paymaster General.

Treasury bench Popular name for the members of the Government, who sit in the House of Commons on the front row of benches.

Treasury Bar Body of **barristers** known as Treasury counsel, nominated by the **Attorney-General** to represent the Government in legal proceedings and to conduct prosecutions on behalf of the **Director of Public Prosecutions**.

Treasury Solicitor Civil servant who directs a department which provides legal advice and conducts litigation on behalf of some Government departments.

treaty International agreement in writing between two or more states or regional organizations which are recognized in **international law**. Treaties are binding in international law. Treaties are made by the **Government,** but do not affect the law of the United Kingdom until given effect to by **Act of Parliament**.

Treaty of Accession International agreement of 1972 between the United Kingdom and the member states of the **European Community** by which the United Kingdom joined the Community and became a party to the **Treaty of Rome**. The European Community Act 1972 was passed in order to give effect to the treaty in British law.

Treaty of Rome International agreement of 1957 between France,

Germany, Italy, Belgium, the Netherlands, and Luxembourg by which the **European Community** was created. The United Kingdom became a party to this Treaty by the **Treaty of Accession**.

trespass Unlawful infringement of a personal right. Trespass against the person is a **tort** and includes **assault** and **battery**. These forms of trespass may also be crimes.

Trespass on land is a **tort** committed by entering another person's land or premises without permission or other lawful authority. Such trespass is not a crime except, under the Criminal Law Act 1977, in residential premises after the **residential occupier** has requested the trespasser to leave, or in foreign embassies or missions and in circumstances in which the trespass is committed with an offensive weapon. Violence to gain entry is also an offence. *See also* **burglary**.

trial Proceeding at which an issue in dispute is considered by a court presided over by a judge or bench of **magistrates** in order to adjudicate that dispute.

triable either way Category of criminal offence, created by the Criminal Law Act 1977 s.16, that may be tried either on **indictment** in the **Crown Court** or summarily in a **Magistrates' Court**. The initial decision whether to hear the case is made by the Magistrates' Court. If that court decides that the case should be heard, the **defendant** is given the option of being tried there or in the Crown Court.

tribunal Body appointed to consider and decide a particular type of dispute according to law. It is usually chaired by a person who is legally qualified but it adopts less formal procedures than courts. Examples include **industrial tribunals** and **rent tribunals**.

Trinity House Body which has statutory duties in relation to the safety of shipping, especially in regard to the training and licensing of pilots and the maintenance of lighthouses, buoys and beacons.

trover Obsolete **tort** of finding and keeping goods belonging to another. The modern equivalent is **conversion**.

trust Arrangement under which property is transferred to a person called the **trustee** or several such persons. Trustees are under an obligation to keep the property or deal with it for the benefit of another person called the **beneficiary** or for some purpose such as a charitable purpose. The document that creates the trust is the trust **deed**. *See also* **secret trust**.

trust corporation Body appointed by a court to act as a trustee of particular funds. Normally, the trust corporation will be the **Public Trustee**.

trustee Person to whom property is given under an obligation to deal with it for the benefit of another or for a particular purpose under a **trust**.

trustee in bankruptcy Person, appointed by a general meeting of a **bankrupt** person's **creditors,** or by the court, whose duty it is to take over all the property of the bankrupt, sell the property for cash and distribute the resulting funds among the creditors according to the rules of **priority** set out in the Insolvency Act 1986, but otherwise in proportion to the debt owed to each creditor.

trust for sale Legal arrangement by which land is held by trustees under an obligation to sell it. The beneficiaries may postpone the sale by agreeing among themselves. Thus, if a woman has three children in her **will** she may leave her house to them all equally, subject to a trust for sale. Under this arrangement the house may be sold and the proceeds divided or, if all agree, the sale postponed and the house kept.

U

umpire Person appointed to adjudicate a dispute which has been referred to the arbitration of two or more persons who are unable to agree (Arbitration Act 1950 ss.8–10).

unborn child Posthumous unborn child, who is presumed to be already born for the purposes of inheritance, according to the doctrine know as *en ventre sa mère* ('in the womb of the mother'). There are two principal offences against the unborn child. It is an offence under the Infant Life Preservation Act s.2 to cause the death of an unborn child that is capable of being born alive. Under the Offences Against the Person Act 1861 s.58, it is an offence to procure a miscarriage, but this offence is not committed if the requirements for a lawful **abortion** under the Abortion Act 1967 are complied with.

uncertainty Condition of being incapable of adequate definition. The law will not enforce an uncertain obligation and accordingly an uncertain gift by **will** or an uncertain **trust** will fail.

uncollected goods Goods, such as items left for cleaning or repair, in the possession of someone other than the owner, which the owner fails to collect when so requested. A bailee has the right to sell the goods in these circumstances, subject to conditions in the Torts (Interference with Goods) Act 1977 s.12.

uncontrollable impulse Explanation for behaviour, not a defence to a criminal charge, although it may be relevant to questions of **insanity** or **diminished responsibility**.

undefended divorce Divorce in which the **respondent** does not dispute the petitioner's right to a divorce. The overwhelming majority of divorces are now undefended. They are dealt with by **registrars**, who use administrative procedure which involves no real court hearing.

underlease Sublease granted by a tenant who owes his own occupancy of premises to the main **lease**. At common law, an underlease comes to an end with the termination of the main lease, but this may be altered by application of the Rent Act. *See also* **rent**; **secure tenancy**; **security of tenure**.

undertaking A promise, most often made to the court by a party to legal proceedings, or his or her lawyer, to act or refrain from acting in a particular way.

undisclosed principal Person on whose behalf an **agent** is in fact acting, although he purports to act on his own behalf. If the agent is acting within the scope of his actual authority, the principal is bound by and can enforce any contract made in such circumstances.

undue influence Improper exercise of mental domination over another. If, for example, a parent persuades a child or a **trustee** persuades a **beneficiary** to do something which is not in his or her interest, the presumption will arise that undue influence has been exercised. If this cannot be rebutted by showing that an independent decision was in fact made, then the transaction can be set aside.

undue preference Payment, made by a debtor within the two years preceding insolvency, which serves to put the payee in a preferential position to other creditors. It is now usually called simply a preference. A preference can be set aside or otherwise reversed by the court on application by the trustee in bankruptcy (Insolvency Act 1986 s.340).

unenforceable Description of anything with which the courts will not compel compliance. An unenforceable contract is valid, but cannot be enforced in the courts.

unfair competition Business competition that is unfair. In particular, abuse of a dominant market position. Competition within the European Community is controlled by the Treaty of Rome Articles 85 and 86.

unfair contract terms Under the Unfair Contract Terms Act 1977, terms in a **contract** which exceed the limits established by the act determine the extent to which parties to contracts can exclude or restrict their liability. Any limitation on liability for negligently caused injury or death is an unfair contract term. Other limitation clauses are subject to a test of reasonableness.

unfair dismissal Dismissal by an employer that does not satisfy the test of fairness in the Employment Protection (Consolidation) Act 1978 s.57. An aggrieved employee can complain to an **industrial tribunal**, which will award **compensation** unless the employer can establish that his or her conduct in dismissing the employee was reasonable.

unfavourable witness Any **witness** who, while displaying no hostile animus, does not give the evidence which the party that called him or her had hoped to elicit. *See also* **hostile witness**.

unfitness to plead Condition of being incapable, by reason of a defect of intellect, of being properly tried on a criminal charge. A defendant who is unfit to plead must be admitted to hospital and may be tried if he later recovers his wits (Criminal Procedure (Insanity) Act 1964 s.5). *See also* **fitness to plead**; **plea**.

unicameralism System of having only one chamber in the legislature. *See also* **bicameralism**.

unincorporated body Group or association of persons bound together for a common purpose, but without a corporate personality. The most common unincorporated bodies are clubs and societies.

universal agent Any agent who has the **authority** to enter into any class of transaction on behalf of his **principal**.

Universal Copyright Convention (UCC) International agreement intended to give protection to the owners of copyright in creative work. The protection given by the UCC is similar to but less extensive than that given by the Berne convention.

universal succession Passing of all the property of a corporation to another corporation.

unlawful Contrary to law; not in accordance with the provisions of the law.

unlawful assembly Gathering of three or more people to commit an unlawful act or to commit a lawful act by unlawful means, in such circumstances as to cause apprehension of a **breach of the peace**. The offence was abolished by the Public Order Act, 1986.

unlawful eviction Removal of an occupier from premises on grounds that the law will not uphold. The eviction of the occupier of a dwelling by any means other than court order is unlawful (Protection from Eviction Act 1977).

unlawful sexual intercourse Sexual intercourse with a girl under 16 years of age, an offence under the Sexual Offences Act 1956 s.6. The consent of the girl is no defence. By section 7 of the same act **sexual intercourse** with a woman who is suffering from severely arrested or retarded development is also unlawful.

unliquidated damages Damages that are not for a fixed amount because they cannot be easily assessed in purely financial terms. A claim for damages for the pain and suffering an injured person experiences is a claim for unliquidated damages. *See also* **liquidated damages**.

unparliamentary language Language contrary to the usages and traditions of Parliament, especially gross insults and imputations of untruthfulness. The **Speaker** will require the withdrawal of an unparliamentary expression; if this is not done he can punish the offending Member of Parliament.

unreasonable behaviour Grounds on which a court may find that a marriage has irretrievably broken down, thus entitling the petitioner to a **divorce**. The court must find that the respondent has behaved in such a way that the petitioner cannot reasonably be expected to continue to live with him or her.

unregistered land Land to which the **title** has not been registered at the Land Registry and for which, accordingly, traditional conveyancing by investigating a chain of title continues to be necessary. *See also* **land registration**.

unsecured creditor Person owed money who is not secured by any rights over the assets of the debtor. The claim of an unsecured **creditor** is inferior to that of a secured creditor; in the event of **insolvency** secured creditors are paid off in full before unsecured creditors receive any payment.

unsecured debenture Form of debenture that does not give the holder any charge over the assets of the company.

unsolicited goods Goods sent to a person who has not requested them. If the sender does not collect the goods within six months, they become the property of the recipient (Unsolicited Goods and Services Act 1971).

unsound mind Archaic term to describe the condition of a person who is incapable of managing his or her own affairs by reason of mental disorder.

urbanization Population increase in towns and cities as a proportion of the total population.

usage Particular way in which a group of persons – for example, inhabitants of an area, or those who carry on a particular trade – do something. An established usage may become a **custom**.

use Term with two applications.
First, the enjoyment of land or other property.
Second, an obsolete equitable device, the predecessor of the **trust** whereby land was held by one person for the use of another.

use and occupation Physical possession and actual use of land.

use classes Categories of use of a building or land. The Town and Country Planning Act 1971 controls the use of land and planning permission can be required for a change of use. Uses are categorized into 18 use classes and no permission is required for a change to a use within the same class.

usher Court official whose function it is to keep order in the courtroom.

usufruct Right to enjoy the yield of an asset without any entitlement to use or deal with the asset itself.

usury Lending of money at interest. The Usury Acts which prohibited the levying of excessive interest were repealed in the 19th century. *See also* **consumer credit**.

utilitarianism Social philosophy emphasizing the satisfaction of the wants of individuals above all else, leading to the notion that the greatest good is the greatest happiness of the greatest number of people.

uterine Description of the offspring of the same mother, but a different father.

utopia Latin for "no place". A theoretical model of an ideal state or society; for example, Plato's *Republic*.

utter To issue or circulate false documents or money.

V

vacation Legal holidays during which the courts do not sit, except for urgent business.

vacant possession Description of premises that are unoccupied by any person.

valuation Setting the value, usually the market value, of an asset.

value added tax (VAT) Indirect tax levied on the supply of goods and services. The tax is payable on the amount by which the value of the goods or services is increased at each stage of its production and distribution (the value is added). It is administered by the Commissioners of **Customs and Excise**.

vandalism Wanton or deliberate destruction of property. *See also* **criminal damage**.

variance Discrepancy or difference, in particular between a **pleading** and the evidence adduced in support of it.

VAT *See* **value added tax.**

veil of incorporation Legal doctrine that a company is a legal person with a separate identity from its members. The court will only pierce the veil of incorporation and ascribe **liability** to individual members in limited circumstances − for example, if **fraud** has occurred.

vendor Person who sells property, products or services.

venue Place in which a case is to be tried and from which, therefore, the jurors who are selected to hear the case must come.

verdict Decision of a jury about a question of fact, most often in regard to the guilt or non-guilt of an accused person. At common law, a verdict was required to be unanimous; a majority verdict is now acceptable if the jury has tried in vain to reach a unanimous verdict for at least two hours (Juries Act 1974 s.17).

verification of flag Investigation of a ship thought to be sailing under false colours.

vested Description of an **estate** to which the holder has an immediate right to present or future possession of the property.

vesting assent Document that transfers land restricted by a **settlement** to a **tenant for life** on the death of the previous tenant for life.

vesting deed Document that transfers land restricted by a **settlement** to a **tenant for life** to give effect to the **settlement**.

vesting order Court order that vests property in a person without the need for a formal **conveyance**. The courts have extensive powers to make vesting orders (Trustee Act 1925 ss.44–56)

veto Power to prevent or prohibit the passing of legislation or some other proposal.

vexatious action Any act that is instituted primarily to annoy or embarrass the **defendant** rather than to obtain the **remedy** sought. The court has the power to strike out a vexatious action.

A vexatious litigant who persists in bringing hopeless actions may be prevented from starting legal proceedings without first obtaining leave of the court to do so. *See also* **striking out pleadings**.

vicarious liability One person's liability for the wrongful act of another, most commonly the liability of an employer for the acts of an employee in the course of his or her employment.

vicarious performance Carrying out of an obligation by someone other than the promisor, on his or her behalf.

Vice-Chancellor Senior judge and vice-president of the **Chancery Division**.

vigilante group Group of citizens organized to protect their homes and district, or to protect other citizens.

visa Entry endorsed in a passport to indicate that the bearer of the passport is allowed to travel to a particular country.

void Without legal effect; a nullity.

voidable Capable of being rescinded at the instance of one party. For example, a person who is tricked into entering a **contract** can have that contract set aside. Until it is rescinded a voidable contract is of full legal effect.

voluntary Of a transaction, unsupported by valuable consideration.

voluntary bill of indictment Criminal charge preferred against the accused by the order of a High Court judge.

voluntary manslaughter Killing of another person with malice aforethought in circumstances that the law regards as mitigating the gravity of the offence, so that the killer is guilty of manslaughter, not murder. The relevant mitigating factors are **provocation, diminished responsibility** or a suicide pact.

volunteer Term with two applications.

First, a person who receives a benefit, such as a gift or legacy, without giving any consideration for it. **Equity** will not assist a volunteer.

Second, a person who performs services for another without any agreement that he or she should be paid for such work.

vote Formal expression of and commitment to a preference in an election, referendum or ballot. All United Kingdom subjects above the age of 18 are entitled to vote in council, Parliamentary and European parliamentary elections, provided that they are not peers, certified as mentally ill or serving a long-term prison sentence.

vote of censure Motion by the Opposition that criticizes some aspect of government policy. A government which lost a vote of censure would probably fall.

Vote Office Office of the House of Commons that is responsible for the distribution of Parliamentary papers.

vote on account Government expenditure is authorized by Parliament each year by the Consolidated Fund Bill and the Consolidated Fund (Appropriation) Bill; until these bills are passed and become law interim government expenditure is authorized by votes of money on account.

Votes and Proceedings Daily publication that records the events of the previous day in the House of Commons.

W

wager Promise to pay money on the result of an event. A wagering contract is unenforceable under the Gaming Act 1845 s.18.

waif Term with two applications.
First, anything found and not claimed; an obsolete term for stolen goods abandoned by a thief.
Second, a homeless or helpless person, especially a child.

waiver Renunciation by a person of a right or remedy to which he or she is legally entitled. A waiver may be express or implied; a waiver is implied from unequivocal conduct inconsistent with the exercise of the right or remedy.

want of age Being below an age limit set by law.

want of prosecution Failure to prosecute a case. A claim or **prosecution** can be dismissed for want of prosecution if an inordinate and inexcusable delay is believed to cause prejudice to the **defendant**.

ward of court Minor under the control and protection of the **High Court**. Arrangements for the care, welfare and education of a ward must be approved by the court.

wardship proceedings Proceedings to make a minor a **ward of court**. The minor becomes a ward as soon as the proceedings are commenced, but ceases to be so at the end of 21 days unless the court makes a formal order of wardship before then.

warned list List of cases that are to be tried in the near future and must be ready to be heard at short notice.

warrant Document, sealed by a court, that authorizes a particular action. *See also* **search warrant; warrant of arrest**.

warrant of arrest Warrant signed by a Justice of the Peace to authorize a police officer to arrest a suspect and bring him or her before the court.

warrant of further detention Warrant issued by a **Magistrates' Court**, that suspends the operation of the clause in the Police and Criminal Evidence Act 1984, by which the police can authorize the detention of a suspect for questioning for no more than 36 hours. The suspect can be held thereafter only if the police obtain a warrant of further detention, which may authorize up to 36 hours further detention. The police can apply for further warrants so long as the total period of detention does not exceed 96 hours (Police and Criminal Evidence Act 1984).

warranty Term with two applications.
First, a promise or assurance.
Second, a term of a contract that is less fundamental than a condition. A breach of warranty entitles the wronged party to damages, but does not entitle him or her to treat the contract as repudiated.

waste Act or omission by an occupier of property that does lasting damage to the property and therefore affects the rights of those with an interest in the property.

wasting asset Any asset that diminishes in value as time passes, for example, a **leasehold** or a **copyright**. **Trustees** must sell wasting trust assets and invest the proceeds in authorized securities.

wasting police time Offence of causing wasteful employment to the police contrary to the Criminal Law Act 1967 s.5(2), for example, by falsely reporting that a crime has been committed.

watch committee Committee of a local authority that previously exercised control over the local police force. This role is now carried out by the police committee for each area police force.

watchdog Dog kept to guard property. The Guard Dogs Act 1975 provides that a guard dog must be controlled by a handler and that a notice warning that a guard dog is present must be displayed.

watermark Identifying mark within the fabric of paper; present in banknotes and postage stamps to make forgery more difficult.

wear and tear Damage and deterioration that is suffered by a **chattel** or building by normal use.

weather permitting clause Term of a **contract** that provides for an extension of time or some other relaxation of a party's contractual obligations in the event of inclement weather.

Weekly Law Reports Series of authoritative and modern law reports on the leading court decisions, first published in 1953.

weight of evidence Overall tendency of the evidence to point to a particular conclusion. It can be a ground of **appeal** that a finding of fact is against the weight of evidence. However, an appeal on this basis is unlikely to succeed, because an appellate court will generally be unwilling to interfere with a lower court's findings of fact.

welfare state Political and social system in which the government takes responsibility for ensuring the welfare of all citizens, and provides benefits for the poor and disadvantaged, paid out of taxation.

whip Official of a political party in Parliament whose principal duty is to ensure that as many MPs as possible vote for the party in any division.

White Book Colloquial name for the *Supreme Court Practice*, the standard work on the procedure and practice of the Supreme Court. It contains the Rules of the Supreme Court as well as other relevant rules and legislation.

white-collar crime Crime committed by a member of the professional middle classes in the course of his or her occupation, using specific professional knowledge and skills.

white paper Publication that sets out details of proposed Government legislation on a particular subject.

wholesaler Middleman, between manufacturer and **retailer**, who purchases goods in large quantities to sell them on.

wilful failure to maintain Failure by a person to maintain his or her spouse. The aggrieved spouse can apply to the **High Court, County Court or Magistrates' Court** for an order for **maintenance** payments.

wilful refusal to consummate Refusal of a person to have sexual intercourse with his or her spouse, and thereby to consummate the marriage. This is a ground for **nullity** of the marriage.

will Declaration, normally in writing, providing for the disposition of the goods of the maker of the will (the testator) on his or her death. Save for wills made by servicemen on active service, certain formalities must be observed. The will must be made in writing, signed by the testator and witnessed by two persons. A witness may not benefit under the will (Wills Act 1837 as amended). A testator may revoke his or her will at any time; any previous will is revoked by the making of a new will. *See also* **codicil**; **intestacy**.

winding-up Dissolution of a company, the bringing of an end to its activities and realizing its assets. A company may be wound up voluntarily, at the instance of its members, or compulsorily by court order.

withdrawal of a juror Procedure to remove a **juror** when a **jury** tries a second issue. There is no provision for challenge of jurors before the second issue is heard. Instead, if a juror might properly have been challenged, he or she can be ordered to withdraw and a further juror selected as a replacement (Juries Act 1974 s.11(6)).

without prejudice Description of a communication which is part of *bona fide* negotiations to settle a dispute and which, being so marked, may not be disclosed to the court except with the leave of the maker.

witness Term with three applications.

First, a person who gives evidence in court. A witness must swear or affirm that he or she will tell the truth. A witness who makes a statement on oath which he or she knows to be false or does not believe to be true commits **perjury**.

Second, a person who sees or hears a particular event.

Third, a person who signs a legal document as testimony to the validity of another person's signature.

woolsack Large cushion, the official seat of the **Lord Chancellor** in his capacity as **Speaker** of the House of Lords.

words of limitation Part of a conveyance or disposition that establishes the duration of an estate. Since 1925, no words of limitation are necessary and, subject to contrary intention, a grantor passes his entire estates.

workmen's compensation Former scheme of state **compensation** for victims of accidents at work. This compensation is now provided within the social security system by Industrial Injury Benefit, Sickness Benefit and Invalidity Benefit.

work to rule Situation in which employees carry out only their contractual obligations, but no work that they usually perform as a matter of goodwill. A form of industrial action.

wounding with intent Offence, under the Offences Against the Person Act 1861 s.18, of wounding a person with the intention of doing **grievous bodily harm** or of resisting or preventing an arrest. The maximum sentence is **life imprisonment**.

writ Court document, bearing the royal arms, which commands a person to do or cease doing a particular thing.

writ of summons Document issued by the High Court which begins most **litigation**. The writ must set out the name and address of the **plaintiff** and the **defendant** and the nature of the plaintiff's claim. The writ must be served on the defendant within one year of its issue.

wrong Infringement of the rights of another person – for example, a **breach of contract** or **tort**, or of the rights and rules of the community – for example a public nuisance or a **crime**.

wrongful dismissal Unjustified dismissal of an employee. The remedy for wrongful dismissal is an action for **breach of contract** in the courts (not in the Industrial Tribunal, which hears cases of alleged

unfair dismissal). The damages will be those sums due under the contract, but this is usually only paid for the period of notice which the employee should have received; an action for wrongful dismissal is therefore usually less useful than a claim of unfair dismissal.

Y

young person Person of 14–16 years of age (Children and Young Persons Act 1933 s.107).

youth culture Attitudes and lifestyles of young people, derived from their association with each other in peer groups.

Glossary of
Foreign Terms

The following is a glossary of foreign terms that are commonly found in a legal context. Most of these are Latin. A few exceptions are from the old French, and these are indicated *Fr.*

Term	Literal meaning	Use
ab extra	(from outside)	
ab initio	(from the beginning)	If at any time a person abuses legally granted authority or licence, any previous actions done under the authority become wrongful (void *ab initio*).
abjuratio	(a denial on oath)	
absente reo	(with the defendant being absent)	
absoluta sententia expositare non indiget	(to explain an unambiguous statement is not required)	
abundans cautela non nocet	(great caution does no harm)	To be certain, things implied should be expressed.
accessio cedit principali	(an accessory thing belongs to the principal thing)	The accessory thing when annexed to the principal thing becomes the property of the owner of the principal thing.

Term	Literal meaning	Use
accusare nemo se debet; accusare nemo se debet nisi coram Deo	(no one is bound to accuse himself; no one is bound to accuse himself except in the presence of God)	A witness does not have to answer any question that would, in the eyes of the court incriminate him or her.
actio	(an action)	
actio personalis moritur cum persona	(a personal action dies with the person)	
actus legis nemini facit injuriam	(the act of the law causes injury to no one)	
actus non facit reum, nisi mens sit rea	(the act does not make the criminal, unless his mind is also guilty)	
actus reus	(a guilty act)	For a crime to be committed there must be an act (actus reus) and an intent (mens rea).
ad diem	(to the appointed day)	
ad hoc	(to or for this)	For a particular purpose; an *ad hoc* committee is one formed to deal with a particular situation.
ad idem	(towards the same)	Indicates that parties to a transaction are in agreement.
ad infinitum	(to infinity; endlessly)	

Term	Literal meaning	Use
ad interim	(for the time being)	
ad litem	(for the law suit)	Relating to the appointed guardian in a custody suit.
ad quod damnum	(at what cost)	Relating to the application of a variety of licences.
aedificatum solo, solo cedit	(what is built on land, becomes part of the land)	Relates to fixtures and fittings sold with premises.
a fortiori	(from the stronger)	Relating to the stronger argument; necessarily.
alia enormia	(other wrongs)	Relating to cases of trespass.
aliud est celare, aliud tacere	(it is one thing to conceal, another to be silent)	
amicus curiae	(a friend of the court)	Usually a barrister who appears in a case to assist the court. A disinterested observer.
animus	(intention)	Usually used in conjunction with another term.
animus deserendi	(the intention of deserting)	Relating to the desertion of a spouse.
animus furandi	(the intention of stealing)	

Term	Literal meaning	Use
animus manendi	(the intention of remaining)	Relating to laws of domicile.
animus possedendi	(the intention of possessing)	
animus revertendi	(the intention of returning)	Relating to the laws of animal ownership.
animus revocandi	(the intention of revoking)	E.g. a will.
animus testandi	(the intention of making a will)	
anni nubiles	(marriageable age)	The marrigeable age of a woman.
a posteriori	(from the later)	Relating to reasoning based on known facts.
a priori	(from the previous)	Relating to reasoning based on presumptions.
aqua cedit solo	(the water goes with the land)	Ownership of water goes with ownership of the land it covers.
a similibus ad similia	(from like to like)	
audi alteram partem	(hear the other side)	One of two of the principles of natural justice.
audita querela	(the complaint having been heard)	The other principle of natural justice.

Term	Literal meaning	Use
autrefois acquit	(*Fr.* previously acquitted)	A plea made by the defendant claiming that he has previously been acquitted from the same (or much the same) indictment.
autrefois convict	(*Fr.* previously convicted)	A plea made by the defendant claiming that he has previously been convicted of the same (or much the same) indictment.
a verbis legis non est recedendum	(you must not vary the words of the law)	
a vinculo matrimonii	(from the bond of marriage)	The forerunner of the modern marriage dissolution decree.
bona fide	(in good faith)	
bona vacantia	(empty goods)	Property or goods without an apparent owner.
caeteris quaestio	(the investigation of the remaining facts)	
cadit quaestio	(the matter falls)	
casus omissus	(an omitted case)	A case that has been overlooked and not provided for in the statute.

Term	Literal meaning	Use
causa mortis	(cause of death)	
caveat	(let him beware)	A notice (usually placed in a registry) which prevents any action taken without previous notice to the person filing the caveat (the caveator).
caveat actor	(let the doer beware)	A person is usually assumed to be aware of the probable results of his acts.
caveat emptor	(let the buyer beware)	Before statutory law the buyer had no warranty of the quality of goods; by statute there now exists a clause whereby the goods must be of merchantable quality.
certiorari	(to be informed)	A writ made by the Crown Court to an inferior court, whereby the inferior court must present a case to the Crown Court. Any procedural error of that case will result in the quashing of the inferior court's ruling.
cessante ratione legis, cessat lex ipsa	(when the reason of the law ceases, the law itself ceases)	A maxim which applies more to common law than statute law.

Term	Literal meaning	Use
cestui que trust	(*Fr.* he who is the trust)	A beneficiary.
commorientes	(those dying together)	Persons who die at the same time.
compos mentis	(of sound mind)	
consensus ad idem	(agreement as to the thing)	Common consent required to a binding contract.
consensus facit legem	(consent makes law)	The legal binding of parties in a contract.
coram	(in the presence of)	
corpus delicti	(body of an offence)	The facts that constitute an offence.
cum testamento annexo	(with the will annexed)	Relating to the court's procedure of a deceased person's will.
curia regis	(the King's Court)	
cy-près	(*Fr. cy*, here; *près*, near)	A doctrine that ensures that a testator's or settlor's wishes are, if not exactly carried out, carried out as closely as possible.
damnum sine injuria	(loss without wrong)	Damage or loss may occur through an act not deemed injurious by a court.

319

Term	Literal meaning	Use
de bene esse	(of well-being)	In order to be fair and cautious.
de bonis non administratis	(of goods not administered)	An estate executor appointed by the court, following the death of the original executor.
de die in diem	(from day to day)	
de facto	(in fact)	
de injuria	(concerning wrong-doing)	A plea of defence made by a defendant.
de jure	(by right)	
de minimis non curat lex	(the law does not concern itself with trivia)	
de novo	(anew)	
delegatus non potest delegare	(a delegate cannot delegate)	
devastavit	(he or she has wasted)	The failure of the executor of an estate to carry out his or her duties properly.
dictum	(a saying)	
donatio mortis causa	(a gift on account of death)	
dum fuit non compos mentis	(while he or she was not of sound mind)	
dum sola et casta	(while unmarried and chaste)	

Term	Literal meaning	Use
durante absentia	(during absence)	
durante minore aetate	(during minor age)	While a person is legally under age.
durante vita	(during life)	
eat inde sine die	(let him go from there without a day)	The dismissal of a defendant.
ei incumbit probatio qui dicit, non qui negat	(the burden of proof rests with the person who accuses, not with the person who denies it)	
ei qui affirmat, non ei qui negat, incumbit probatio	(the burden of proof rests with the person who affirms, not the person who denies)	
ejusdem generis	(of the same kind)	The rule which states that when particular words are followed by general words the general words are construed as having the same implication as the particular words.
en autre droit	(*Fr.* in the right of another)	The property of the testator is held by his executor.
et seq (et sequentes)	(and those following)	
ex abundante cautela	(from excessive caution)	

321

Term	Literal meaning	Use
ex aequo et bono	(in fair dealing and good faith)	
ex contractu	(arising from contract)	
ex curia	(out of court)	
ex debitato justitae	(from the requirements of justice)	Relating to those remedies that the court is obliged to give, as opposed to discretionary remedies.
ex delicto	(arising from the offence)	Relating to actions of tort.
ex gratia	(as a favour)	
ex nudo pacto non oritur actio	(no action arises from a bare contract)	A contract cannot be enforced without proper consideration.
ex officio	(by virtue of office)	
ex parte	(partly)	Relating to court applications made by (1) an interested person who is not a party to the proceedings or (2) a party in the absence of another.
expensae litis	(expenses of the suit)	Costs.
ex post facto	(from subsequent action)	A legal act that works retrospectively.
ex turpi causa non oritur actio	(an action does not arise from a shameful case)	Relating to void transactions because of illegality.

Term	Literal meaning	Use
factum	(act, deed, fact)	
factum probanda	(a fact that must be proved)	
factum probantia	(a substantiated fact)	
feme covert	(*Fr.* a married woman)	
feme sole	(*Fr.* an unmarried woman)	
fiat	(let it be done)	
fiat justitia	(let justice be done)	
fieri facias	(you may bring into being)	Relating to cases of debt instructing goods to be taken from the debtor to the value of the judgment debt and interest.
filius nullius	(son of nobody)	An illegitimate child.
forum rei	(place of the matter)	The court of the country in which the subject of the lawsuit resides or is situated.
fraus omnia vitiat	(fraud corrupts everything)	
fructus industriales	(fruits of labour)	Crops or produce that grow with the help of human cultivation.
fructus naturales	(fruits of nature)	Crops or produce that grow naturally.

Term	Literal meaning	Use
gratis dictum	(a gratuitous assertion)	
habeas corpus	(you may have the body)	A writ issued requiring a person who has detained another to come before the court to justify the lawfulness of that detention or release the person detained.
ibid	(in the same place)	
id certum est quod certum reddi potest	(that which can be made is certain)	
idem	(the same)	
ignorantia facti excusat; ingorantia juris non excusat	(ignorance of the fact excuses, ignorance of law does not excuse)	
impossibilium nulla obligatio est	(impossibility nullifies obligation)	
impotentia excusat legem	(impotency excuses law)	
in aequali jure melior est conditio possidentis	(in cases of equal rights the possessor's claim is stronger)	
in Anglia non est interregnum	(in England there is no interval)	For example, there is no interval between the

Term	Literal meaning	Use
		rule of the monarchy and that of the heir.
in articulo mortis	(at the point of death)	
in bonis	(in the goods of)	
in camera	(in the chamber)	A case conducted in private.
inclusio unius est exclusio alterius	(the inclusion of one is the exclusion of the other)	
in curia	(in court)	
in custodia legis	(in custody of the law)	
in delicto	(in an offence)	
in extenso	(at full length)	
in flagrante delicto	(while the offence still glows with heat)	Relating to certain types of arrest which can only be made when the person is caught in the act of committing the offence.
in futuro	(in the future)	
injuria	(a legal wrong-doing)	
injuria non excusat injuriam	(one wrong does not excuse another)	
in loco parentis	(in place of a parent)	When children are at school, the school temporarily has the rights and duties of the parents.

Term	Literal meaning	Use
in nomine	(in the name of)	
in perpetuum	(forever)	
in personam	(against a person)	Relating to lawsuits or claims against a specific person.
in pleno	(in full)	
in praesenti	(for the present)	
in propria persona	(in one's own person)	
in re	(in the matter of)	Concerning.
in rem	(against a thing)	Relating to the general principle that people should respect other people's property.
in situ	(on its original site)	
inter alia	(among others)	
inter vivos	(among living persons)	
in transitu	(while in transit)	
intra vires	(within the powers)	
ipso facto	(by the very fact)	
jus	(the law or right)	
jus acrescendi	(the right of accrual)	The right of one person of a jointly-owned property to acquire the

Term	Literal meaning	Use
		entire property on the death of the other owner(s).
jus gentium	(the right of nations)	
jus scriptum	(the written law)	
jus tertii	(the right of a third party)	
laesae majestatis crimen	(the crime of injured majesty)	Treason.
lex domicilii	(the law of domicile)	In private international law, the law of the person's country decides certain cases, such as validity of wills and marriage.
lex fori	(the law of the forum)	The law of the court of the country in which a case is being heard governs matters of procedure.
lex loci contractus	(the law of a place of contract)	The law of the court of the country governs matters of formal requirements of the contract.
lex mercatoria	(mercantile law)	
lex non cogit ad impossibilia	(the law does not enforce impossibility)	

Term	Literal meaning	Use
lex scripta	(the written law)	Statute law.
lex situs	(the law of the place where an object is located)	
locus in quo	(the place where)	In criminal law, the place where the crime is alleged to have been committed.
locus sigilli	(the place of the seal)	
locus standi	(the place of standing)	The right to bring or challenge actions in court.
mala fide	(in bad faith)	
mala in se; mala prohibita	(crimes wrong in themselves; crimes prohibited by law)	Relating to immoral crimes such as murder compared to crimes such as white collar crime.
mala praxis	(bad practice; bad business)	Medical incompetence or negligence.
mandamus	(we command)	A writ from the High Court instructing a person or body to carry out a specified public duty.
mens rea	(guilty mind)	The knowledge or evil intention of a crime
ne exeat regno	(he is not to leave the kingdom)	A writ restraining a person from leaving the

Term	Literal meaning	Use
		country without prior agreement from the crown or high court.
necessitas non habet legem	(necessity has no law)	
necessitas publica major est quam privata	(public necessity is greater than private)	
nec per vim nec clam nec precario	(neither through violence, stealth nor entreaty)	
nemo debet bis puniri pro uno delicto	(no one should be punished twice for one crime)	
nemo debet esse judex in propria causa	(no one may be a judge for his own cause)	Magistrates and judges must declare any personal or pecuniary interests in any case that comes before them.
nemo tenetur ad impossibile	(no one is constrained to achieve the impossible)	
nemo tenetur se ipsum accusare	(no one is bound to accuse himself)	
nisi	(if not)	Relating to court adjucations that come into effect on a specified date unless cause is shown within a certain period why it should not; e.g. decree nisi in divorce proceedings.

Term	Literal meaning	Use
nolle prosequi	(to be unwilling to prosecute)	An action taken by the Attorney-General that suspends court proceedings if the defendant is unable to stand trial, or if the Attorney-General does not consider a trial to be in the public interest.
non compos mentis	(not of sound mind)	
non constat	(it does not correspond; it is not consistent)	
non culpabilis	(not guilty)	
non obstante veredicto	(notwithstanding the verdict)	
non sequitur	(it does not follow)	
novus actus interveniens	(a new intervening act)	An event that removes direct responsibility from the defendant due to the intervention of the act of a third party.
nudum pactum	(a bare agreement)	A contract drawn up without consideration.
nunc pro tunc	(now instead of then)	A court action that takes effect at an earlier date than when it was actually taken.
obiter dictum	(an incidental remark)	A remark made by a judge in his judgment

Term	Literal meaning	Use
		which does not effect the final decision, or which relates to a similar, but not the same, set of circumstances as apply in the case, and cannot therefore be cited as a precedent.
omnia praesumuntur rite et solemniter esse acta	(all acts are presumed to have been done properly and regularly)	
onus probandi	(the burden of proof)	
opere citato (op. cit.)	(in the work already cited)	
pari passu	(in equal step)	Unbiased, without preference.
particeps criminis	(a partner in crime)	An accessory.
per	(through, by, because of, for)	
pur autre vie	(*Fr.* for another life)	Relating to matters of estate, in which B's property is given to A for the duration of B's life?
per capita	(by heads)	For each person.
per curiam	(by the court)	
per incuriam	(through negligence)	A court decision which is mistaken because of lack

Term	Literal meaning	Use
		of attention to relevant authorities or statutes. The decision is annulled.
per pro (per procurationem)	(through the agency of)	On behalf of another.
per se	(by itself)	Taken alone.
per stirpes	(by roots)	Relating to the equal distribution of an estate or funds. If the beneficiary predeceases the testator, the beneficiary's children receive an equal share of the property.
plene administravit	(he has fully administered)	The defence of a personal executor against a creditor's action to recover the testator's debt. The creditor must prove that the executor still retains some of the testator's estate before he can recover the debt.
prima facie	(from prima facies, first appearance)	On the face of things.
primo loco	(in the first place)	
pro bono publico	(for the public good)	
pro forma	(as a matter of form)	
pro rata	(in proportion)	
pro tanto	(for so much)	To that extent?

Term	Literal meaning	Use
pro tempore	(for the time being)	
qua	(as)	In the capacity of.
quantum	(how much)	Amount of damages.
quantum meruit	(as much as he, she or it deserved)	An action taken by a person who has provided a service for another person in the expectation of receiving some renumeration but has not done so. He is entitled to sue for the amount the service deserves.
quantum valebant	(as much as they were worth)	An action claiming for money for goods that were sold without a fixed price, but payment was implied.
quasi	(as it were)	Seemingly or not quite.
quia timet	(because he fears)	An injunction that prevents an anticipated injurious action.
quid pro quo	(this for that)	
qui prior est tempore, potior est jure	(whoever is first in time has the better claim in law)	
quicquid plantatur solo, solo cedit	(whatever is annexed to the soil belongs to the soil)	

Term	Literal meaning	Use
quorum	(of whom)	The minimum number of people required to constitute a valid meeting.
ratio decidendi	(the grounds for deciding)	The reason for a judicial decision which subsequently creates a precedent for the future.
reddendum	(that which must be rendered or paid)	Money to be paid.
res	(affair, matter, thing)	
res gestae	(achievements)	Relating to facts and contemporaneous facts concerning evidence?
res ipsa loquitur	(the thing speaks for itself)	A maxim which states that negligence was clearly the cause of an accident. The defendant must prove that negligence was not the cause.
res judicata	(a matter that has been adjudicated)	
res nova	(new affair)	A matter awaiting a decision.
res nullius	(a thing belonging to no one)	Ownerless property.
restitutio in integrum	(restoration in full)	The principle that in awarding damages the

Term	Literal meaning	Use
		courts aim to restore aggrieved parties to their previous position.
sans recours	(*Fr.* without recourse)	Relating to bills of exchange, where an agent adds his signature without being liable if the bill is dishonoured
scienter	(knowingly)	
semble	(*Fr.* it appears)	
similiter	(similarly)	
simpliciter	(simply, absolutely, unconditional)	
sine die	(without a day being appointed)	Indefinitely.
stare decisis	(to stand by settlements)	A basic principle of English law by which precedents are consistently upheld.
status quo	(the state in which)	The existing state of affairs.
sub judice	(under trial)	Case that is not yet decided and may not be reported in the press or publicly discussed outside the courtroom for fear of prejudicing the proceedings.
subpoena	(under penalty)	A court order requiring a person to

Term	Literal meaning	Use
		appear at a specified place and time and for a specified purpose.
subpoena ad testificandum	(under penalty to give evidence)	A court order requiring a person to appear in court for the specific purpose of giving evidence.
subpoena duces tecum	(under penalty that you bring with you)	A court order requiring a person to attend court for the purpose of giving evidence and to bring specified documentation.
testatum	(deed)	
travaux préparatoires	(*Fr.* groundwork)	Preparatory work which forms a basis for final legislation.
uberrimae fidei	(of the utmost good faith)	Relating to contracts in which one party must disclose any relevant facts which have bearing on the contract to the other party.
ubi jus, ibi remedium	(where there is justice, there is a remedy)	
ubi remedium, ibi jus	(where there is a remedy, there is justice)	
ultra vires	(beyond the powers)	Relating to acts by a public authority or body

Term	Literal meaning	Use
		that go beyond the power granted to it, such acts are void.
venire de novo	(to come anew)	A writ from the Court of Appeal ordering a trial to be nullified on the grounds of a fundamental mistake in the court proceedings, and a new trial to be set.
videlicet (viz.)	(namely)	
vis major	(greater force)	Relating to irresistible forces such as floods, earthquakes and armed forces.
voire dire	(*Fr.* to speak the truth)	Relating to preliminary examinations of witnesses and jurors to test their competence, if they prove to be not of sound mind they will be rejected.
volenti non fit injuria	(with consent no injury is done)	Applies as a defence in personal injury actions.

Notes

Crime
Anti social behaviour order
— Asbo

Notes

Notes

Notes

Notes

Notes

Notes

Notes